Middle School 2-1

기말고사 완벽대비

적중 100

영어 기출 문제집

중 2

천재 | 이재영

Best Collection

KB084806

구성과 특징

교과서의 주요 학습 내용을 중심으로 학습 영역별 특성에 맞춰 단계별로 다양한 학습 기회를 제공하여 단원별 학습능력 평가는 물론 중간 및 기말고사 시험 등에 완벽하게 대비할 수 있도록 내용을 구성

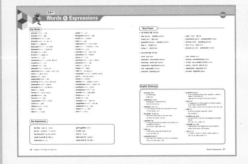

Words & Expressions

Step1 Key Words 단원별 핵심 단어 설명 및 풀이
Key Expression 단원별 핵심 숙어 및 관용어 설명
Word Power 반대 또는 비슷한 뜻 단어 배우기
English Dictionary 영어로 배우는 영어 단어

Step2 실력평가 단원별 수시평가 대비 주관식, 객관식 문제풀이

Step3 서술형 대비 학업성취도 및 수행능력평가 대비 서술형 문제풀이

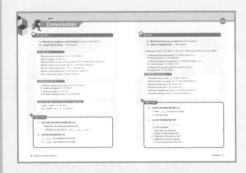

Conversation

Step1 핵심 의사소통 의사소통에 필요한 주요 표현 방법 요약
핵심 Check 기본적인 표현 방법 및 활용능력 확인

Step2 대화문 익히기 상황에 따른 대화문 활용 및 연습

Step3 기본평가 시험대비 기초 학습 능력 평가

Step4 실력평가 단원별 수시평가 대비 주관식, 객관식 문제풀이

Step5 서술형 대비 학업성취도 및 수행능력평가 대비 서술형 문제풀이

Grammar

Step1 주요 문법 단원별 주요 문법 사항과 예문을 알기 쉽게 설명
핵심 Check 기본 문법사항에 대한 이해 여부 확인

Step2 기본평가 시험대비 기초 학습 능력 평가

Step3 실력평가 단원별 수시평가 대비 주관식, 객관식 문제풀이

Step4 서술형 대비 학업성취도 및 수행능력평가 대비 서술형 문제풀이

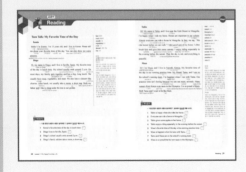

Reading

Step1 구문 분석 단원별로 제시된 문장에 대한 구문별 분석과 내용 설명
확인문제 문장에 대한 기본적인 이해와 인지능력 확인

Step2 확인학습A 빈칸 채우기를 통한 문장 완성 능력 확인

Step3 확인학습B 제시된 우리말을 영어로 완성하여 작문 능력 키우기

Step4 실력평가 단원별 수시평가 대비 주관식, 객관식 문제풀이

Step5 서술형 대비 학업성취도 및 수행능력평가 대비 서술형 문제풀이
교과서 구석구석 교과서에 나오는 기타 문장까지 완벽 학습

Composition

|영역별 핵심문제|

단어 및 어휘, 대화문, 문법, 독해 등 각 영역별 기출문제의 출제 유형을 분석하여 실전에 대비하고 연습할
수 있도록 문제를 배열

|서술형 실전 및 창의사고력 문제|

학교 시험에서 점차 늘어나는 서술형 시험에 집중 대비하고 고득점을 취득하는데 만전을 기하기 위한
학습 코너

|단원별 예상문제|

기출문제를 분석한 후 새로운 시험 출제 경향을 더하여 새롭게 출제될 수 있는 문제를 포함하여 시험에 완벽
하게 대비할 수 있도록 준비

|단원별 모의고사|

영역별, 단계별 학습을 모두 마친 후 실전 연습을 위한 모의고사

on the textbook .... 교과서 파헤치기

- 단어Test1~2 영어 단어 우리말 쓰기와 우리말을 영어 단어로 쓰기

- 대화문Test1~2 대화문 빈칸 완성 및 전체 대화문 쓰기

- 본문Test1~5 빈칸 완성, 우리말 쓰기, 문장 배열연습, 영어 작문하기 복습 등 단계별 반복 학습을
　　　　　　　통해 교과서 지문에 대한 완벽한 습득

- 구석구석지문Test1~2 지문 빈칸 완성 및 전문 영어로 쓰기

Contents

Lesson 3

Healthy Life, Happy Life

🎤 의사소통 기능

- 증상 묻고 답하기
  A: What's wrong with you?
  B: I have a toothache.

- 약속 정하기
  A: Can you make it at three?
  B: That's fine with me.

🔧 언어 형식

- 가주어 it
  It is good **to exercise** regularly.

- to부정사의 형용사적 용법
  I need something **to eat** for lunch.

Words & Expressions

Key Words

- **actually** [ǽktʃuəli] 부 실제로, 정말로
- **against** [əgénst] 전 ~에 붙여[맞아], ~에 반대하여
- **antibody** [ǽntibadi] 명 항체
- **appointment** [əpɔ́intmənt] 명 약속
- **attack** [ətǽk] 동 공격하다 명 공격
- **bacteria** [bæktíəriə] 명 박테리아, 세균
- **bad breath** 입 냄새
- **balanced** [bǽlənst] 형 균형 잡힌, 안정된
- **break** [breik] 동 부러지다
- **cell** [sel] 명 세포
- **copy** [kápi] 동 복제하다, 복사하다
- **creature** [krí:tʃər] 명 생물
- **dangerous** [déindʒərəs] 형 위험한 (↔ safe)
- **defend** [difénd] 동 방어하다 (↔ attack)
- **defense** [diféns] 명 방어
- **different** [dífərənt] 형 다른 (↔ same)
- **digest** [didʒést] 동 소화하다, 소화시키다
- **everywhere** [evriwer] 부 모든 곳, 어디나
- **exercise** [éksərsàiz] 동 운동하다
- **fever** [fí:vər] 명 열
- **finally** [fáinəli] 부 마지막으로, 마침내 (= at last)
- **flu** [flu:] 명 독감
- **form** [fɔːrm] 명 형태
- **germ** [dʒəːrm] 명 세균, 미생물
- **happen** [hǽpən] 동 발생하다, 일어나다
- **hard** [ha:rd] 형 어려운 (↔easy)
- **healthy** [hélθi] 형 건강한
- **hiccup** [híkʌp] 명 딸꾹질

- **hurt** [həːrt] 동 다치게 하다, 아프다
- **impossible** [impásəbl] 형 불가능한 (↔ possible)
- **invade** [invéid] 동 침입하다
- **luckily** [lʌ́kili] 부 다행히도
- **macrophage** [mǽkrəfèidʒ] 명 대식 세포
- **major** [méidʒər] 형 주요한, 중대한
- **medicine** [medsn] 명 약
- **multiply** [mʌ́ltəplài] 동 증식[번식]하다
- **necessary** [nésəsèri] 형 필요한
- **regularly** [régjulərli] 부 규칙적으로
- **remember** [rimémbər] 동 기억하다 (↔ forget)
- **scratch** [skrætʃ] 동 긁다, 할퀴다
- **several** [sévərəl] 형 몇의
- **shot** [ʃot] 명 주사
- **skin** [skin] 명 피부
- **sore throat** 인후염
- **spot** [spat] 명 (특정한) 곳[장소/자리]
- **step** [step] 명 단계
- **stomachache** 명 위통, 복통
- **success** [səksés] 명 성공
- **terrible** [térəbl] 형 끔찍한, 소름끼치는
- **through** [θru:] 전 ~을 통하여
- **trick** [trik] 동 속이다
- **victim** [víktim] 명 피해자, 희생자
- **virus** [váiərəs] 명 바이러스
- **white blood cell** 백혈구
- **zone** [zoun] 명 지역

Key Expressions

- **at last** 마침내, 드디어
- **be famous for** ~으로 유명하다
- **be good for** ~에 좋다
- **be ready to** ~할 준비가 되어 있다
- **be thinking of** ~을 생각하고 있다
- **by the way** 그런데
- **catch a cold** 감기에 걸리다
- **give up** 포기하다

- **go well** 잘되어 가다
- **in a few days** 며칠 후에
- **make it** (모임 등에) 가다[참석하다]
- **plenty of** 많은
- **protect A from B** A를 B로부터 보호하다
- **show up** 나타나다
- **such as** ~와 같은
- **watch out** 조심하다

Word Power

※ 동사에 -er, -or을, 명사에 -ist를 붙여서 행위자를 나타내는 단어

□ act (연기하다) → actor (배우)

□ paint (그리다) → painter (화가)

□ invent (발명하다) → inventor (발명가)

□ write (쓰다) → writer (작가)

□ science (과학) → scientist (과학자)

□ visit (방문하다) → visitor (방문객)

□ translate (번역[통역]하다) → translator (번역가, 통역사)

□ direct (감독하다) → director (감독)

□ art (미술, 예술) → artist (미술가, 예술가)

□ cartoon (만화) → cartoonist (만화가)

English Dictionary

□ **appointment** 약속
→ an agreement to meet with someone at a particular time 특정한 때에 어떤 사람을 만나기로 하는 약속

□ **bacteria** 박테리아, 세균
→ any one of a group of very small living things that often cause disease
흔히 질병을 일으키는 아주 작은 생물 무리의 하나

□ **balanced** 균형 잡힌
→ having good or equal amounts of all the necessary parts of something
필요한 요소를 빠짐없이 잘 또는 고르게 갖춘

□ **cell** 세포
→ any one of the very small parts that together form all living things
모든 생물을 구성하는 아주 작은 부분들의 어느 하나

□ **defend** 방어하다
→ to fight in order to keep someone or something safe
누군가 또는 어떤 것을 안전하게 지키기 위해 싸우다

□ **digest** 소화하다, 소화시키다
→ to change food that you have eaten by a biological process into simpler forms that can be used by the body
섭취한 음식물을 신체가 사용할 수 있도록 생리 과정을 거쳐 더 단순한 형태로 변화시키다

□ **flu** 독감
→ an infectious disease like a very bad cold, which causes fever, pains, and weakness
고열, 통증, 약화를 일으키는 매우 심한 감기 같은 전염병

□ **germ** 세균, 미생물
→ a very small living thing that causes disease
병을 일으키는 아주 작은 생물

□ **invade** 침입하다
→ to enter or be in a place where you are not wanted
남이 원하지 않는 곳에 들어가거나 있다

□ **luckily** 다행히도
→ used to say that something good or lucky has happened
좋은 일이나 다행스러운 일이 일어났다고 말할 때 사용되는

□ **major** 주요한, 중대한
→ very important
매우 중요한

□ **multiply** 증식[번식]하다
→ to increase in number by reproducing
번식해서 수가 증가하다

□ **scratch** 긁다
→ to rub your skin with your fingernails because it feels uncomfortable
불편해서 손톱 같은 날카로운 것으로 피부를 긁다

□ **shot** 주사
→ an act of putting something such as medicine or vaccine into the body with a needle
약이나 백신 같은 어떤 것을 바늘로 몸 안에 주입하는 일

□ **success** 성공
→ the fact of getting or achieving wealth, respect, or fame
부, 존경 또는 명성을 얻거나 달성함

□ **victim** 피해자, 희생자
→ a person who has been attacked, injured, robbed, or killed by someone else
다른 누군가에게 공격받거나 다치거나 강탈당하거나 죽임을 당한 사람

01 다음 중 단어의 성격이 <u>다른</u> 하나는?

① writer   ② danger

③ traveler   ④ director

⑤ invader

중요
02 다음 빈칸에 알맞은 말이 바르게 짝지어진 것은?

> • Mary didn't show _____ for the meeting yesterday.
> • Eating too many snacks is not good _____ your health.

① into – at   ② up – for

③ on – in   ④ out – with

⑤ off – over

중요
03 다음 영영풀이에 해당하는 단어로 알맞은 것은?

> to increase in number by reproducing

① defend   ② scratch

③ invade   ④ multiply

⑤ protect

서답형
04 다음 짝지어진 단어의 관계가 같도록 빈칸에 알맞은 말을 쓰시오.

> hard : easy = defend : _____

05 다음 우리말에 맞게 빈칸에 알맞은 것은?

> 너는 다음 월요일에 참석할 수 있니?
> ➡ Can you _____ it next Monday?

① do   ② take

③ get   ④ have

⑤ make

서답형
06 다음 영영풀이에 해당하는 단어를 쓰시오.

> any one of the very small parts that together form all living things

➡ _____

서답형
07 다음 우리말에 맞게 빈칸에 알맞은 말을 쓰시오.

> 그런데, 너는 누구와 함께 갔니?
> ➡ _____ _____ _____, who did you go with?

08 다음 빈칸에 공통으로 알맞은 것은?

> • I like films with plenty _____ action.
> • I can't think _____ her name at the moment.

① in   ② of

③ up   ④ about

⑤ at

01 다음 짝지어진 두 단어의 관계가 같도록 빈칸에 알맞은 말을 쓰시오.

(1) paint : painter = act : _____
(2) art : artist = cartoon : _____
(3) invent : _____ = write : writer

02 다음 우리말에 맞게 빈칸에 알맞은 말을 쓰시오.

(1) 바이러스는 독감과 같은 질병을 일으킨다.
   ➡ Viruses cause diseases _____
   _____ the flu.
(2) 그녀는 그녀의 독특한 그림으로 유명하다.
   ➡ She _____ _____ _____ her
   unique paintings.
(3) 며칠 후에, 너는 기분이 좋아지기 시작한다.
   ➡ In a _____ _____, you start to
   feel better.

03 다음 빈칸에 들어갈 알맞은 말을 <보기>에서 골라 쓰시오.

┌─ 보기 ┐
digest balanced germs multiply
└────────┘

(1) When _____ enter your body, they
   can make you sick.
(2) When we eat, our bodies _____ food.
(3) Bacteria _____ quickly in warm food.
(4) A _____ diet will keep your body
   strong and healthy.

04 다음 괄호 안의 말을 문맥에 맞게 고쳐 쓰시오.

(1) I hope you are always _____ and
   happy. (health)
(2) _____, we arrived there on time.
   (luck)
(3) Some robots do _____ jobs for
   humans. (danger)

05 다음 빈칸에 알맞은 말을 <보기>에서 골라 쓰시오.

┌─ 보기 ┐
plenty of   good for
show up   catch a cold
└────────┘

(1) Still, Jane does not _____.
(2) Fruits are _____ your health.
(3) That store has _____ customers.
(4) If you _____, you will cough a
   lot.

06 다음 영영풀이에 해당하는 단어를 주어진 철자로 시작하여 쓰시오.

(1) s_____ : to rub your skin with your
   fingernails because it feels
   uncomfortable
(2) v_____ : a person who has been
   attacked, injured, robbed, or
   killed by someone else
(3) b_____ : any one of a group of very
   small living things that often
   cause disease

Conversation

1 증상 묻고 답하기

A What's wrong with you? 무슨 일이니?
B I have a toothache. 이가 아파.

■ What's wrong with you?는 '무슨 일이니?'의 뜻으로 상대방이 몸이 아파 보이거나 우울해 보일 때 사용하는 표현이다.
  - A: What's wrong with you, Jake? 너 왜 그래, Jake?
    B: I have a terrible headache. 머리가 몹시 아파.

증상을 묻는 표현

- What's wrong (with you)?
- What's the matter (with you)?
- What happened (to you)?
- What's the problem (with you)?
- What seems to be the problem?

증상 묻기에 답하기

- I have a cold. 감기에 걸렸어.
- I have a stomachache. 배가 아파.
- I have a sore throat. 목이 아파.
- I cut my finger. 손가락을 베었어.
- I broke my leg. 다리가 부러졌어.

- I have a toothache. 이가 아파.
- I have a runny nose. 콧물이 나와.
- I have a headache. 머리가 아파.
- I have a fever. 열이 나.

핵심 Check

1. 다음 우리말과 일치하도록 빈칸에 알맞은 말을 쓰시오.

(1) A: What's _____? (무슨 일이야?)
   B: I have a _____. (배가 아파.)

(2) A: What's the _____? You look worried. (무슨 일이야? 걱정돼 보인다.)
   B: I have a _____ _____. (콧물이 나와.)

(3) A: _____ seems to be the _____? (무슨 문제가 있니?)
   B: I _____ _____ _____. (이가 아파.)

2 약속 정하기

A Can you make it at three? 3시에 올 수 있니?

B That's fine with me. 난 괜찮아.

- Can you make it at three?는 '3시에 올 수 있니?'라는 뜻으로 약속을 정할 때 쓰는 표현이다. make it 은 '해내다, 성공하다'라는 의미를 갖고 있지만, 시간이나 장소의 표현과 함께 쓰여 '시간에 맞춰 가다' 또는 '도착하다'라는 의미를 갖는다.

약속 정하기 표현

- Can we meet at six? 6시에 만날까?
- Why don't we meet at six?
- How[What] about meeting at six?
- Shall we meet at six?
- Let's meet at six.

약속 정하기에 답하는 표현

승낙하기 • That's fine with me. / No problem. / Why not? / Sure, I'd love to. / That's a good idea. / (That) Sounds great.

거절하기 • I'm sorry, I can't. / I'm afraid not. / I'd love to, but I can't. / Not this time, thanks. / Maybe next time.

핵심 Check

2. 다음 우리말과 일치하도록 빈칸에 알맞은 말을 쓰시오.

(1) **A:** Can you _____ _____ at five at the bus stop? (너는 5시에 버스 정류장에 올 수 있니?)

  B: _____. See you _____. (물론이지. 그때 보자.)

(2) **A:** _____ _____ _____ to the movie theater tomorrow?
  (우리 내일 영화관에 가는 게 어때?)

  B: No _____. (문제없어.)

(3) **A:** _____ _____ basketball this Saturday. (이번 토요일에 농구하자.)

  B: _____, _____ _____. (미안하지만, 못하겠어.)

Communicate: Listen - Listen and Answer Dialog 1

B: ❶Can I go home early, Ms. Song? I don't feel so good.

W: ❷What seems to be the problem?

B: ❸I have a terrible stomachache. ❹It really hurts.

W: ❺Why don't you get some medicine at the nurse's office?

B: I already did. But it didn't help.

W: Okay. ❻You can go. ❼Go see a doctor, okay?

B: ❽Sure. Thanks.

B: 송 선생님. 집에 일찍 가도 될까요? 몸이 너무 안 좋아요.

W: 무슨 문제가 있니?

B: 배가 너무 아파요. 정말 아파요.

W: 양호실에서 약을 좀 먹는 게 어떠니?

B: 벌써 먹었어요. 하지만 도움이 되지 않았어요.

W: 알겠다. 가도 돼. 병원에 가 봐, 알았지?

B: 물론이죠. 고맙습니다.

❶ Can{May] I + 동사원형 ~?: 내가 ~해도 될까?(상대방에게 허락을 구할 때 쓰는 표현) ❷ What seems to be the problem?: 어디가 안 좋으니? (증상을 물을 때 쓰는 표현) ❸ have a terrible stomachache: 배가 너무 아프다 ❹ hurt: 아프다 ❺ Why don't you + 동사원형 ~?: ~하는 게 어때? / get some medicine: 약을 좀 먹다 / nurse's office: 양호실 ❻ can: ~해도 좋다, ~해도 된다(허락의 의미를 나타냄) ❼ go see a doctor = go and see a doctor = go to see a doctor / 명령어, okay?: ~해라, 알았지? (제안, 권유하는 표현) ❽ 제안이나 권유에 승낙하는 표현이다.

Check(√) True or False

(1) The boy has a terrible stomachache. T ☐ F ☐

(2) The boy got some medicine at the hospital. T ☐ F ☐

Communicate: Listen - Listen and Answer Dialog 2

(*The phone rings.*)

B: Hello, Sora.

G: Hi, Jongha. ❶I heard you were sick. ❷Are you okay now?

B: Yes, ❸I went to the doctor, and I feel better now.

G: Good to hear that. ❹By the way, I called you to talk about our science project.

B: Yeah, we should meet. ❺Can you make it tomorrow?

G: Okay. ❻Let's meet at Simpson's Donuts at nine.

B: At nine? That's too early. I sleep late on the weekend.

G: ❼How about 10 then?

B: ❽That sounds fine.

(전화벨이 울린다.)

B: 여보세요, 소라야.

G: 안녕, 종하야. 아프다고 들었어. 이제 좀 괜찮니?

B: 응, 병원에 갔었는데, 이제 좀 나아졌어.

G: 다행이구나. 그런데, 우리 과학 프로젝트에 대해 얘기하려고 전화했어.

B: 그래, 우리 만나야겠다. 내일 만날 수 있니?

G: 좋아. 9시에 Simpson's Donuts에서 만나자.

B: 9시? 너무 일러. 난 주말에 늦잠을 자.

G: 그럼 10시는 어때?

B: 괜찮아.

❶ I heard (that) + 주어 + 동사 ~: 나는 ~라고 들었어.(들은 사실을 말할 때 쓰는 표현) ❷ 상대방이 안 좋아 보일 때 사용하는 표현이다. ❸ go to the doctor: 의사의 진찰을 받다, 병원에 가다 / feel better: 몸이 나아지다 ❹ by the way: 그런데, 그건 그렇고(화제를 바꿀 때 사용하는 표현) / to talk: to부정사의 부사적 용법(목적) ❺ Can you make it ~?: ~에 만날 수 있니? (약속 시간을 제안하는 표현) ❻ Let's meet + 동사원형 ~: ~에서 만나자 ❼ How about ~?: ~은 어때? ❽ 약속 제안에 승낙하는 표현이다.

Check(√) True or False

(3) Sora called Jongha to talk about their science project. T ☐ F ☐

(4) Sora and Jongha will meet at nine. T ☐ F ☐

Communicate: Listen - Listen More

M: Hi, Minsol. ❶What's wrong with your dog?

G: ❷She keeps scratching herself. ❸Actually, she lost some hair.

M: When did she first have the problem?

G: ❹About three days ago.

M: ❺Let me see. (pause) She has a virus on her skin. ❻I'll give you some medicine.

G: Thank you.

M: I need to check your dog again. Can you make it next Monday?

G: ❽That's fine with me.

M: Okay. See you.

❶ What's wrong with ~?: ~에게 무슨 문제가 있니?
❷ keep -ing: 계속해서 ~하다
❸ actually: 사실 / lose some hair: 털이 좀 빠지다
❹ about three days ago: 약 3일 전에
❺ Let me see.: 어디 보자
❻ give + 간접목적어 + 직접목적어 = give + 직접목적어 + to + 간접목적어: ~에게 ...을 주다
❼ Can you make it ~?: ~에 올 수 있니?
❽ That's fine with me.: 전 괜찮아요.

Communicate: Listen - All Ears

W: 1. ❶Can you make it next Friday?
2. ❷What's wrong with your cat?

❶ Can you make it ~?: ~에 만날까?
❷ What's wrong with ~?: ~에게 무슨 문제가 있니?

Communicate: Speak 2 - Talk in pairs

A: ❶What's wrong with you?

B: ❷I have a sore throat.

A: ❸That's too bad. ❹You should drink some water.

B: ❺Okay, I will.

❶ What's wrong with you?: 무슨 일 있니? = What's the matter? = Is something wrong? = What's the problem? = What happened (to you)?
❷ have a sore throat: 목이 아프다
❸ That's too bad.: 안됐구나. (동정하는 표현)
❹ You should + 동사원형 ~.: 너는 ~해야 해. (충고하는 표현)
❺ 충고에 수락하는 표현이다.

Communicate: Speak 2 - Talk in groups

A: ❶Let's play basketball this Saturday.

B: ❷Sure, why not?

A: ❸Can you make it at ten?

B: That's fine with me. ❹Where should we meet?

A: ❺Let's meet at the school gym.

B: ❻Okay. See you there.

❶ Let's ~: ~하자
❷ 제안에 수락하는 표현이다. / Why not?: 좋고말고.
❸ Can you make it at ~?: ~에 만날 수 있니?
❹ 약속 장소를 정할 때 사용하는 표현이다.
❺ Let's meet at ~: ~에서 만나자.(약속 장소를 정할 때 쓰는 표현) / school gym: 학교 체육관
❻ Okay.: 좋아. (제안을 수락하는 표현) = Sure. = Of course. = No problem. = Why not? 등

Wrap Up - Listening ❺

B: Mom, ❶I don't feel well.

W: ❷What seems to be the problem?

B: ❸I think I have a fever.

W: Really? Let me see. Umm, ❹you do have a fever. ❺I'll get you some medicine.

B: Thank you, Mom.

❶ I don't feel well: 몸이 좋지 않아.
❷ What seems to be the problem?: 어디가 안 좋으니?
❸ have a fever: 열이 나다
❹ do: 동사를 강조하는 do
❺ get + 간접목적어 + 직접목적어 = get + 직접목적어 + for + 간접목적어: ~에게 ...을 갖다 주다

Wrap Up - Listening ❻

G: ❶I'm thinking of going to the Comics Museum tomorrow. ❷Will you come with me?

B: I really want to go.

G: ❸Can you make it at 11?

B: ❹That's fine with me.

G: Okay. ❺Let's meet at the subway station.

❶ I'm thinking of -ing ~: 나는 ~할 생각이다
❷ Will you + 동사원형 ~?: ~할 거니?
❸ Can you make it at ~?: ~에 만날 수 있니?
❹ That's fine with me. 난 괜찮아. (제안에 수락하는 표현) = Sure. = Of course. = No problem. = Why not? 등
❺ Let' meet at + 장소: ~에서 만나자. / subway station: 지하철역

● 다음 우리말과 일치하도록 빈칸에 알맞은 말을 쓰시오.

Communicate: Listen - Listen and Answer Dialog 1

B: _____ I go home _____, Ms. Song? I _____ _____ so good.

W: What _____ _____ be the problem?

B: I _____ a terrible _____. It really _____.

W: _____ _____ you get some _____ at the nurse's office?

B: I _____ did. But it _____ _____.

W: Okay. You _____ go. _____ _____ a doctor, okay?

B: _____. Thanks.

Communicate: Listen - Listen and Answer Dialog 2

(*The phone rings.*)

B: Hello, Sora.

G: Hi, Jongha. I _____ you were sick. Are you _____ now?

B: Yes, I went to _____ _____, and I _____ _____ now.

G: Good _____ _____ that. _____ _____, I called you _____ _____ about our science project.

B: Yeah, we _____ _____. Can you _____ _____ tomorrow?

G: Okay. _____ _____ at Simpson's Donuts _____ nine.

B: At nine? That's too _____. I sleep _____ on the weekend.

G: _____ _____ 10 then?

B: That _____ fine.

Communicate: Listen - Listen More

M: Hi, Minsol. What's _____ _____ your dog?

G: She keeps _____ herself. Actually, she _____ some _____.

M: When did she first _____ _____ _____?

G: _____ three days _____.

M: _____ me _____. (*pause*) She _____ _____ _____ on her skin. I'll give you some medicine.

G: Thank you.

M: I _____ _____ _____ your dog again. _____ you _____ it next Monday?

G: That's _____ _____ me.

M: Okay. _____ you.

해석

B: 송 선생님, 집에 일찍 가도 될까요? 몸이 너무 안 좋아요.
W: 무슨 문제가 있니?
B: 배가 너무 아파요. 정말 아파요.
W: 양호실에서 약을 좀 먹는 게 어떠니?
B: 벌써 먹었어요. 하지만 도움이 되지 않았어요.
W: 알겠다. 가도 돼. 병원에 가봐, 알았지?
B: 물론이죠. 고맙습니다.

(전화벨이 울린다.)
B: 여보세요, 소라야.
G: 안녕, 종하야. 아프다고 들었어. 이제 좀 괜찮니?
B: 응, 병원에 갔었는데, 이제 좀 나아졌어.
G: 다행이구나. 그런데, 우리 과학 프로젝트에 대해 얘기하려고 전화했어.
B: 그래, 우리 만나야겠다. 내일 만날 수 있니?
G: 좋아. 9시에 Simpson's Donuts에서 만나자.
B: 9시? 너무 일러. 난 주말에 늦잠을 자.
G: 그럼 10시는 어때?
B: 괜찮아.

M: 안녕, 민솔. 너의 개에게 무슨 문제가 있니?
G: 계속 자기 몸을 긁어요. 사실, 털이 좀 빠졌어요.
M: 너의 개는 언제 처음으로 문제가 생겼니?
G: 약 3일 전에요.
M: 어디 보자. (잠시 멈춘다) 피부에 바이러스가 있어. 약을 좀 줄게.
G: 감사합니다.
M: 네 개를 다시 확인할 필요가 있어. 다음 주 월요일에 올 수 있니?
G: 좋아요.
M: 알겠다. 나중에 보자.

Communicate: Listen - All Ears

M: 1. Can you _____ it next Friday?

2. What's _____ with your cat?

Communicate: Speak 2 - Talk in pairs

A: _____ _____ with you?

B: I _____ a _____ _____.

A: That's too _____. You _____ _____ some water.

B: Okay, I _____.

Communicate: Speak 2 - Talk in groups

A: _____ play basketball this Saturday.

B: Sure, _____ _____?

A: _____ _____ _____ it at ten?

B: That's fine _____ me. Where _____ we _____?

A: _____ meet _____ the school gym.

B: Okay. _____ _____ there.

Wrap Up - Listening ❺

B: Mom, I _____ _____ well.

W: _____ seems to be the _____?

B: I think I _____ _____ _____.

W: Really? _____ _____ _____. Umm, you _____ have a fever. I'll _____ _____ _____ _____.

B: _____ you, Mom.

Wrap Up - Listening ❻

G: I'm _____ _____ going to the Comics Museum tomorrow. Will you _____ _____ me?

B: I really want _____ _____.

G: Can you _____ _____ _____ 11?

B: That's _____ _____ me.

G: Okay. _____ meet _____ the subway station.

해석

W 1. 다음 주 금요일에 만날까?
2. 너의 고양이에게 무슨 문제가 있니?

A: 무슨 일 있니?
B: 목이 아파.
A: 그것 참 안됐구나. 너는 물을 좀 마셔야 해.
B: 알았어, 그럴게.

A: 이번 토요일에 농구하자.
B: 물론, 좋고말고.
A: 10시에 만날 수 있니?
B: 난 괜찮아. 우리 어디서 만날까?
A: 학교 체육관에서 만나자.
B: 알았어, 거기서 보자.

B: 엄마, 몸이 안 좋아요.
W: 뭐가 문제인 것 같니?
B: 열이 있는 것 같아요.
W: 정말? 어디 보자. 음, 정말 열이 있네. 약을 좀 갖다 줄게.
B: 고마워요, 엄마.

G: 내일 만화 박물관에 갈 생각이야. 나하고 같이 갈래?
B: 정말 가고 싶어.
G: 11시에 만날 수 있니?
B: 난 괜찮아.
G: 좋아. 지하철역에서 만나자.

[01~02] 다음 밑줄 친 말과 바꾸어 쓸 수 있는 것을 고르시오.

01

> A: What time should we meet tomorrow?
> B: Can you make it at five?

① Let's go there.
② Let's meet tomorrow.
③ Let's meet at five.
④ How about meeting together?
⑤ I can't make it at five.

02

> A: What's wrong?
> B: I have a terrible headache.

① Why not?
② What's that?
③ How are you?
④ What's the problem?
⑤ What are you doing?

[03~04] 다음 대화의 빈칸에 알맞은 것을 고르시오.

03

> A: Let's go see a movie tomorrow.
> B: Good idea!
> A: _____
> B: Okay. Let's meet at 5 o'clock.

① Where can we meet?
② When can you come?
③ How would you like it?
④ Can you make it at 5?
⑤ What time shall we meet?

04

> A: _____
> B: Well, I have a sore throat.

① How come?
② What's wrong?
③ How are you?
④ How do you do?
⑤ What are you doing?

[01~05] 다음 대화를 읽고, 물음에 답하시오.

B: Can I go home early, Ms. Song? I don't feel so good.

W: ⓐWhat seems to be the problem?

B: I have a terrible stomachache. It really hurts.

W: ⓑWhy don't you get some medicine at the nurse's office?

B: I already did. But it didn't help.

W: Okay. You ⓒcan go. Go see a doctor, okay?

B: Sure. Thanks.

 위 대화의 밑줄 친 ⓐ와 바꿔 쓸 수 있는 것은?

① What's your opinion?

② How's it going?

③ How did it happen?

④ Why is it a problem?

⑤ What's the matter with you?

02 위 대화의 밑줄 친 ⓑ를 다음과 같이 바꿔 쓸 때 빈칸에 알맞은 말을 쓰시오.

_____ _____ _____ some medicine at the nurse's office?

 위 대화의 밑줄 친 ⓒ와 쓰임이 같은 것은?

① The child can't walk yet.

② He can speak German very well.

③ Can the rumor be true?

④ You can go out and play outdoors.

⑤ Can you speak any foreign languages?

04 위 대화에서 다음 영영풀이에 해당하는 단어를 찾아 쓰시오.

pain in or near your stomach

➡ _____

05 위 대화의 내용과 일치하지 않는 것은?

① 소년은 몸이 좋지 않다.

② 소년은 배가 약간 아프다.

③ 소년은 약을 먹었지만 소용이 없었다.

④ 송 선생님은 소년이 집에 가는 것을 허락해 주었다.

⑤ 소년은 병원에 갈 것이다.

[06~09] 다음 대화를 읽고, 물음에 답하시오.

A: Let's play basketball this Saturday.

B: _____ ⓐ

A: ⓑCan you make it at ten?

B: That's fine with me. _____ ⓒ

A: Let's meet at the school gym.

B: Okay. See you there.

 위 대화의 빈칸 ⓐ에 알맞지 않은 것은?

① Of course.

② No problem.

③ That's a good idea.

④ I'm afraid I can't.

⑤ Sure, why not?

07 위 대화의 밑줄 친 ⓑ를 다음과 같이 바꿔 쓸 때 빈칸에 알맞은 말을 쓰시오.

Can we _____ at ten?

08 위 대화의 빈칸 ⓒ에 알맞은 것은?

① When can you come?

② Where should we meet?

③ How would you like it?

④ Who can play with us?

⑤ What time shall we meet?

09 위 대화를 읽고, 다음 질문에 완전한 문장으로 답하시오.

> Q: What time and where will "A" and "B" meet?
>
> A: _____

[10~15] 다음 대화를 읽고, 물음에 답하시오.

> (*The phone rings.*)
>
> B: Hello, Sora.
>
> G: Hi, Jongha. I heard you were sick.
> _____
>
> B: Yes, I went to the doctor, and I feel better now.
>
> G: Good to hear that. ⓑ그런데, I called you to talk about our science project.
>
> B: Yeah, we should meet. ⓒCan you make it tomorrow?
>
> G: Okay. _____ⓓ_____ meet at Simpson's Donuts at nine.
>
> B: At nine? That's too early. I sleep _____ⓔ_____ on the weekend.
>
> G: How about 10 then?
>
> B: That sounds fine.

10 위 대화의 빈칸 ⓐ에 알맞은 것은?

① Are you busy now?

② Do you feel sad?

③ Are you okay now?

④ What are you doing?

⑤ Did you take your medicine?

11 위 대화의 밑줄 친 ⓑ의 우리말을 세 단어로 쓰시오.

➡ _____

12 위 대화의 밑줄 친 ⓒ와 바꿔 쓸 수 <u>없는</u> 것은?

① Let's meet tomorrow.

② Shall we meet tomorrow?

③ How about meeting tomorrow?

④ Will you meet tomorrow?

⑤ Why don't we meet tomorrow?

13 위 대화의 빈칸 ⓓ에 알맞은 것은?

① You can   ② Let's

③ I'd like to   ④ We will

⑤ You have to

14 위 대화의 빈칸 ⓔ에 다음 영영풀이에 해당하는 단어를 쓰시오.

> after the usual or expected time

➡ _____

15 위 대화를 읽고, 답할 수 <u>없는</u> 질문은?

① Why did Jongha go to the doctor?

② Why did Sora call Jongha?

③ Where will Sora and Jongha meet?

④ What time will they meet?

⑤ Until when should they finish their science project?

[01~02] 다음 대화를 읽고, 물음에 답하시오.

A: _____ ⓐ _____
B: Well, I have a headache.
A: That's too bad. ⓑ좀 쉬는 게 어때?
B: OK, I will.

01 위 대화의 빈칸 ⓐ에 들어갈 말을 2가지 이상 쓰시오.

➡ _____
_____

02 위 대화의 밑줄 친 ⓑ의 우리말을 괄호 안의 단어를 이용하여 영어로 쓰시오.

(why, get, rest)

➡ _____

[03~05] 다음 대화를 읽고, 물음에 답하시오.

A: Let's play basketball this Saturday.
B: Sure, why not?
A: ⓐCan you make it at ten?
B: That's fine with me. ⓑ우리 어디서 만날까?
A: Let's meet at the school gym.
B: Okay. See you ⓒthere.

03 위 대화의 밑줄 친 ⓐ를 다음과 같이 바꿔 쓸 때 빈칸에 알맞은 말을 쓰시오.

How about _____ at ten?

04 위 대화의 밑줄 친 ⓑ의 우리말을 주어진 단어를 이용하여 영작하시오. (4 words)

(should)

➡ _____

05 위 대화의 밑줄 친 ⓒ가 가리키는 말을 영어로 쓰시오.

➡ _____

[06~09] 다음 대화를 읽고, 물음에 답하시오.

M: Hi, Minsol. ⓐWhat's wrong with your dog?
G: She keeps (A)[scratching / to scratch] herself. Actually, she lost some hair.
M: When did she first have the problem?
G: About three days (B)[before / ago].
M: Let me see. (pause) She has a virus on her skin. I'll give you some medicine.
G: Thank you.
M: I need to check your dog again. ⓑ다음 월요일에 올 수 있니?
G: That's fine with me.
M: Okay. See you.

06 위 대화의 밑줄 친 ⓐ를 다음과 같이 바꿔 쓸 때 빈칸에 알맞은 말을 쓰시오.

What's the _____ with your dog?

07 위 대화의 밑줄 친 ⓑ의 우리말을 주어진 단어를 이용하여 영작하시오.

(make)

➡ _____

08 위 대화의 (A)~(B)에서 어법상 알맞은 것을 골라 쓰시오.

(A) _____ (B) _____

09 위 대화를 읽고, 민솔이네 개의 증상을 우리말로 모두 쓰시오.

➡ _____

1 가주어 it

> - **It** is not easy **to take** good care of a pet. 애완동물을 잘 돌보는 것은 쉽지 않다.
> - **It** is fun **to learn** to swim. 수영을 배우는 것은 재미있다.
> - **It** will be nice **to become** a musician. 음악가가 되는 것은 멋질 거야.

■ **가주어 it**

to부정사구가 문장 안에서 주어로 쓰일 경우, to부정사구를 문장의 뒤로 보내고 그 자리에 it을 쓴다. 이 때의 it은 아무런 의미가 없는 주어로 '가주어'라고 하고, to부정사구를 '진주어'라고 한다.

- To master English in a month is impossible. 영어를 한 달 동안에 습득하는 것은 불가능하다.

  → **It** is impossible **to master** English in a month.
  　　가주어　　　　　　진주어

cf. to부정사 이외에도 진주어로 명사절이 쓰일 때가 있다. 이때 명사절을 이끄는 접속사는 보통 that이 쓰인다.

- **It** is a bad habit **that** people read in bed. 침대에서 독서하는 것은 나쁜 버릇이다.

■ **to부정사의 의미상의 주어**

to부정사의 의미상 주어가 문장의 주어와 일치하지 않는 경우, 일반적으로 「for+목적격」의 형태로 진주어 앞에 쓴다. kind, foolish, wise, honest, polite 등과 같이 사람의 성격을 나타내는 형용사가 보어로 쓰이면 의미상의 주어로 「of+목적격」의 형태를 쓴다.

- **It** is natural **for** your parents **to get** angry. 너의 부모님이 화를 내시는 것은 당연하다.

- **It** is very kind **of** you **to help** me. 나를 도와주다니 넌 참 친절하다.

핵심 Check

1. 다음 괄호 안에서 알맞은 것을 고르시오.

(1) It is hard (understanding / to understand) his words.

(2) (It / That) is interesting to watch basketball.

(3) It is good for your health (to exercise / exercise) every day.

(4) It is honest (for / of) you to say so.

(5) It is not easy (for / of) us to learn foreign languages.

② to부정사의 형용사적 용법

- Jay has the ability **to make** people happy. Jay는 사람들을 행복하게 만드는 능력이 있다.
- They need something **to drink**. 그들은 마실 것이 필요하다.
- I have a lot of homework **to do** tonight. 나는 오늘밤 해야 할 숙제가 많다.

■ to부정사의 형용사적 용법은 명사나 대명사 뒤에서 '~하는, ~할'의 뜻으로 쓰인다. 이 때 앞의 명사는 to부정사의 주어 또는 목적어 역할을 한다.

- I have no money **to give** you. (목적어) 나는 너에게 줄 돈이 없다.
  = I have no money that I can give you.

- He had no friends **to help** him. (주어) 그는 자기를 도와줄 친구가 하나도 없었다.
  = He had no friends who would help him.

■ to부정사의 수식을 받는 명사가 전치사의 목적어일 경우, to부정사 뒤에 전치사가 온다.

- Ann has elderly parents **to look** after. Ann은 돌보아야 할 나이 드신 부모가 있다.
- I want a small room **to live** in by myself. 나는 혼자 살 작은 방을 원한다.

■ -thing으로 끝나는 부정대명사는 「-thing+(형용사+)to부정사」의 어순을 따른다.

- I want something cold **to drink**. 나는 차가운 마실 것을 원한다.
- You think that you have nothing **to wear**. 너는 입을 것이 아무것도 없다고 생각한다.

핵심 Check

2. 다음 괄호 안에서 알맞은 것을 고르시오.

(1) It's time (going / to go) to school.

(2) Jack has a lot of friends (helping / to help).

(3) Give me a pen (to write / to write with).

(4) Would you like something (to cold drink / cold to drink)?

Grammar 시험대비 기본평가

01 다음 괄호 안에서 알맞은 것을 고르시오.

(1) (It / That) is fun to travel to some countries in Asia.

(2) Do you have anything (to do / doing) this evening?

(3) There are many places (visit / to visit) in Jeju.

(4) It is hard (of / for) me to solve this problem.

(5) It is very kind (of / for) you to help me.

> travel 여행하다
> solve 풀다

02 다음 우리말과 일치하도록 빈칸에 알맞은 말을 쓰시오.

(1) 우리는 일정을 바꿀 시간이 없다.

➡ We have no time _____ _____ the schedule.

(2) 그는 우리나라를 방문한 최초의 미국인이었다.

➡ He was the first American _____ _____ our country.

(3) 우리에게 그늘을 드리워줄 나무가 전혀 없었다.

➡ There were no trees _____ _____ us shade.

> schedule 일정
> offer 제공하다
> shade 그늘

03 다음 문장에서 어법상 틀린 것을 찾아 바르게 고쳐 쓰시오.

(1) It's difficult exercise every day.

_____ ➡ _____

(2) It is impossible finish this work in an hour.

_____ ➡ _____

(3) That is very important to learn a foreign language.

_____ ➡ _____

(4) It was brave for him to save the child.

_____ ➡ _____

(5) It was easy of me to answer all the questions.

_____ ➡ _____

> exercise 운동하다
> impossible 불가능한
> save 구하다

01 다음 중 밑줄 친 부분의 쓰임이 나머지 넷과 <u>다른</u> 것은?

① He is always the first <u>to come</u>.

② He has nothing <u>to write</u> with.

③ He went to England <u>to study</u> English.

④ There are a lot of things for him <u>to do</u>.

⑤ He was looking for an apartment <u>to live</u> in.

[02~03] 다음 문장의 빈칸에 알맞은 것을 고르시오.

02

It is good for the health _____ early.

① get up   ② got up

③ to get up   ④ to getting up

⑤ to be getting up

03

Do you have anything _____?

① read   ② reads

③ reading   ④ to read

⑤ to be reading

서답형
04 다음 두 문장의 뜻이 같도록 빈칸에 알맞은 말을 쓰시오.

I have a lot of letters _____ _____.
= I have a lot of letters that I should write.

서답형
05 다음 두 문장의 뜻이 같도록 빈칸에 알맞은 말을 쓰시오.

To change the schedule is very difficult.
= _____ is very difficult _____ the schedule.

중요
06 다음 중 밑줄 친 부분의 쓰임이 〈보기〉와 같은 것은?

─┤ 보기 ├─
I have lots of books <u>to read</u> by next month.

① Jina has no chair <u>to sit</u> on.

② My hobby is <u>to listen</u> to music.

③ She is glad <u>to get</u> a letter from Ted.

④ He wants <u>to play</u> baseball after school.

⑤ I went to the market <u>to buy</u> some eggs.

07 다음 우리말과 같도록 할 때, 빈칸에 알맞은 말이 바르게 짝지어진 것은?

자전거를 탈 때는 헬맷을 쓰는 것이 안전하다.
= _____ is safe _____ a helmet when you ride a bike.

① It − to wear   ② This − wear

③ It − wears   ④ It − wear

⑤ That − to wear

서답형

08 다음 우리말과 일치하도록 주어진 단어를 바르게 배열하여 문장을 완성하시오.

> 너 뭐 좀 먹을래?
> (anything, you, want, do, eat, to)

➡ _____

_____

09 다음 밑줄 친 it의 쓰임이 나머지 넷과 다른 하나는?

① It's important to be kind to others.
② Is it fun to play computer games?
③ It is not surprising for him to say so.
④ It's hard to believe, but it's a flower.
⑤ It's not easy to understand other cultures.

중요

10 다음 중 어법상 어색한 문장은?

① It's almost time to go to bed.
② It's time to get aboard a plane.
③ It is time to eat dinner.
④ It's time for the children to going to bed.
⑤ It's time for my dad to buy a new car.

서답형

11 다음 괄호 안에 주어진 말을 사용하여 우리말을 영작하시오.

> 그 기계를 고치는 것은 어렵다.
> (it, difficult, fix, machine)

➡ _____

12 다음 빈칸에 알맞은 말이 바르게 짝지어진 것은?

> • It is very kind _____ you to say so.
> • It is natural _____ a baby to cry.

① of – of
② of – for
③ for – for
④ for – of
⑤ for – with

중요

13 다음 빈칸에 공통으로 알맞은 것은?

> • It was honest _____ you to tell the truth.
> • It is wise _____ her to make such a decision.

① of
② for
③ with
④ at
⑤ upon

14 다음 빈칸에 들어갈 동사의 형태로 적절한 것은?

> It's necessary _____ on time.

① to be
② is
③ be
④ are
⑤ will be

서답형

15 다음 빈칸에 공통으로 알맞은 말을 쓰시오.

> • You don't have _____ worry about it.
> • I have no reason _____ be angry at you.

16 다음 문장의 빈칸에 to를 쓸 수 없는 것은?

① It is natural for your mom _____ get angry.
② She hopes _____ visit her uncle.
③ He is kind enough _____ help us.
④ It is easy _____ speak English.
⑤ She made me _____ wash the dishes.

서답형

17 다음 문장에서 어법상 어색한 부분을 찾아 바르게 고쳐 쓰시오.

> I need a chair to sit.

_____ ➡ _____

18 다음 중 밑줄 친 부분의 쓰임이 나머지 넷과 다른 것은?

① It will soon be a new year.
② Is it easy to use this camera?
③ It is a lot of fun to ski in winter.
④ It isn't difficult to use the computer.
⑤ It is interesting to read English books.

19 다음 밑줄 친 부분의 쓰임이 바르지 않은 것은?

① There is no chair to sit on.
② I have no money to give you.
③ Judy has a lot of friends to talk.
④ She doesn't have a house to live in.
⑤ Do you have a pen to write with?

20 다음 중 밑줄 친 to부정사의 쓰임이 나머지와 다른 하나는?

① It is important to try your best.
② My dream is to be a singer.
③ I want a house to live in.
④ I decided to study Spanish.
⑤ It is very kind of you to help me.

서답형

21 다음 주어진 어구를 이용하여 〈보기〉와 같이 문장을 쓰시오.

> ┤ 보기 ├
> boring, watch news on TV
> → It is boring to watch news on TV.

> pleasant, listen to music
> ➡ _____

22 다음 빈칸에 들어갈 말이 바르게 짝지어진 것은?

> • It's time for our children _____ to bed.
> • You don't have _____ an umbrella with you.

① go – take
② to go – taken
③ going – taking
④ going – to take
⑤ to go – to take

서답형

23 다음 문장에서 어법상 어색한 부분을 찾아 바르게 고쳐 쓰시오.

> It is necessary for you going there as soon as possible.

_____ ➡ _____

01 다음 빈칸에 공통으로 알맞은 말을 쓰시오.

> • Mike had no time _____ do his homework.
> • We are going to buy some paper _____ write on.

02 다음 두 문장의 뜻이 같도록 빈칸에 알맞은 말을 쓰시오.

> To cook French food is difficult.
> = _____ is difficult _____ cook French food.

03 다음 주어진 단어를 바르게 배열하여 문장을 완성하시오.

(1) (difficult / it / learn / is / to / English)
➡ _____

(2) (a magazine / on / he / read / the train / bought / to)
➡ _____

04 다음 밑줄 친 단어를 알맞은 형태로 고쳐 쓰시오.

> It is strange for her receive fan letters.

➡ _____

05 다음 괄호 안에 주어진 말을 사용하여 우리말을 영작하시오. (가주어 – 진주어 구문을 사용할 것.)

(1) 주말마다 그를 방문하는 것은 쉽지 않았다.
(visit, easy, every)

➡ _____

(2) 다른 나라에서 사는 것은 재미있는 경험이다.
(it, exciting, live, another)

➡ _____
_____

06 다음 괄호 안에 주어진 단어를 이용하여 우리말을 영어로 옮기시오.

(1) 그녀는 가수가 되려는 강한 욕망을 갖고 있다.
(strong desire, be, singer)

➡ _____

(2) 우리는 이야기할 것이 있었다.
(something, talk about)

➡ _____

(3) 나는 쓸 종이를 한 장 원한다.
(want, write)

➡ _____

(4) 제게 뜨거운 마실 것을 좀 주십시오.
(please, something, drink)

➡ _____

07 다음 문장에서 어법상 어색한 곳을 찾아 바르게 고쳐 쓰시오.

(1) He doesn't have time play with his friends.

_____ ➡ _____

(2) It is important of you to study hard.

_____ ➡ _____

08 다음 빈칸에 알맞은 말을 〈보기〉에서 골라 쓰시오. (중복해서 사용할 수 없음)

┌─── 보기 ───┐
to   on   with   it

(1) _____ is hard to follow good advice.
(2) Do you have anything to write _____?
(3) I need a knife to cut the rope _____.
(4) I have a lot of things _____ do today.

09 다음 두 문장의 뜻이 같도록 빈칸에 알맞은 말을 쓰시오

나는 같이 놀 친한 친구가 필요하다.
= I need my best friend _____
_____ _____.

10 다음 빈칸에 공통으로 들어갈 알맞은 말을 쓰시오.

• It's time for my father _____ come home.
• You don't have _____ water the flowers.

11 다음 두 문장이 같은 뜻이 되도록 빈칸에 알맞은 말을 쓰시오.

To learn to ride a bike was not difficult.
= _____ was not difficult _____ _____ to ride a bike.

12 다음 문장에서 어법상 어색한 곳을 찾아 바르게 고쳐 쓰시오.

(1) It was stupid for you to believe the rumor.

_____ ➡ _____

(2) It isn't necessary of you to come here today.

_____ ➡ _____

13 다음 주어진 단어를 이용하여 우리말을 영어로 옮기시오.

그곳은 24시간 동안 많은 물건들을 파는 장소이다.
(it's, a place, to sell, things)

➡ _____

Reading

Germs: The War Inside

Germs are everywhere, but it is impossible to see them with your
(~에) 있다   가주어   진주어
eyes.

There are two major kinds of germs: bacteria and viruses. Bacteria
~이 있다   두 가지 주요한 종류의   bacterium의 복수형
are very small creatures. Some are good. They can help you digest the
= Some bacteria   help+목적어(A)+원형부정사: A가 ~하는 것을 돕다
food that you eat. Others are bad and can make you sick. Viruses are
목적격 관계대명사   = Other bacteria   make+목적어+목적보어(형용사)
germs that can only live inside the cells of other living bodies. They
= which(주격 관계대명사) 오직(부사구 inside the cells of other living bodies를 수식) 살아 있는   = Viruses
cause diseases such as the flu.
~와 같은

"Bad" germs can enter your body through your skin, mouth, nose,
enter into (x)   ~을 통해
and eyes. What happens when they invade?
문장의 주어가 되는 의문대명사   ~할 때(접속사)

The germs multiply in the body. Your body becomes a war zone. You
~이 되다   주격보어
start to feel tired and weak.
start to: ~하기 시작하다

Luckily, your body has an army of defense. The T cells sound the
다행히도(문장 수식 부사)   경보를 발하다
alarm! The B cells arrive to fight the germs with antibodies. The
싸우기 위해(목적을 나타내는 부사적 용법)
macrophage cells show up and eat the germs. Together, this army is
나타나다   be동사+과거분사(수동태)
called the white blood cells. If all goes well, they win the fight. In a
주어 all이 사물을 나타내므로 단수동사로 받는다. 싸움에 이기다
few days, you start to feel better.
며칠 후에   good의 비교급

germ 세균	
everywhere 도처에	
impossible 불가능한	
major 주요한	
bacteria 박테리아	
virus 바이러스	
creature 생물	
digest 소화하다	
inside ~ 안에서	
cell 세포	
body 신체, 몸	
cause 일으키다, 야기하다	
disease 병	
such as ~와 같은	
flu 독감	
skin 피부	
happen 일어나다	
invade 침략하다	
multiply 증식하다	
zone 지역	
army 부대, 군대	
defense 방어	
antibody 항체	

 확인문제

● 다음 문장이 본문의 내용과 일치하면 T, 일치하지 않으면 F를 쓰시오.

1 We can see germs with our eyes. ☐

2 Bacteria and viruses are two major germs. ☐

3 Most bacteria are bad. ☐

4 Viruses cause diseases like the flu. ☐

5 Our body has an army of defense. ☐

The body remembers the invader, so it cannot make copies of itself
again. But the germs are smart, too. They can change form and trick
the body. There are several ways to protect yourself from germs. First,
wash your hands with soap and warm water. A balanced diet will keep
your body strong and healthy. It is also important to exercise regularly
and get plenty of sleep. Finally, get the necessary shots. They are the
best defense against germs. If you follow these steps, you will not be a
victim of "bad" germs.

Watch out! This is my spot! Hands off! Time to attack! Make more
copies of me. It's my job to defend the body. That was a nice meal! Are
there any more germs to eat? Next year, I'll send in my cousin. He'll
see you then for another fight! I'm ready to fight any germs. We give
up. We can't make you sick.

invader 침입자
copy 복사, 복제
smart 영리한
form 형태
trick 속이다
several 몇 개의
protect 보호하다
soap 비누
balanced 균형 잡힌
diet 다이어트, 식단
heathy 건강한
important 중요한
regularly 규칙적으로
plenty of 충분한
finally 마지막으로
necessary 필요한
shot 주사
step 단계, 조치
victim 희생자

확인문제

● 다음 문장이 본문의 내용과 일치하면 T, 일치하지 않으면 F를 쓰시오.

1　The invader can make copies of itself again though the body remembers it. ☐

2　The germs are smart enough to trick the body. ☐

3　You should wash your hands with soap and warm water to protect yourself from germs. ☐

4　The shots are not the best defense against the germs ☐

● 우리말을 참고하여 빈칸에 알맞은 말을 쓰시오.

1 Germs are _____, but it is impossible to _____ them with your eyes.

2 There are two major _____ of germs: _____ and viruses.

3 Bacteria are very small _____.

4 _____ are good.

5 They can help you _____ the food _____ you eat.

6 _____ are bad and can _____ you sick.

7 Viruses are germs _____ can only live _____ the cells of other _____ bodies.

8 They _____ diseases _____ as the flu.

9 "Bad" germs can _____ your body _____ your skin, mouth, nose, and eyes.

10 What _____ when they invade?

11 The germs _____ in the body.

12 Your _____ _____ a war _____.

13 You _____ to feel tired and _____.

14 Luckily, your _____ has an army of _____.

15 The T cells _____ the alarm!

16 The B cells _____ to fight the _____ with antibodies.

17 The macrophage cells _____ up and _____ the germs.

18 Together, this army is _____ the white blood _____.

19 If all _____ well, they win the _____.

20 In a _____ days, you start to _____ better.

1 세균은 어디에나 있지만 눈으로 세균을 보는 것은 불가능하다.

2 세균에는 두 가지 주요한 종류가 있다: 박테리아와 바이러스이다.

3 박테리아는 매우 작은 생물이다.

4 어떤 것들은 좋다.

5 그것들은 당신이 먹는 음식을 소화하는 데 도움을 줄 수 있다.

6 다른 것들은 나쁘고 당신을 아프게 할 수 있다.

7 바이러스는 다른 살아 있는 몸의 세포 안에서만 살 수 있는 세균이다.

8 그들은 독감과 같은 질병을 일으킨다.

9 '나쁜' 세균은 피부, 입, 코, 눈을 통해 몸에 들어갈 수 있다.

10 그들이 침입하면 어떻게 되는가?

11 세균은 몸속에서 증식한다.

12 당신의 몸은 전쟁 지역이 된다.

13 당신은 피곤하고 약해지는 것을 느끼기 시작한다.

14 다행히도, 당신의 몸은 방어 부대를 가지고 있다.

15 T세포가 경보를 발한다!

16 B세포는 항체로 세균과 싸우기 위해 도착한다.

17 대식 세포가 나타나서 세균을 먹는다.

18 이 군대는 함께 백혈구라고 부른다.

19 모든 것이 잘되면 싸움에서 이긴다.

20 며칠 후면 당신은 회복되기 시작한다.

21 The body remembers the _____, so it cannot make _____ of _____ again.

22 But the germs are _____, too.

23 They can _____ form and _____ the body.

24 There are _____ ways to _____ yourself from germs.

25 First, _____ your hands with soap and _____ water.

26 A balanced _____ will keep your body strong and _____.

27 It is also important to _____ regularly and get _____ of sleep.

28 _____, get the necessary _____.

29 They are the best _____ against _____.

30 If you follow these _____, you will not be a _____ of "bad" germs.

31 Make more _____ of me.

32 It's my job to _____ the body.

33 That was a nice _____!

34 Are _____ any more germs to _____?

35 _____ year, I'll _____ in my cousin.

36 He'll _____ you then for _____ fight!

37 What _____ I do now?

38 I'm _____ to fight _____ germs.

39 We give _____.

40 We can't _____ you sick.

21 몸은 침입자를 기억하므로 침입자는 다시 복세할 수 없다.

22 하지만 세균들도 영리하다.

23 그들은 형태를 바꿀 수 있고 몸을 속일 수 있다.

24 세균으로부터 당신 자신을 보호하는 몇 가지 방법이 있다.

25 먼저 비누와 따뜻한 물로 손을 씻어라.

26 균형 잡힌 식단은 당신의 몸을 튼튼하고 건강하게 해줄 것이다.

27 규칙적으로 운동하고 충분한 잠을 자는 것도 중요하다.

28 마지막으로 필요한 주사를 맞아라.

29 그것들은 세균을 막는 최고의 방어이다.

30 만약 당신이 이 단계를 따른다면, 당신은 "나쁜" 세균의 희생자가 되지 않을 것이다.

31 나를 더 복제해 줘.

32 몸을 지키는 게 내 일이야.

33 정말 맛있는 식사였어!

34 먹을 세균이 더 있니?

35 내년에는 내 사촌을 보낼게.

36 그때 그가 또 싸우려고 널 보게 될 거야!

37 지금 내가 무엇을 할 수 있을까?

38 나는 어떤 세균과도 싸울 준비가 되어 있어.

39 우리는 포기한다.

40 우리는 널 아프게 할 수 없어.

Reading 교과서 확인학습 B

● 우리말을 참고하여 본문을 영작하시오.

1 ▷ 세균은 어디에나 있지만 눈으로 세균을 보는 것은 불가능하다.
➡ _____

2 ▷ 세균에는 두 가지 주요한 종류가 있다: 박테리아와 바이러스이다.
➡ _____

3 ▷ 박테리아는 매우 작은 생물이다.
➡ _____

4 ▷ 어떤 것들은 좋다.
➡ _____

5 ▷ 그것들은 당신이 먹는 음식을 소화하는 데 도움을 줄 수 있다.
➡ _____

6 ▷ 다른 것들은 나쁘고 당신을 아프게 할 수 있다.
➡ _____

7 ▷ 바이러스는 다른 살아 있는 몸의 세포 안에서만 살 수 있는 세균이다.
➡ _____

8 ▷ 그들은 독감과 같은 질병을 일으킨다.
➡ _____

9 ▷ '나쁜' 세균은 피부, 입, 코, 눈을 통해 몸에 들어갈 수 있다.
➡ _____

10 ▷ 그들이 침입하면 어떻게 되는가?
➡ _____

11 ▷ 세균은 몸속에서 증식한다.
➡ _____

12 ▷ 당신의 몸은 전쟁 지역이 된다.
➡ _____

13 ▷ 당신은 피곤하고 약해지는 것을 느끼기 시작한다.
➡ _____

14 ▷ 다행히도, 당신의 몸은 방어 군대를 가지고 있다.
➡ _____

15 ▷ T세포가 경보를 발한다!
➡ _____

16 ▷ B세포는 항체로 세균과 싸우기 위해 도착한다.
➡ _____

17 ▷ 대식 세포가 나타나서 세균을 먹는다.
➡ _____

18 ▷ 이 군대는 함께 백혈구라고 부른다.
➡ _____

19 ▷ 모든 것이 잘되면 싸움에서 이긴다.
➡ _____

20 ▷ 며칠 후면 당신은 회복되기 시작한다.
➡ _____

21 몸은 침입자를 기억하므로 다시 복제할 수 없다.

➡ _____

22 하지만 세균들도 영리하다.

➡ _____

23 그들은 형태를 바꿀 수 있고 몸을 속일 수 있다.

➡ _____

24 세균으로부터 여러분 자신을 보호하는 몇 가지 방법이 있다.

➡ _____

25 먼저 비누와 따뜻한 물로 손을 씻어라.

➡ _____

26 균형 잡힌 식단은 당신의 몸을 튼튼하고 건강하게 해줄 것이다.

➡ _____

27 규칙적으로 운동하고 충분한 잠을 자는 것도 중요하다.

➡ _____

28 마지막으로 필요한 주사를 맞아라.

➡ _____

29 그것들은 세균을 막는 최고의 방어이다.

➡ _____

30 만약 당신이 이 단계를 따른다면, 당신은 "나쁜" 세균의 희생자가 되지 않을 것이다.

➡ _____

31 나를 더 복제해 주세요.

➡ _____

32 몸을 지키는 게 내 일이야.

➡ _____

33 정말 맛있는 식사였어!

➡ _____

34 먹을 세균이 더 있니?

➡ _____

35 내년에는 내 사촌을 보낼게.

➡ _____

36 그때 그가 또 싸우려고 널 보게 될 거야!

➡ _____

37 지금 내가 무엇을 할 수 있을까?

➡ _____

38 나는 어떤 세균과도 싸울 준비가 되어 있어.

➡ _____

39 우리는 포기한다.

➡ _____

40 우리는 널 아프게 할 수 없어.

➡ _____

[01~06] 다음 글을 읽고, 물음에 답하시오.

> Germ 1: Watch ___ⓐ___ !
>
> Germ 2: This is my spot!
>
> Germ 3: ⓑHands off!
>
> Germ 4: Hey!
>
> (①) Germs are everywhere, ___ⓒ___ it is impossible to see them with your eyes. (②)
>
> There are two major kinds of germs: bacteria and viruses. (③) Bacteria are very small creatures. (④) They can help you digest the food ⓓthat you eat. (⑤) Others are bad and can make you sick.

01 위 글의 ①~⑤ 중 다음 주어진 문장이 들어갈 알맞은 곳은?

> Some are good.

① ② ③ ④ ⑤

02 위 글의 빈칸 ⓐ에 알맞은 것은?

① on   ② out

③ at   ④ for

⑤ with

서답형

03 위 글의 밑줄 친 ⓑ를 우리말로 옮기시오.

➡ _____

중요

04 위 글의 빈칸 ⓒ에 알맞은 것은?

① and   ② or

③ but   ④ for

⑤ because

중요

05 위 글의 밑줄 친 ⓓ와 바꿔 쓸 수 있는 것은?

① who   ② whom

③ what   ④ where

⑤ which

06 위 글의 내용과 일치하지 않는 것은?

① 균은 어디에나 있다.

② 균을 눈으로 볼 수 없다.

③ 박테리아와 바이러스는 균이다.

④ 박테리아는 아주 작은 생명체다.

⑤ 박테리아는 대부분 몸에 해롭다.

[07~10] 다음 글을 읽고, 물음에 답하시오.

> Germ 1: I'm in! Time to ___ⓐ___ !
>
> Germ 2: Yay! Success!
>
> Germ 3: Make more copies of me. Now!
>
> Viruses are germs ___ⓑ___ can only live inside the cells of other living bodies. They cause diseases ⓒsuch as the flu.
>
> "Bad" germs can enter your body through your skin, mouth, nose, and eyes. What happens when they invade? The germs ___ⓓ___ in the body. Your body becomes a war zone. You start to feel tired and weak.

07 위 글의 빈칸 ⓐ에 알맞은 것은?

① attack   ② eat

③ die   ④ escape

⑤ repair

08 위 글의 빈칸 ⓑ에 알맞은 것은? (정답 2개)

① who   ② that
③ what   ④ why
⑤ which

09 위 글의 밑줄 친 ⓒ를 한 단어로 바꿔 쓰시오.

➡ _____

10 위 글의 빈칸 ⓓ에 다음 정의에 해당하는 단어를 쓰시오.

to increase greatly in number or amount

➡ _____

[11~15] 다음 글을 읽고, 물음에 답하시오.

A: We have an ⓐinvade! Come quickly.
B: It's my job to ___ⓑ___ the body.
C: That was a nice meal! Are there any more germs to eat?

 Luckily, your body has an army of defense. The T cells sound the alarm! The B cells arrive ⓒto fight the germs with antibodies. The macrophage cells show ___ⓓ___ and eat the germs.

 Together, this army is called the white blood cells. If all goes well, they win the fight. In a few days, you start to feel better.

11 위 글의 밑줄 친 ⓐ를 알맞은 형으로 바꿔 쓰시오.

➡ _____

12 위 글의 빈칸 ⓑ에 알맞은 것은?

① defend   ② attack
③ live   ④ fix
⑤ fight

13 위 글의 밑줄 친 ⓒ와 같은 용법으로 쓰인 것은?

① My hope is to become a doctor.
② It's time to go to bed now.
③ My job is to report the news.
④ He tried to find the lost key.
⑤ Kathy came to Korea to be a K pop singer.

14 위 글의 빈칸 ⓓ에 알맞은 것은?

① on   ② up
③ off   ④ with
⑤ from

15 위 글의 내용으로 보아 대답할 수 없는 질문은?

① What did 'C' eat?
② What does our body have?
③ Why does B cells arrive?
④ How does the T cells sound the alarm?
⑤ What is the army called?

[16~21] 다음 글을 읽고, 물음에 답하시오.

> **The army of defense:** Game ⓐ .
>
> **Germ:** Fine. Next year, I'll send ⓑ my cousin. He'll see you then for ⓒ(other, another) fight!
>
> ⓓThe body remembers the invader, so it cannot make copies of it again. But the germs are smart, too. ⓔThey can change form and trick the body.

16 위 글의 빈칸 ⓐ에 알맞은 것은?

① Up   ② On
③ Over   ④ Off
⑤ From

17 위 글의 빈칸 ⓑ에 알맞은 것은?

① on   ② to
③ off   ④ in
⑤ for

서답형
18 위 글의 괄호 ⓒ에서 알맞은 것을 고르시오.

➡ _____

서답형
19 위 글의 밑줄 친 ⓓ에서 어법상 어색한 것을 고치시오.

_____ ➡ _____

서답형
20 위 글의 밑줄 친 ⓔ를 우리말로 옮기시오.

➡ _____

21 위 글의 내용에서 언급되지 않은 것은?

① 방어 군대가 전쟁에서 승리했다.
② 균들은 내년에 다시 올 것이다.
③ 균들은 자신들이 침입한 몸을 기억하고 있다.
④ 한 번 침입한 균들은 자신을 복제할 수 없다.
⑤ 균들은 형태를 바꿀 수 있다.

[22~24] 다음 글을 읽고, 물음에 답하시오.

> **Germ:** Oh, no! I can't hold on.
> What can I do now?
> There are several ways ⓐprotect yourself ⓑ germs. First, wash your hands ⓒwith soap and warm water.

서답형
22 위 글의 밑줄 친 ⓐ를 알맞은 형태로 고쳐 쓰시오.

➡ _____

23 위 글의 빈칸 ⓑ에 알맞은 것은?

① of   ② from
③ in   ④ off
⑤ with

24 위 글의 밑줄 친 ⓒ와 같은 의미로 쓰인 것은?

① That's all right with me.
② What's the matter with you?
③ Cut the bread with this knife.
④ Do you agree with him?
⑤ Ann was in bed with the flu.

[25~28] 다음 글을 읽고, 물음에 답하시오.

A: I'm ready to ___ⓐ___ any germs.
B: Me, too. ⓑBring it on.
ⓒA balanced diet will keep your body strong and healthy. ⓓIt is also important to exercise regularly and get plenty of sleep.

25 위 글의 빈칸 ⓐ에 알맞은 것은?

① lose   ② win
③ fight   ④ hit
⑤ follow

서답형

26 위 글의 밑줄 친 ⓑ를 우리말로 옮기시오.

➡ _____

중요

27 위 글의 밑줄 친 ⓒ와 문형이 같은 것은?

① These shirts are very small.
② The song made me sad.
③ There are some apples in the basket.
④ She made us some cookies.
⑤ My grandfather planted some trees.

서답형

28 위 글의 밑줄 친 ⓓ가 가리키는 것을 우리말로 쓰시오.

➡ _____

[29~33] 다음 글을 읽고, 물음에 답하시오.

Germ 1: What? ⓐIt's "Game Over" for my cousins, too?
Germ 2: We give ___ⓑ___ .
Germ 3: We can't make you sick.
ⓒFinal, get the necessary shots. They are the best defense ___ⓓ___ germs. ___ⓔ___ you follow these steps, you will not be a victim of "bad" germs.

서답형

29 위 글의 밑줄 친 ⓐ를 우리말로 옮기시오.

➡ _____

30 위 글의 빈칸 ⓑ에 알맞은 것은?

① on   ② in
③ for   ④ up
⑤ over

서답형

31 위 글의 밑줄 친 ⓒ를 알맞은 형으로 고치시오.

➡ _____

32 위 글의 빈칸 ⓓ에 알맞은 것은?

① to   ② with
③ over   ④ across
⑤ against

중요

33 위 글의 빈칸 ⓔ에 알맞은 것은?

① If   ② As
③ While   ④ Since
⑤ Though

[01~04] 다음 글을 읽고, 물음에 답하시오.

Germ 1: ⓐ조심해!
Germ 2: This is my spot!
Germ 3: Hands off!
Germ 4: Hey!

Germs are everywhere, ⓑbut it is impossible to see them with your eyes.

There are two major kinds of germs: bacteria and viruses. Bacteria are very small creatures. Some are good. They can help you digest the food that you eat. ____ⓒ____ are bad and can make you sick.

01 위 글의 밑줄 친 ⓐ와 같은 뜻이 되도록 빈칸에 알맞은 말을 쓰시오.

| _____ out! |

02 위 글의 밑줄 친 ⓑ와 같은 뜻이 되도록 빈칸에 알맞은 말을 쓰시오.

| but you _____ see them with your eyes. |

03 위 글의 빈칸 ⓒ에 알맞은 말을 쓰시오.

➡ _____

04 How do good bacteria help you? Answer in Korean.

➡ _____

[05~08] 다음 글을 읽고, 물음에 답하시오.

Germ 1: I'm in! Time to attack!
Germ 2: Yay! Success!
Germ 3: Make more copies ___ⓐ___ me. Now!

Viruses are germs that can only live inside the cells of other living bodies. They cause diseases such as the flu. ⓑ"Bad" germs can enter into your body through your skin, mouth, nose, and eyes. What happens when ⓒthey invade? The germs multiply in the body. Your body becomes a war zone. You start to feel tired and weak.

05 위 글의 빈칸 ⓐ에 알맞은 말을 쓰시오.

➡ _____

06 위 글의 밑줄 친 ⓑ에서 어법상 어색한 것을 고치시오.

_____ ➡ _____

07 위 글의 밑줄 친 ⓒ가 가리키는 것을 우리말로 쓰시오.

➡ _____

08 Why does your body become a war zone? Answer in English.

➡ _____

[09~13] 다음 글을 읽고, 물음에 답하시오.

A: We have an invader! Come quickly.

B: It's my job to defend the body.

C: That was a nice meal! ⓐ먹을 균들이 좀 더 있냐?

Luckily, your body has an army of ⓑ defend. The T cells sound the alarm! The B cells arrive to fight the germs with antibodies. The macrophage cells show up and eat the germs.

ⓒTogether, this army is calling the white blood cells. If all goes well, they win the fight. ⓓIn a few days, you start to feel better.

09 위 글의 밑줄 친 ⓐ와 같은 뜻이 되도록 주어진 단어를 써서 영어로 옮기시오.

(there, any, germs, eat)

➡ _____

10 위 글의 밑줄 친 ⓑ를 알맞은 형으로 고치시오.

➡ _____

11 위 글의 밑줄 친 ⓒ에서 어법상 어색한 것을 고치시오.

_____ ➡ _____

12 위 글의 밑줄 친 ⓓ를 우리말로 옮기시오.

➡ _____

13 What do the T cells do for the body?

➡ _____

[14~18] 다음 글을 읽고, 물음에 답하시오.

Every day you use your hands to touch ⓐdiffer things. You touch your phone and computer. You open and close doors with your hands, too. There are germs on everything ____ⓑ____ you touch. If you eat ____ⓒ____ with your hands, the germs on your hands can get into your body. Then what should you do? Wash your hands ____ⓓ____ soap!

14 위 글의 밑줄 친 ⓐ를 알맞은 형으로 고치시오.

➡ _____

15 위 글의 빈칸 ⓑ에 알맞은 관계대명사를 쓰시오.

➡ _____

16 위 글의 빈칸 ⓒ에 다음 정의에 해당하는 단어를 쓰시오. (필요하면 어형 변화를 할 것.)

a simple meal that is quick to cook and to eat

➡ _____

17 위 글의 빈칸 ⓓ에 알맞은 말을 쓰시오.

➡ _____

18 위 글의 내용으로 보아 손으로 음식을 먹으면 안 되는 이유를 우리말로 간단히 쓰시오.

➡ _____

구석구석

My Writing Portfolio - Step 1

Sit Less, Move More

- It is dangerous to play online games too much.
  「가주어 It, 진주어 to부정사」 구문
- It is time to go out and exercise.
  밖에 나가다

Stay Healthy

- Eating too many snacks is not good for your health.
  동명사 주어(동사는 단수 취급)
- It is important to eat enough fruit and vegetables.

구문해설 • less: 더 적게, 덜하게 • dangerous: 위험한 • exercise: 운동하다 • healthy: 건강한
• be not good for: ~에 좋지 않다 • important: 중요한 • enough: 충분한
• vegetables: 채소

덜 앉고, 더 움직여라
- 온라인 게임을 너무 많이 하는 것은 위험하다.
- 이제 외출해서 운동할 시간이다.

건강을 유지해라
- 과자를 너무 많이 먹는 것은 건강에 좋지 않다.
- 과일과 채소를 충분히 먹는 것이 중요하다.

Words in Action - B

1. Frida Kahlo was a Mexican painter[artist]. She is famous for her unique paintings.
   ~으로 유명하다

2. Charles Schulz was a cartoonist who created the famous character Charlie Brown.
   주격 관계대명사(선행사: a cartoonist)

3. Park Gyeongri was a great Korean writer. She spent 25 years writing *Toji*.
   spend time -ing: ~하면서 시간을 보내다

4. James Cameron is the director of the movie, *Avatar*.
   the movie와 Avatar는 동격 관계

5. Jang Yeongsil was a(n) inventor[scientist] who created water clocks.
   주격 관계대명사

구문해설 • painter: 화가 • unique: 독특한 • painting: 그림 • cartoonist: 만화가
• create: 창조하다 • director: 감독 • inventor: 발명가 • water clock: 물시계

1. Frida Kahlo는 멕시코 화가[예술가]였다. 그녀는 독특한 그림으로 유명하다.

2. Charles Schulz는 유명한 캐릭터인 Charlie Brown을 만든 만화가였다.

3. 박경리는 위대한 한국 작가였다. 그녀는 토지를 쓰는 데 25년이 걸렸다.

4. James Cameron은 영화 '아바타'의 감독이다.

5. 장영실은 물시계를 만든 발명가[과학자]였다.

Wrap Up - Reading

Every day you use your hands to touch different things. You touch your phone
매일   to부정사의 부사적 용법(목적)
and computer. You open and close doors with your hands, too. There are
                                      ~으로   There are + 복수명사 ~: ~이 있다
germs on everything that you touch. If you eat snacks with your hands, the
                      목적격 관계대명사   조건을 나타내는 접속사 if: (만약) ~이면
germs on your hands can get into your body. Then what should you do? Wash
                          ~에 들어가다   명령문: 동사원형 ~: ~해라
your hands with soap!

구문해설 • use: 사용하다 • touch: 만지다 • different: 다른 • close: (문을) 닫다
• too: ~도 (또한) • everything: 모든 것 • germ: 세균 • wash: 씻다 • soap: 비누

여러분은 매일 다른 것들을 만지기 위해 손을 사용한다. 여러분은 여러분의 전화기와 컴퓨터를 만진다. 여러분은 또한 손으로 문을 열고 닫는다. 여러분이 만지는 모든 것에는 세균이 있다. 만약 여러분이 손으로 과자를 먹는다면, 손에 있는 세균은 여러분의 몸으로 들어갈 수 있다. 그럼 어떻게 해야 할까? 비누로 손을 씻어라!

영역별 핵심문제

01 다음 중 짝지어진 단어의 관계가 나머지 넷과 <u>다른</u> 것은?

① write – writer
② paint – painter
③ act – actor
④ science – scientist
⑤ direct – director

02 다음 빈칸에 들어갈 말로 적절하지 <u>않은</u> 것은?

> • This is a very _____ problem.
> • The key to _____ is hard work.
> • The old bill is too easy to _____.
> • She has a virus on her _____.

① skin
② hard
③ germ
④ copy
⑤ success

03 다음 두 단어의 관계가 같도록 빈칸에 알맞은 말을 쓰시오.

> easy : difficult = safe : _____

04 다음 빈칸에 들어갈 말이 바르게 짝지어진 것은? (대·소문자 무시)

> • _____ the way, what should we eat?
> • Watch _____! There's a car coming!

① in – on
② on – off
③ by – out
④ for – after
⑤ from – for

05 다음 영영풀이에 해당하는 단어는?

> any one of the very small parts that together form all living things

① shot
② cell
③ germ
④ virus
⑤ spot

06 다음 문장의 밑줄 친 부분과 바꿔 쓸 수 있는 것은?

> <u>At last</u>, the guests began to arrive.

① Usually
② Finally
③ Actually
④ Extremely
⑤ Especially

07 다음 우리말에 맞게 빈칸에 알맞은 말을 쓰시오.

> 왜 너는 기타 치는 걸 포기했니?
> ➡ Why did you _____ _____ playing the guitar?

08 다음 대화의 빈칸에 알맞지 <u>않은</u> 것은?

> A: _____
> B: Well, I have a stomachache.

① What's wrong?
② Is something wrong?
③ What's the problem?
④ What did you eat for lunch?
⑤ What seems to be the problem?

09 다음 대화의 빈칸에 알맞은 말을 쓰시오.

> A: Can you make it at two?
> B: No _____. Let's meet at the park.

➡ _____

10 다음 대화의 빈칸에 알맞은 것은?

> A: Let's go to the history museum. How about 12 o'clock?
> B: _____ Why don't we meet at 2 o'clock?
> A: Sure, no problem.

① Of course.
② That's a good idea.
③ What time will they meet?
④ Good, I am so excited.
⑤ I'm sorry. I will meet my friend at that time.

11 다음 대화의 순서를 바르게 배열하시오.

> (A) I have a sore throat.
> (B) Okay, I will.
> (C) What's wrong with you?
> (D) That's too bad. You should drink some water.

➡ _____

12 다음 대화의 빈칸에 알맞은 말은?

> A: Let's go to the movies this afternoon.
> _____
> B: I'm sorry, I can't.

① Can you make it at 5?
② Are you interested in films?
③ Do you go to the movies often?
④ Would you like to see the movie?
⑤ What kind of movies do you like?

[13~16] 다음 대화를 읽고, 물음에 답하시오.

> B: Can I go home early, Ms. Song? I don't feel so good.
> W: ⓐWhat seems to be the problem?
> B: I have a terrible stomachache. It really hurts.
> W: Why don't you get some medicine at the nurse's office?
> B: I already did. But ⓑit didn't help.
> W: Okay. You can go. _____ⓒ_____
> B: Sure. Thanks.

13 위 대화의 밑줄 친 ⓐ와 바꿔 쓸 수 없는 것은?

① What's wrong?
② What's the problem?
③ Is something wrong?
④ Why are you so upset?
⑤ What's the matter?

14 위 대화의 밑줄 친 ⓑ가 의미하는 것을 우리말로 구체적으로 쓰시오.

➡ _____

15 위 대화의 빈칸 ⓒ에 알맞은 것은?

① Do exercise, okay?
② Ride a bike, okay?
③ Go see a doctor, okay?
④ Play basketball, okay?
⑤ Have some pizza, okay?

16 위 대화를 읽고, 다음 질문에 완전한 문장으로 답하시오.

> Q: What's the problem with the boy?
> A: _____

[17~18] 다음 문장의 빈칸에 알맞은 것을 고르시오.

17

Do you have anything _____ this evening?

① do   ② did
③ doing   ④ to do
⑤ to doing

18

It is dangerous _____ swim in this river.

① to   ② in
③ of   ④ for
⑤ with

19 다음 빈칸에 공통으로 알맞은 것은?

- It was stupid _____ you to believe him.
- It is clever _____ him to solve the problem.

① at   ② of
③ for   ④ from
⑤ with

20 다음 대화의 빈칸에 알맞은 말을 쓰시오.

A: I think _____ _____ difficult to find the things I want to buy.
B: You know, they have the information desk.

21 다음 중 어법상 어색한 것은?

① She doesn't have a pen to write with.
② She wants someone to travel with.
③ She wants interesting something to read.
④ She kept her promise to enter a university.
⑤ She was the first woman to land on the moon.

22 다음 밑줄 친 부분의 쓰임이 나머지 넷과 다른 것은?

① It is necessary for you to study hard.
② It is too cold to go swimming in the lake.
③ It's good to try to solve the problem.
④ It is difficult for us to achieve the goal.
⑤ It is dangerous to walk alone at midnight.

23 다음 중 밑줄 친 부분의 쓰임이 〈보기〉와 다른 것은?

┌─ 보기 ─┐
I have a lot of work to do today.
└─────┘

① I need somebody to talk to.
② He must be crazy to quit his job.
③ I don't have time to chat with you.
④ She couldn't find any chairs to sit on.
⑤ Do you know the way to get to City Hall?

24 다음 문장에서 어법상 <u>어색한</u> 부분을 찾아 바르게 고쳐 쓰시오.

> I need a ball point to write.

_____ ➡ _____

25 다음 우리말을 영어로 바르게 옮긴 것은?

> 냉장고에는 먹을 음식이 많이 있다.

① There are a lot of food to eat in the refrigerator.
② There are a lot of food eating in the refrigerator.
③ There is a lot of food eating in the refrigerator.
④ There is a lot of foods to eat in the refrigerator.
⑤ There is a lot of food to eat in the refrigerator.

26 다음 두 문장이 같은 뜻이 되도록 빈칸에 알맞은 말을 쓰시오.

> To read this book is important.
> = _____ is important _____ read this book.

27 다음 단어를 바르게 배열하여 알맞은 문장을 만드시오.

> to / anything / myself / I / do / make / slimmer / look / will

➡ _____

[28~32] 다음 글을 읽고, 물음에 답하시오.

Germ 1: I'm in! Time to ___ⓐ___ !
Germ 2: Yay! Success!
Germ 3: Make more copies of me. Now!
  Viruses are germs that can only live inside the cells of other ⓑ<u>live</u> bodies. (①) They cause diseases such as the flu. (②) "Bad" germs can enter your body through your skin, mouth, nose, and eyes. (③) What happens ___ⓒ___ they invade? (④) The germs multiply in the body. (⑤) You start to feel tired and weak.

28 위 글의 ①~⑤ 중 다음 주어진 문장이 들어갈 알맞은 곳은?

> Your body becomes a war zone.

①   ②   ③   ④   ⑤

29 위 글의 빈칸 ⓐ에 알맞은 것은?

① play   ② attack
③ rest   ④ defend
⑤ advise

30 위 글의 밑줄 친 ⓑ를 알맞은 형으로 고치시오.

➡ _____

31 위 글의 빈칸 ⓒ에 알맞은 것은?

① that   ② till
③ when   ④ since
⑤ which

32 위 글의 내용과 일치하지 <u>않는</u> 것은?

① 균은 자신을 복제할 수 없다.
② 바이러스는 다른 살아 있는 몸의 세포 안에서만 살 수 있다.
③ 바이러스는 병을 유발한다.
④ 나쁜 균은 피부, 입, 코, 눈을 통해 신체로 들어온다.
⑤ 균은 몸 안에서 번식한다.

[33~35] 다음 글을 읽고, 물음에 답하시오.

The army of defense: Game Over
Germ: Fine. Next year, I'll send in my cousin. ⓐHe'll see you then for another fight!
The body remembers the invader, ___ⓑ___ it cannot make copies of itself again. But the germs are smart, too. They can change form and ___ⓒ___ the body.

33 위 글의 밑줄 친 ⓐ를 우리말로 옮기시오.

➡ _____

34 위 글의 빈칸 ⓑ에 알맞은 것은?

① or   ② so
③ but   ④ for
⑤ though

35 위 글의 빈칸 ⓒ에 알맞은 것은?

① save   ② live
③ trick   ④ fix
⑤ protect

[36~39] 다음 글을 읽고, 물음에 답하시오.

Every day you use your hands to touch different things. (①) You touch your phone and computer. (②) There are germs on everything that you touch. (③) If you eat snacks with your hands, the germs ___ⓐ___ your hands can get into your body. (④) Then what should you do? (⑤) Wash your hands with ___ⓑ___!

36 위 글의 ①~⑤ 중 다음 주어진 문장이 들어갈 알맞은 곳은?

You open and close doors with your hands, too.

①   ②   ③   ④   ⑤

37 위 글의 빈칸 ⓐ에 알맞은 것은?

① on   ② to
③ at   ④ in
⑤ over

38 위 글의 빈칸 ⓑ에 다음 정의에 해당하는 단어를 쓰시오.

a substance that you use with water for washing yourself or sometimes for washing clothes

➡ _____

39 Where are germs? Answer in English.

➡ _____

단원별 예상문제

출제율 90%

01 다음 중 짝지어진 단어의 관계가 나머지 넷과 다른 것은?

① defend : attack
② remember : forget
③ different : same
④ hard : difficult
⑤ dangerous : safe

출제율 95%

02 다음 빈칸에 공통으로 알맞은 것은?

> • I won't give _____ easily.
> • He didn't show _____ for the appointment.

① in   ② up
③ out   ④ off
⑤ onto

출제율 90%

03 다음 짝지어진 두 단어의 관계가 같도록 빈칸에 알맞은 말을 쓰시오.

> paint : painter = invent : _____

출제율 85%

04 다음 중 영영풀이가 잘못된 것은?

① easy: not hard to do
② major: very important
③ fever: a body temperature that is higher than normal
④ germ: a very small living thing that causes disease
⑤ safe: involving possible injury, harm, or death

출제율 90%

05 다음 우리말에 맞게 빈칸에 알맞은 말을 쓰시오.

(1) 우리는 하루 이틀 뒤에 떠날 준비를 하고 있어야 해.
  ➡ We should _____ _____ _____ leave in a day or two.
(2) 콧물이 나고 목도 아프고 기침도 납니다.
  ➡ I have a _____ _____, _____ _____ and a cough.

출제율 90%

06 다음 대화의 빈칸에 알맞은 말이 바르게 짝지어진 것은?

> A: What's wrong?
> B: I have _____.
> A: That's too bad. Why don't you _____?
> B: OK. I will.

① a bad cold − see a doctor
② a pet − get some fresh air
③ a lot of homework − go to sleep
④ some stress − go to see a dentist
⑤ long hair − take some medicine

출제율 85%

07 다음 대화의 빈칸에 알맞은 것은?

> A: Let's go to the concert this Saturday.
> B: Sounds good. _____
> A: Fine with me.

① Can I join you?
② May I go to the concert?
③ How about going to the concert?
④ Do you like the concert?
⑤ Can you make it at 3?

46 Lesson 3. Healthy Life, Happy Life

[08~10] 다음 대화를 읽고, 물음에 답하시오.

B: Hello, Sora.
G: Hi, Jongha. I heard you were sick. Are you okay now?
B: (①) Yes, I went to the doctor, and I feel better now.
G: (②) By the way, I called you to talk about our science project.
B: (③) Yeah, we should meet. _____ⓐ
G: Okay. ⓑLet's meet at Simpson's Donuts at nine.
B: At nine? That's too early. I sleep late on the weekend.
G: (④) How about 10 then?
B: (⑤) That sounds fine.

08 위 대화의 ①~⑤ 중 다음 주어진 문장이 들어갈 알맞은 곳은?

> Good to hear that.

①   ②   ③   ④   ⑤

09 위 대화의 빈칸 ⓐ에 들어갈 말을 주어진 단어를 바르게 배열하여 완성하시오.

> (it / you / tomorrow / can / make)

➡ _____

10 위 대화의 밑줄 친 ⓑ를 다음과 같이 바꿔 쓸 때 빈칸에 알맞은 말을 쓰시오.

> _____ _____ _____ meet at Simpson's Donuts at nine?

11 다음 빈칸에 들어갈 동사의 형태로 적절한 것은?

> It's necessary for you _____ the piano every day.

① practice   ② practiced
③ practicing   ④ to practice
⑤ to practicing

12 다음 빈칸에 알맞은 말이 바르게 짝지어진 것은?

> • It was wise _____ you to agree to the proposal.
> • It is impossible _____ us to win the game.

① of – of   ② of – for
③ for – for   ④ for – of
⑤ for – with

13 다음 문장에서 어법상 어색한 부분을 찾아 바르게 고쳐 쓰시오.

> I need some paper to write.

_____ ➡ _____

14 다음 두 문장의 뜻이 같도록 빈칸에 알맞은 말을 쓰시오.

> To finish this homework is hard.
> = _____ is hard _____ finish this homework.

출제율 85%

15 다음 중 어법상 어색한 문장은?

① I need a chair to sit.
② Columbus was the first man to discover the American continent.
③ We have no house to live in.
④ He has a wish to become a pilot.
⑤ She forgot to bring something to write with.

출제율 90%

16 다음 중 〈보기〉의 밑줄 친 it과 쓰임이 같은 것은?

┌─── 보기 ───┐
It is bad to use cell phones in class.
└──────────┘

① It is very hot in this room.
② It is not my lost puppy.
③ It is fun to play soccer with my friends.
④ It rained a lot yesterday morning.
⑤ It was built by Koreans.

출제율 85%

17 다음 우리말을 영어로 바르게 옮긴 것은?

┌──────────────────────┐
한국에는 방문할 장소가 많이 있다.
└──────────────────────┘

① There is many places visit in Korea.
② There are visiting many places in Korea.
③ There are many places visiting in Korea.
④ There are to visit many places in Korea.
⑤ There are many places to visit in Korea.

출제율 100%

18 다음 밑줄 친 부분의 쓰임이 다른 하나는?

① There's nothing to be afraid of any more.
② Ann is coming to Seoul to visit us.
③ I'm going to the park to walk my dogs.
④ Paul drove very quickly to get there on time.
⑤ I went to the post office to send the parcel.

[19~21] 다음 글을 읽고, 물음에 답하시오.

┌──────────────────────────────────┐
A: ⓐI'm ready to fight any germs.
B: Me, too. Bring it ⓑ .
 A balanced diet will keep your body strong and healthy. It is also important to exercise ⓒregular and get plenty of sleep.
└──────────────────────────────────┘

출제율 90%

19 위 글의 밑줄 친 ⓐ를 우리말로 옮기시오.

➡ _____

출제율 85%

20 위 글의 빈칸 ⓑ에 알맞은 것은?

① in   ② on
③ to   ④ for
⑤ from

출제율 90%

21 위 글의 밑줄 친 ⓒ를 알맞은 어형으로 고치시오.

➡ _____

[22~26] 다음 글을 읽고, 물음에 답하시오.

Every day you use your hands ⓐto touch different things. You touch your phone and computer. You ___ⓑ___ and close doors with your hands, too. ⓒ여러분이 손대는 모든 것에 균들이 있다. ___ⓓ___ you eat snacks with your hands, the germs on your hands can get ___ⓔ___ your body. Then what should you do? Wash your hands with soap!

출제율 90%

22 위 글의 밑줄 친 ⓐ와 같은 용법으로 쓰인 것은?

① My hope is to work as a doctor in Africa.
② It's time to go to bed now.
③ My job is to report the news.
④ The boys hoped to find the hidden treasure.
⑤ Kevin came to Korea to be a K pop singer.

출제율 100%

23 위 글의 빈칸 ⓑ에 알맞은 단어를 쓰시오.

➡ _____

출제율 90%

24 위 글의 밑줄 친 ⓒ를 주어진 단어를 써서 영어로 옮기시오.

there, germs, on, touch

➡ _____

출제율 85%

25 위 글의 빈칸 ⓓ에 알맞은 것은?

① But   ② If
③ Since   ④ Though
⑤ Because

출제율 90%

26 위 글의 빈칸 ⓔ에 알맞은 것은?

① at   ② to
③ into   ④ from
⑤ out of

[27~30] 다음 글을 읽고, 물음에 답하시오.

Germ 1: ⓐWhat? It's "Game Over" for my cousins, too?
Germ 2: We give up.
Germ 3: We can't ___ⓑ___ you sick.
　Finally, get the necessary shots. ⓒThey are the best defense against germs. If you follow these steps, you will not be a ___ⓓ___ of "bad" germs.

출제율 90%

27 위 글의 Germ 1이 밑줄 친 ⓐ를 말한 이유를 우리말로 간단히 쓰시오.

➡ _____

출제율 100%

28 위 글의 빈칸 ⓑ에 알맞은 것은?

① make   ② get
③ do   ④ let
⑤ become

출제율 90%

29 위 글의 밑줄 친 ⓒ를 우리말로 옮기시오.

➡ _____

출제율 85%

30 위 글의 빈칸 ⓓ에 다음 정의에 해당하는 단어를 쓰시오.

someone who has been hurt or killed

➡ _____

[01~02] 다음 대화를 읽고, 물음에 답하시오.

> A: ⓐWhat's wrong with you?
> B: ⓑ나는 목이 아파.
> A: That's too bad. You should drink some water.
> B: Okay, I will.

01 위 대화의 밑줄 친 부분과 바꿔 쓸 수 있는 표현을 두 가지 쓰시오.

➡ _____

_____

_____

02 위 대화의 밑줄 친 우리말을 영어로 쓰시오. (5 words)

➡ _____

03 다음 우리말과 같도록 빈칸에 알맞은 말을 넣어 대화를 완성하시오.

> A: _____ go to the library this Saturday. (우리 이번 토요일에 도서관에 가자.)
> B: Sounds good. Can you _____ _____ at 9? (좋아. 너는 9시에 시간 되니?)
> A: I'm _____ I can't. _____ about 10? (난 안 될 것 같아. 10시는 어떠니?)
> B: Okay. _____ you then. (좋아. 그때 보자.)

04 다음 대화의 순서를 바르게 배열하시오.

> (A) OK, I will.
> (B) What's wrong?
> (C) Well, I have a toothache.
> (D) That's too bad. Why don't you go see a dentist?

➡ _____

05 다음 우리말 의미에 맞도록 주어진 표현을 이용하여 영작하시오.

(1) 언덕을 내려가는 것은 쉽지 않다.
(it, easy, go down)

➡ _____

(2) 나는 내 남동생이 찍는 사진들을 좋아한다.
(photographs, which, takes)

➡ _____

_____

06 다음 〈조건〉에 맞게 괄호 안의 단어를 이용하여 우리말을 영어로 옮기시오.

> ┤ 조건 ├
> 1. 주어진 단어를 모두 이용할 것.
> 2. 필요시 관사를 붙이거나 단어를 추가할 것.
> 3. It으로 시작할 것.
> 4. 대·소문자 및 구두점에 유의할 것.

(1) 내가 자동차를 주차하기는 어렵다.
(difficult, me, park, car)

➡ _____

(2) 헬멧을 쓰고 자전거를 타는 것이 안전하다.
(safe, ride, bike, with, helmet)

➡ _____

(3) 다른 나라에서 사는 것은 흥미진진한 경험이다.
(exciting, experience, live, another, country)

➡ _____

07 다음 하루 일과표를 보고 빈칸에 알맞은 내용을 쓰시오.

8:00 a.m.	school
12:10 p.m.	lunch
5:00 p.m.	playground
6:30 p.m.	homework

(1) It's 8 a.m. It's time _____.

(2) It's 12:10 p.m. It's time _____.

(3) It's 5 p.m. It's time _____.

(4) It's 6:30 p.m. It's time _____.

[08~11] 다음 글을 읽고, 물음에 답하시오.

> **Germ:** Oh, no! I can't hold on.
> _____ⓐ_____ can I do now?
>   There are several ways to protect ⓑyou from germs. First, wash your hands _____ⓒ_____ soap and warm water.

08 위 글의 빈칸 ⓐ에 알맞은 말을 쓰시오.

➡ _____

09 위 글의 밑줄 친 ⓑ를 알맞은 형으로 고치시오.

➡ _____

10 위 글의 빈칸 ⓒ에 알맞은 말을 쓰시오.

➡ _____

11 위 글의 Germ이 밑줄 친 부분과 같이 말한 이유를 본문에서 유추하여 답하시오.

➡ _____

[12~15] 다음 글을 읽고, 물음에 답하시오.

> **Germ 1:** What? It's "Game Over" for my cousins, too?
> **Germ 2:** ⓐ우리는 포기한다.
> **Germ 3:** We can't make you sick.
>   Finally, get the necessary shots. ⓑThey are the best ⓒdefend against germs. ⓓIf you follow these steps, you will not be a victim of "bad" germs.

12 위 글의 밑줄 친 ⓐ와 같은 뜻이 되도록 빈칸에 알맞은 말을 쓰시오.

We give _____.

13 위 글의 밑줄 친 ⓑ가 가리키는 것을 영어로 쓰시오.

➡ _____

14 위 글의 밑줄 친 ⓒ를 알맞은 형으로 고치시오.

➡ _____

15 위 글의 밑줄 친 ⓓ를 우리말로 옮기시오.

➡ _____

01 다음 주어진 상황에 맞게 to부정사와 괄호 안의 단어를 이용하여 〈보기〉처럼 문장을 완성하시오.

> 보기
>
> I'm hungry. <u>I need some food to eat.</u>(eat)

(1) I'm very thirsty. _____ (drink)

(2) There's no chair here. _____ (sit)

(3) Tony feels lonely. _____ (talk)

02 다음 어구들을 연결하여 〈보기〉와 같이 한 문장으로 쓰시오.

• happy	• him	• to visit	• his hometown
• kind	• foreigners	• to watch	• Korean
• exciting	• us	• to play	• the work on time
• boring	• her	• to finish	• the poor
• possible	• you	• to help	• basketball games
• difficult	• me	• to learn	• the game

> 보기
>
> It is happy for him to visit his hometown.

(1) _____

(2) _____

(3) _____

(4) _____

(5) _____

03 Jessica의 이번 주 일정표를 보고, 내용에 맞도록 문장을 완성하시오.

Mon.	Tue.	Wed.	Thu.	Fri.
a movie / watch	a piano lesson / take	a baseball game / watch	a piano lesson / take	four comic books / read

(1) Jessica has _____ this Monday.

(2) Jessica has _____ on TV this Wednesday.

(3) Jessica has _____ on Tuesday and Thursday.

(4) Jessica has _____ on Friday.

단원별 모의고사

01 다음 영영풀이에 해당하는 단어로 알맞은 것은?

to change food that you have eaten by a biological process into simpler forms that can be used by the body

① multiply　　　　② scratch
③ invade　　　　④ digest
⑤ exercise

02 다음 중 우리말 뜻이 <u>잘못된</u> 것은?

① at last: 마침내
② feel better: 몸이 좋아지다
③ go well: 잘되어 가다
④ watch out for: ~을 구경하다
⑤ can't hold on: 견뎌낼 수 없다

03 다음 빈칸에 공통으로 알맞은 것은?

• The nurse gave him a flu _____.
• Taylor scored with a low _____ into the corner of the net.

① mask　　　　② zone
③ way　　　　④ shot
⑤ spot

04 다음 짝지어진 두 단어의 관계가 같도록 빈칸에 알맞은 말을 쓰시오.

art : artist = cartoon : _____

05 다음 빈칸에 공통으로 들어갈 말을 쓰시오.

• It is important to get plenty _____ sleep.
• I'm thinking _____ going to Greece this summer.

➡ _____

[06~08] 다음 대화를 읽고, 물음에 답하시오.

A: Let's play basketball this Saturday.
B: _____ⓐ_____
A: ⓑCan you make it at ten?
B: That's fine with me. Where should we meet?
A: Let's meet at the school gym.
B: Okay. See you there.

06 위 대화의 빈칸 ⓐ에 알맞은 것은?

① No, thanks.　　② I'm afraid not.
③ It doesn't matter.　④ Sure, why not?
⑤ Sorry, but I can't.

07 위 대화의 밑줄 친 ⓑ와 바꿔 쓸 수 <u>없는</u> 것은?

① Let's meet at ten.
② Do you meet at ten?
③ Shall we meet at ten?
④ What about meeting at ten?
⑤ Why don't we meet at ten?

08 위 대화의 내용과 일치하도록 빈칸에 알맞은 말을 쓰시오.

"A" and "B" will meet at _____
_____ _____ at _____ o'clock
this Saturday to _____ _____.

[09~11] 다음 대화를 읽고, 물음에 답하시오.

> G: I'm thinking ___ⓐ___ going to the Comics Museum tomorrow. Will you come with me?
> B: I really want to go.
> G: Can you ___ⓑ___ it at 11?
> B: That's fine ___ⓒ___ me.
> G: Okay. ⓓLet's meet at the subway station.

09 위 대화의 빈칸 ⓐ와 ⓒ에 알맞은 말이 바르게 짝지어진 것은?

① at – by
② about – to
③ of – with
④ in – on
⑤ on – to

10 위 대화의 빈칸 ⓑ에 알맞은 단어를 쓰시오.

➡ _____

11 위 대화의 밑줄 친 ⓓ를 다음과 같이 바꿔 쓸 때 빈칸에 알맞은 말을 쓰시오.

_____ _____ meeting at the subway station?

[12~14] 다음 문장의 빈칸에 알맞은 것을 고르시오.

12
He has many things _____ tonight.

① do
② does
③ doing
④ to do
⑤ to be doing

13
I'm looking for a friend to travel _____.

① at
② in
③ with
④ on
⑤ for

14
Alice and Ken are going to enter Berkeley. They need a dormitory _____.

① live
② to live
③ to live in
④ to live with
⑤ to living

15 다음 밑줄 친 부분의 쓰임이 〈보기〉와 같은 것은?

> ─┤ 보기 ├─
> I have nothing special to eat in my bag.

① She packed her bag to go home.
② I was happy to find my cell phone.
③ He needs someone to look after his cat.
④ To eat breakfast is good for your brain.
⑤ We went to the store to buy some snacks.

16 다음 괄호 안에 주어진 단어의 알맞은 형태를 쓰시오.

Is it possible _____ the project by tomorrow? (finish)

[17~18] 다음 중 어법상 알맞지 <u>않은</u> 문장을 고르시오.

17
① It's hard to climb the tree.
② It's great fun skate on ice.
③ It's exciting to watch a baseball game.
④ It's important for us to study English.
⑤ It's interesting to take a trip to strange lands.

18
① Let me get you a chair to sit on.
② She has no house to live in.
③ There's nothing to worry about.
④ Give me a pen to write with.
⑤ You seem to have important something to tell me.

19 다음 밑줄 친 ⓐ, ⓑ를 어법상 올바른 형태로 쓰시오.

I think shopping on the Internet is good.
It's easy ⓐfind the things I want to buy.
It's also easy ⓑfind good prices.

ⓐ _____ ⓑ _____

20 다음 괄호 안의 단어 형태가 바르게 짝지어진 것은?

• I have something (tell) you.
• Do you have anything (read)?

① tell – read
② tell – to read
③ to tell – read
④ telling – read
⑤ to tell – to read

[21~24] 다음 글을 읽고, 물음에 답하시오.

Germ 1: Watch out!
Germ 2: This is my spot!
Germ 3: Hands off!
Germ 4: Hey!
  Germs are everywhere, but it is ⓐpossible to see them with your eyes.
  There are two major kinds of germs: bacteria and viruses. Bacteria are very small creatures. ____ⓑ____ are good. They can help you ____ⓒ____ the food that you eat. ____ⓓ____ are bad and can make you sick.

21 위 글의 밑줄 친 ⓐ를 알맞은 어형으로 고치시오.

➡ _____

22 위 글의 빈칸 ⓑ와 ⓓ에 알맞은 것으로 짝지어진 것은?

① Any – Other
② Any – Others
③ Some – Others
④ Some – Other
⑤ Some – The others

23 위 글의 빈칸 ⓒ에 알맞은 것은? (2개)

① digest
② digestion
③ digesting
④ to digest
⑤ to digesting

24 위 글의 내용으로 보아 알 수 <u>없는</u> 것은?

① 균들은 도처에 있다.
② 박테리아와 바이러스는 균이다.
③ 박테리아는 아주 작은 생물체이다.
④ 박테리아 중에는 이로운 것들이 있다.
⑤ 바이러스는 박테리아보다 더 해롭다.

[25~28] 다음 글을 읽고, 물음에 답하시오.

A: We have an invader! Come quickly.

B: It's my job to defend the body.

C: That was a nice meal! Are there any more germs ___ⓐ___ ?

Luckily, your body has an army of defense. The T cells sound the alarm! (①) The B cells arrive to fight the germs with antibodies. (②) The macrophage cells ⓑshow up and eat the germs. (③)

Together, this army is ⓒcall the white blood cells. (④) In a few days, you start to feel better. (⑤)

25 위 글의 ①~⑤ 중 다음 주어진 문장이 들어갈 알맞은 곳은?

If all goes well, they win the fight.

①   ②   ③   ④   ⑤

26 위 글의 빈칸 ⓐ에 알맞은 것은?

① eat   ② eating
③ to eat   ④ for eat
⑤ to eating

27 위 글의 밑줄 친 ⓑ와 뜻이 같은 것은?

① seem   ② turn
③ get   ④ become
⑤ appear

28 위 글의 밑줄 친 ⓒ를 알맞은 형으로 고치시오.

➡ _____

[29~31] 다음 글을 읽고, 물음에 답하시오.

The army of defense: Game Over.

Germ: Fine. Next year, I'll send in my cousin. He'll see you then for ___ⓐ___ fight!

The body remembers the invader, so it cannot make copies of itself again. But the germs are smart, too. They can change form and trick the body.

29 위 글의 빈칸 ⓐ에 알맞은 것은?

① other   ② another
③ others   ④ the other
⑤ the others

30 위 글의 내용과 일치하지 않는 것은?

① The army of defense won the fight.
② The germ's cousin will come next year.
③ The invader can't make copies of itself again.
④ The body will remember the germ's cousin.
⑤ The germs can change form.

31 Why can't the invader make copies of itself again? Answer in English.

➡ _____

Lesson 4

Earth, Our Only Home

의사소통 기능

- 허락 구하기
  A: Is it okay to put up a poster?
  B: Sure, go ahead.

- 금지하기
  A: Can I feed the animal?
  B: No, you're not supposed to do that.

언어 형식

- 수동태
  This shirt **was designed** by my sister.

- as ~ as ...
  Grandma is **as** old **as** that tree.

Words & Expressions

Key Words

- **allow** [əláu] 동 허락하다(= permit)
- **almost** [ɔ́:lmoust] 부 거의
- **artificial** [à:rtəfíʃəl] 형 인공의, 인위적인(↔ natural)
- **bright** [brait] 형 밝은(↔ dark)
- **bulletin board** 게시판
- **careful** [kɛ́ərfəl] 형 주의 깊은(↔ careless)
- **carefully** [kɛ́ərfəli] 부 주의 깊게
- **cause** [kɔːz] 동 ~을 야기하다[초래하다]
- **clearly** [klíərli] 부 분명히
- **create** [kriéit] 동 창조[창작]하다
- **dark** [da:rk] 형 어두운(↔ bright)
- **disturb** [distə́:rb] 동 방해하다
- **effect** [ifékt] 명 영향, 결과
- **enough** [inʌf] 부 충분히 형 충분한
- **environment** [inváiərənmənt] 명 환경
- **especially** [ispéʃəli] 부 특히, 특별히
- **everywhere** [evriwər] 부 모든 곳에서
- **famous** [féiməs] 형 유명한(= well-known)
- **feed** [fiːd] 동 먹이를 주다
- **follow** [fálou] 동 ~을 따르다
- **human** [hjúːmən] 명 인간, 사람
- **lastly** [lǽstli] 부 마지막으로
- **lay** [lei] 동 (알을) 낳다
- **leash** [liːʃ] 명 가죽 끈[줄]
- **leftover** [leftouvər] 명 남은 음식
- **light** [lait] 명 빛 형 가벼운(↔ heavy)
- **migrate** [máigreit] 동 이동하다, 이주하다
- **natural** [nǽtʃərəl] 형 자연의, 자연적인(↔ artificial)
- **ocean** [óuʃən] 명 바다
- **painting** [péintiŋ] 명 그림
- **pick** [pik] 동 (꽃을) 꺾다
- **pollution** [pəlúːʃən] 명 오염
- **protect** [prətékt] 동 보호하다
- **recent** [ríːsnt] 형 최근의
- **report** [ripɔ́ːrt] 명 보고, 보고서
- **rhythm** [ríðm] 명 리듬
- **rule** [ruːl] 명 규칙
- **serious** [síəriəs] 형 심각한
- **sleep** [sliːp] 명 잠, 수면
- **solve** [salv] 동 해결하다
- **starry** [stáːri] 형 별이 총총한
- **threaten** [θrétn] 동 위협하다, 위태롭게 하다
- **toothbrush** [tuθbrəʃ] 명 칫솔
- **trash** [træʃ] 명 쓰레기(= waste)
- **volume** [váljuːm] 명 음량, 볼륨
- **volunteer** [vàləntíər] 동 자원 봉사로 일하다 명 자원 봉사자
- **wildlife** [waildlaif] 명 야생 동물
- **wrong** [rɔ́ːŋ] 형 잘못된, 틀린(↔ right)

Key Expressions

- **according to** ~에 따르면
- **be familiar with** ~에 익숙하다, ~을 잘 알다
- **be over** 끝나다
- **because of** ~ 때문에
- **be not supposed to** ~해서는 안 된다
- **care about** ~에 관심을 가지다
- **feel proud** 긍지를 느끼다
- **have an effect** 영향을 주다
- **in danger** 위험에 처한
- **in fact** 사실
- **look up** 올려다보다, 쳐다보다
- **make a fire** 불을 붙이다
- **millions of** 수백만의
- **most of** ~의 대부분
- **suffer from** ~로 고통 받다
- **take action** 조치를 취하다
- **take care of** ~을 처리하다, ~을 돌보다
- **throw away** ~을 버리다
- **turn down** (볼륨을) 줄이다
- **wander off** ~에서 벗어나다

Word Power

※ 명사에 -ful, -y 등을 붙여 형용사가 되는 단어

□ **luck**(행운) → **lucky**(운이 좋은)

□ **care**(주의) → **careful**(주의 깊은)

□ **help**(도움) → **helpful**(도움이 되는)

□ **harm**(해) → **harmful**(해로운)

□ **wonder**(경이) → **wonderful**(경이로운)

□ **beauty**(아름다움) → **beautiful**(아름다운)

□ **cloud**(구름) → **cloudy**(흐린)

□ **wind**(바람) → **windy**(바람이 부는)

□ **star**(별) → **starry**(별이 총총한)

□ **thirst**(갈증) → **thirsty**(갈증이 나는)

□ **mess**(엉망인 상태) → **messy**(지저분한)

English Dictionary

□ **allow** 허락하다
→ to let someone do something
누군가가 뭔가를 하도록 하게 두다

□ **artificial** 인공의, 인위적인
→ not natural or real
자연적이거나 진짜가 아닌

□ **create** 창조[창작]하다
→ to make or produce something
어떤 것을 만들거나 생산하다

□ **disturb** 방해하다
→ to stop someone from working, sleeping, etc.
어떤 사람의 작업, 수면 등을 방해하다

□ **effect** 영향
→ a change that results when something is done or happens
어떤 일이 행해지거나 일어날 때 초래되는 변화

□ **environment** 환경
→ the natural world in which people, animals, and plants live
사람, 동물, 식물이 사는 자연 세계

□ **feed** 먹이를 주다
→ to give food to someone or something
어떤 사람이나 어떤 것에게 먹을 것을 주다

□ **lay** (알을) 낳다
→ to produce an egg outside of the body
몸 밖으로 알을 낳다

□ **leftover** 남은 음식
→ food that has not been finished at a meal and that is often served at another meal
식사 때 다 먹지 않고 종종 또 다른 식사 때 제공되는 음식

□ **migrate** 이동하다
→ to move from one area to another at different times of the year
계절에 따라 한 지역에서 다른 지역으로 이동하다

□ **pollution** 오염
→ the process of making air, water, soil, etc. dirty
공기, 물, 토양 등을 더럽게 만드는 과정

□ **protect** 보호하다
→ to keep someone or something from being harmed, lost, etc.
누군가 또는 어떤 것이 해를 입거나 없어지거나 하지 않게 하다

□ **rhythm** 리듬
→ a regular, repeated pattern of events, changes, activities, etc.
일정하고 반복적인 형태의 사건, 변화, 활동 따위

□ **solve** 해결하다
→ to find an answer to a problem or a question
어떤 문제나 질문에 대한 답을 발견하다

□ **starry** 별이 총총한
→ full of stars
별이 가득한

□ **trash** 쓰레기
→ things that are no longer useful or wanted and that have been thrown away
못쓰게 되거나 필요하지 않아서 버린 것

□ **wildlife** 야생 동물
→ animals living in nature
자연에서 사는 동물

 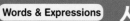

01 다음 중 〈보기〉와 같은 형태로 변화하는 단어가 <u>아닌</u> 것은?

┌─── 보기 ───┐

help : helpful

① harm   ② care

③ mess   ④ beauty

⑤ wonder

02 다음 빈칸에 들어갈 동사가 바르게 짝지어진 것은?

• Don't _____ a fire or cook in the park.

• He wants to _____ action to solve the problem.

① build – bring   ② start – get

③ take – make   ④ get – turn

⑤ make – take

03 다음 영영풀이에 해당하는 단어로 알맞은 것은?

to stop someone from working, sleeping, etc.

① allow   ② throw

③ defend   ④ disturb

⑤ protect

서답형

04 다음 짝지어진 단어의 관계가 같도록 빈칸에 알맞은 말을 쓰시오.

dark : bright = natural : _____

05 다음 빈칸에 알맞은 말이 바르게 짝지어진 것은?

• We are familiar _____ this process.

• There are many species of animals _____ danger.

① in – with   ② of – at

③ to – from   ④ with – in

⑤ about – with

서답형

06 다음 문장의 빈칸에 영영풀이에 해당하는 단어를 주어진 철자로 시작하여 쓰시오.

a change that results when something is done or happens

➡ Light pollution can have a serious e_____ on humans and wildlife.

07 다음 문장의 밑줄 친 부분의 의미로 가장 적절한 것은?

<u>In fact</u>, she is the tallest woman in the world!

① Exactly   ② Clearly

③ Actually   ④ Recently

⑤ Especially

서답형

08 다음 빈칸에 공통으로 알맞은 말을 쓰시오.

• According _____ the weather forecast, it will rain tomorrow.

• You're not supposed _____ pick flowers or fruits.

➡ _____

01 다음 짝지어진 두 단어의 관계가 같도록 빈칸에 알맞은 말을 쓰시오.

(1) same : different = dark : _____

(2) easy : difficult = _____ : right

(3) kind : sort = famous : _____

(4) delicious : tasty = trash : _____

02 다음 우리말에 맞게 빈칸에 알맞은 말을 쓰시오.

(1) 소리 좀 줄여 주시겠어요?

➡ Will you _____ _____ the volume, please?

(2) 수백만의 사람들이 그들의 집을 잃었다.

➡ _____ _____ people lost their homes.

(3) 그는 교통 체증 때문에 비행기를 놓쳤다.

➡ He missed his airplane _____ _____ a traffic jam.

03 다음 빈칸에 공통으로 들어갈 말을 〈보기〉에서 골라 쓰시오.

┌─ 보기 ─────────────┐
│   volunteer   light   effect   │
└────────────────────┘

(1) • Colors have an _____ on our moods.
   • Cause and _____ react upon each other.

(2) • I'm looking for a _____ overcoat.
   • Wildlife is threatened by _____ pollution.

(3) • You can be a _____ to help them!
   • I don't want her to _____.

04 다음 빈칸에 들어갈 알맞은 말을 〈보기〉에서 골라 쓰시오.

┌─ 보기 ─────────────┐
│   trash   environment   rhythm   │
└────────────────────┘

(1) He is dancing to the _____.

(2) We have to protect the _____ from pollution.

(3) The children are picking up the _____.

05 다음 빈칸에 알맞은 말을 〈보기〉에서 골라 쓰시오.

┌─ 보기 ─────────────┐
│ suffer from   care about   be over │
└────────────────────┘

(1) The concert will _____ by about 8:00.

(2) They _____ noise and dirty water.

(3) People should _____ our oceans.

06 다음 영영풀이에 해당하는 단어를 주어진 철자로 시작하여 쓰시오.

(1) a_____ : not natural or real

(2) a_____ : to let someone do something

(3) m_____ : to move from one area to another at different times of the year

(4) p_____ : to keep someone or something from being harmed, lost, etc.

Conversation

1 허락 구하기

> **A** Is it okay to put up a poster? 포스터를 붙여도 될까요?
> **B** Sure, go ahead. 물론, 어서 해.

■ Is it okay to ~?는 어떤 행동을 하기 전에 허가 여부를 묻는 표현으로, '~해도 될까요?'라고 해석한다.

> • A: Is it okay to stay out until late? 늦게까지 밖에 있어도 될까요?
> B: Sorry, you can't. 미안하지만, 안 돼.

허락 구하기 표현

> • Is it OK to open the window? 창문을 열어도 될까요?
> • Can[May] I take pictures? 사진을 찍어도 될까요?
> • Am I allowed to use a cellphone here? 여기서 휴대전화를 사용해도 될까요?
> • Is it OK if I leave now? 제가 지금 떠나도 될까요?
> • Do[Would] you mind if I sit here? 제가 여기 앉아도 될까요?

허락 구하기에 답하기

(허가할 때) • Sure. Go ahead. • Why not? • Of course. • No problem. • Okay.
   • That's fine with me. • Certainly. • I think it's okay.

(불허할 때) • I'm afraid not. • No, I'm sorry. • Not now. • Certainly not.
   • Not for any reason. • No, don't do that.

■ Do[Would] you mind if I ~?처럼 mind(꺼리다, 싫어하다)를 사용하여 허락을 구하는 질문에 답할 때는 Yes라고 하면 허락을 하지 않는다는 의미이고, No나 not이 들어가면 허락한다는 의미이므로 주의해야 한다.

> • A: Do you mind if I close the window? 창문을 닫아도 될까요?
> B: Not at all. 그렇게 하세요.

핵심 Check

1. 다음 우리말과 일치하도록 빈칸에 알맞은 말을 쓰시오.

  (1) **A:** Is it _____ _____ ride a bike? (자전거를 타도 돼요?)

    B: _____, you _____. (아니, 안 돼.)

  (2) **A:** _____ I _____ to use this computer? (이 컴퓨터를 써도 될까요?)

    B: Sure. (물론이지.)

② 금지하기

A Can I feed the animal? 동물에게 먹이를 줘도 되나요?

B No, you're not supposed to do that. 아니요, 그러면 안 됩니다.

■ You're not supposed to ~.는 상대방의 어떤 행동을 금지할 때 쓰는 표현으로, '너는 ~해서는 안 된다.'라고 해석한다.

• A: Is it okay if I practice the guitar here? 여기서 기타를 연습해도 될까요?

B: No, you're not supposed to do that. 아니요, 그러면 안 됩니다.

금지를 나타내는 표현

• You're not supposed to take pictures at the museum. 박물관에서는 사진을 찍어서는 안 된다.

= Don't[Do not] take pictures at the museum.

= You can't take pictures at the museum.

= You shouldn't take pictures at the museum.

= You're not allowed to take pictures at the museum.

= You're not permitted to take pictures at the museum.

핵심 Check

2. 다음 우리말과 일치하도록 빈칸에 알맞은 말을 쓰시오.

(1) **A:** Excuse me. You _____ _____ your cellphone here.

(실례합니다. 이곳에서 휴대 전화를 사용하시면 안 됩니다.)

B: Oh, I'm _____ . (오, 죄송합니다.)

(2) **A:** _____ _____ snacks in here. (이 안에서 과자를 드시지 마세요.)

B: Oh, I'm sorry. (오, 죄송합니다.)

(3) **A:** Can I bring friends home? (집에 친구를 데려와도 돼요?)

B: _____, you _____. You're _____ _____ _____ bring friends

home. (아니, 안 돼. 너는 집에 친구를 데려오면 안 돼.)

(4) **A:** Is it okay if I _____ _____ _____ at the museum?

(박물관에서 사진을 찍어도 될까요?)

B: No, you're not _____ to do that. (아니요, 그건 허가되지 않습니다.)

Communicate: Listen - Listen and Answer Dialog 1

G: ❶Is it okay to put a poster on the bulletin board, Mr. Cha?

M: A poster?

G: Here. ❷It's a poster about World Oceans Day.

M: ❸Let me see. It's a great poster. Did you make it?

G: My club members made it together. ❹I think people should care more about our oceans.

M: I agree. ❺Well, we don't have space right now.

G: ❻Then can I put it on the door?

M: ❼Sure. Go ahead.

G: 게시판에 포스터를 붙여도 될까요, 차 선생님?

M: 포스터?

G: 이거요. 이것은 세계 해양의 날에 대한 포스터예요.

M: 어디 보자. 포스터가 멋지네. 네가 만들었니?

G: 저희 동아리 회원들이 함께 그것을 만들었어요. 저는 사람들이 우리의 바다에 대해 더 관심을 가져야 한다고 생각해요.

M: 나도 그렇게 생각해. 음, 지금은 공간이 없어.

G: 그럼 문에 붙여도 될까요?

M: 물론. 어서 해.

❶ Is it okay to ~?: ~해도 괜찮을까요? (허가 여부를 묻는 표현) / bulletin board: 게시판
❷ It은 A poster를 가리킨다. / World Oceans Day: 세계 해양의 날
❸ Let me see.: 어디 보자.
❹ I think (that) 주어 + should + 동사원형 ~: 나는 ~해야 한다고 생각해. / care about: ~에 관심을 가지다
❺ space: 공간 / right now: 지금
❻ Can I + 동사원형 ~?: ~해도 될까요? (허가 여부를 묻는 표현)
❼ Go ahead.: 어서 해.

Check(√) True or False

(1) The girl made the poster by herself. T ☐ F ☐

(2) The girl will put the poster on the door. T ☐ F ☐

 Communicate: Listen - Listen and Answer Dialog 2

G: What are you doing, Minsu?

B: ❶I'm throwing away unused medicine.

G: ❷Well, you're not supposed to do that.

B: Why not?

G: ❸It can pollute the water. ❹It can also put people and animals in danger.

B: I see. ❺Then what should I do?

G: ❻You must take it to a drugstore. ❼They'll take care of it.

B: Oh, I didn't know that. I'll be more careful.

G: 뭐 하고 있니, 민수야?

B: 사용하지 않는 약을 버리고 있어.

G: 음, 그렇게 해서는 안 돼.

B: 왜 안 돼?

G: 그것은 물을 오염시킬 수 있어. 또한 사람과 동물을 위험에 빠뜨릴 수 있어.

B: 알겠어. 그럼 내가 어떻게 해야 하지?

G: 약국에 가져가야 해. 그들이 그것을 처리할 거야.

B: 오, 난 몰랐어. 더 주의할게.

❶ be동사+-ing: ~하고 있다(현재진행형) / throw away: 버리다 / unused medicine: 사용하지 않는 약
❷ You're not supposed to ~.: 너는 ~해서는 안 된다. (금지하기 표현)
❸ It은 'throwing away unused medicine'을 가리킨다. / pollute: 오염시키다
❹ put ~ in danger: ~을 위험에 빠뜨리다
❺ What should I do?: 내가 어떻게 해야 하니?(충고를 구하는 표현)
❻ must: ~해야 한다 / it= unused medicine
❼ take care of: ~을 처리하다

Check(√) True or False

(3) The unused medicine can pollute the water. T ☐ F ☐

(4) The girl will take care of the unused medicine. T ☐ F ☐

Communicate: Listen - Listen More

G: Wow! I love this place, Dad.

M: Oh, I forgot something. I didn't bring our toothbrushes.

G: ❶I saw a store on our way here.

M: Okay. ❷I'll go get some toothbrushes.

G: Sure. ❸It's getting dark. ❹You should drive carefully.

M: ❺Don't worry.

G: ❻Dad, is it okay to cook some *ramyeon*?

M: ❼Of course. ❽But you're not supposed to throw away any leftovers.

G: I know that. ❾I really care about the environment.

❶ on one's way here: 여기 오는 길에
❷ go와 get 사이에는 and가 생략되었다. / get=buy
❸ It: 명암을 나타내는 비인칭 주어 / get dark: 어두워지다
❹ should+동사원형: ~해야 한다 / carefully: 주의 깊게
❺ 부정명령문: Don't[Never]+동사원형 ~.
❻ Is it okay to + 동사원형 ~?: ~해도 돼?
❼ 허가할 때 사용하는 표현이다.
❽ You're not supposed to + 동사원형 ~: 너는 ~해서는 안 된다 / throw away: 버리다 / leftover: 남은 음식
❾ care about: ~에 관심을 가지다 / environment: 환경

Communicate: Listen - All Ears

M: 1. ❶You're not supposed to do that.
   2. ❷People should care more about our oceans.

❶ You're not supposed to + 동사원형 ~: 너는 ~해서는 안 된다
❷ should+동사원형: ~해야 한다 / care about: ~에 관심을 가지다

Communicate: Speak - Talk in groups

A: ❶You're not supposed to study during breaks.

B: ❷What's wrong with that?

A: ❸It's a new class rule. ❹You shouldn't do that.

B: Okay. I'll ❺remember the rule.

❶ You're not supposed to + 동사원형 ~: 너는 ~해서는 안 된다 / during breaks: 쉬는 시간에
❷ What's wrong with that?: 그게 뭐가 문젠데?
❸ class rule: 학급 규칙
❹ You shouldn't+동사원형 ~: 너는 ~해서는 안 돼.
❺ remember: 기억하다(↔forget)

My Speaking Portfolio - Step 1

M: ❶Welcome to K-Zoo. ❷Please listen carefully and follow the rules. First, ❸you're not supposed to feed the animals. ❹It can make them sick. ❺And you're not supposed to touch the animals. It can be very dangerous. ❻Lastly, don't throw stones or trash at them. Enjoy your time at K-Zoo. Thank you.

❶ Welcome to ~: ~에 온 걸 환영합니다
❷ follow the rules: 규칙을 따르다
❸ be not supposed to+동사원형: ~해서는 안 된다 / feed: 먹이를 주다
❹ make+목적어+목적격 보어: ~을 …하게 만들다 / them=the animals
❺ touch the animals: 동물들을 만지다
❻ lastly: 마지막으로 / Don't+동사원형: ~하지 마라(부정명령문) / trash: 쓰레기

Wrap Up - Listening ❺

G: ❶Dad, is it okay to go out with my friends this Saturday?

M: ❷What are your plans?

G: ❸Well, my favorite singer is going to have a concert at Olympic Park.

M: ❹Okay, but come home by 9 o'clock.

G: ❺No problem. ❻The concert will be over by about 8:00.

❶ Is it OK to ~?: ~해도 될까?(= Am I allowed to ~? = Is it OK if I ~?) / go out: 외출하다
❷ What are your plans?: 너희 계획들은 무엇이니?(계획을 묻는 표현)
❸ favorite: 아주 좋아하는 / be going to: ~할 것이다 / have a concert: 콘서트를 하다
❹ come home: 집에 오다 / by: ~까지는
❺ No problem.: 그럼요.[전혀 문제되지 않아요.]
❻ be over: 끝나다 / about: 약, ~쯤

Wrap Up - Listening ❻

W: ❶Hey, look at the sign!

B: What sign?

W: ❷The one over there. ❸You're not supposed to pick flowers here.

B: Oh, I'm sorry. I didn't know that.

❶ look at: ~을 보다 / sign: 표지판
❷ one = sign / over there: 저쪽에
❸ You're not supposed to + 동사원형 ~: 너는 ~해서는 안 된다 / pick flowers: 꽃을 따다

다음 우리말과 일치하도록 빈칸에 알맞은 말을 쓰시오.

Communicate: Listen - Listen and Answer Dialog 1

G: Is it _____ _____ _____ a poster on the _____ board, Mr. Cha?

M: A poster?

G: Here. It's a poster _____ World Oceans Day.

M: _____ me _____. It's a great poster. _____ you _____ it?

G: My club _____ made it _____. I think people should care more _____ our oceans.

M: I _____. Well, we don't have space _____ _____.

G: Then _____ I _____ it on the door?

M: Sure. Go _____.

Communicate: Listen - Listen and Answer Dialog 2

G: What _____ you _____, Minsu?

B: I'm _____ _____ unused medicine.

G: Well, you're not _____ to do that.

B: Why _____?

G: It _____ _____ the water. It can also _____ people and animals _____ _____.

B: I _____. Then _____ should I _____?

G: You _____ _____ it to a drugstore. They'll take _____ of it.

B: Oh, I _____ know that. I'll _____ more _____.

Communicate: Listen - Listen More

G: Wow! I _____ this _____, Dad.

M: Oh, I _____ something. I _____ _____ our toothbrushes.

G: I saw a store _____ _____ _____ here.

M: Okay. I'll _____ _____ some toothbrushes.

G: Sure. It's _____ _____. You _____ drive _____.

M: _____ worry.

G: Dad, is _____ okay _____ _____ some *ramyeon*?

M: Of _____. But you're _____ _____ _____ throw away any leftovers.

G: I know that. I really _____ _____ the environment.

해석

G: 게시판에 포스터를 붙여도 될까요, 차 선생님?
M: 포스터?
G: 이거요. 이것은 세계 해양의 날에 대한 포스터예요.
M: 어디 보자. 포스터가 멋지네. 네가 만들었니?
G: 저희 동아리 회원들이 함께 그것을 만들었어요. 저는 사람들이 우리의 바다에 대해 더 관심을 가져야 한다고 생각해요.
M: 나도 그렇게 생각해. 음, 지금은 공간이 없어.
G: 그럼 문에 붙여도 될까요?
M: 물론. 어서 해.

G: 뭐 하고 있니, 민수야?
B: 사용하지 않는 약을 버리고 있어.
G: 음, 그렇게 해서는 안 돼.
B: 왜 안 돼?
G: 그것은 물을 오염시킬 수 있어. 또한 사람과 동물을 위험에 빠뜨릴 수 있어.
B: 알겠어. 그럼 내가 어떻게 해야 하지?
G: 약국에 가져가야 해. 그들이 그것을 처리할 거야.
B: 오, 난 몰랐어. 더 주의할게.

G: 와우! 이곳이 정말 좋아요, 아빠.
M: 오, 깜빡 잊은 게 있어. 칫솔을 가져오지 않았어.
G: 여기 오는 길에 가게를 봤어요.
M: 좋아, 내가 가서 칫솔 좀 사 올게.
G: 그래요. 어두워지고 있어요. 운전 조심하세요.
M: 걱정하지 마.
G: 아빠, 라면을 좀 요리해도 돼요?
M: 물론이지. 하지만 남은 음식은 버리면 안 돼.
G: 알아요. 저는 환경에 정말 관심이 많아요.

Communicate: Listen - All Ears

M: 1. You're _____ _____ _____ do that.

2. People should _____ _____ _____ our oceans.

Communicate: Speak - Talk in groups

A: _____ _____ supposed to study _____ breaks.

B: What's _____ with that?

A: It's a new _____ _____. You _____ do that.

B: Okay. I'll _____ the rule.

My Writing Portfolio - Step 1

M: _____ _____ K-Zoo. Please _____ carefully and _____ the rules. First, you're not _____ to feed the animals. It can _____ them _____. And you're not supposed _____ _____ the animals. It can be very _____. _____, don't _____ stones or trash _____ them. Enjoy your time _____ K-Zoo. Thank you.

Wrap Up - Listening ❺

G: Dad, _____ _____ _____ _____ go out with my friends this Saturday?

M: What are your _____?

G: Well, my _____ singer is going to _____ _____ _____ at Olympic Park.

M: Okay, but come home _____ 9 o'clock.

G: No _____. The concert will _____ _____ by about 8:00.

Wrap Up - Listening ❻

W: Hey, _____ _____ the sign!

B: _____ sign?

W: The one _____ _____. You're not supposed to _____ flowers here.

B: Oh, I'm _____. I _____ _____ that.

해석

M: 1. 너는 그렇게 해서는 안 돼.
2. 사람들은 우리의 바다에 대해 더 관심을 가져야 해.

A: 쉬는 시간에 공부하면 안 돼.
B: 그게 뭐가 문젠데?
A: 새로운 학급 규칙이야. 그렇게 해선 안 돼.
B: 알았어. 규칙을 기억할게.

M: K-Zoo에 오신 것을 환영합니다. 주의 깊게 듣고 규칙을 따르세요. 첫 번째, 동물들에게 먹이를 주면 안 돼요. 그것은 동물들을 아프게 할 수 있습니다. 그리고 동물들을 만지면 안 돼요. 그것은 매우 위험할 수 있습니다. 마지막으로, 동물들에게 돌이나 쓰레기를 던지지 마세요. K-Zoo에서 즐거운 시간을 보내세요. 감사합니다.

G: 아빠, 이번 토요일에 친구들과 외출해도 될까요?
M: 너희들의 계획이 뭐니?
G: 음, 제가 가장 좋아하는 가수가 올림픽 공원에서 콘서트를 할 예정이에요.
M: 좋아, 하지만 9시까지는 집에 오거라.
G: 그럼요. 콘서트는 8시쯤에 끝날 거예요.

W: 이봐요, 표지판을 보세요!
B: 무슨 표지판이요?
W: 저쪽에 있는 거요. 여기서 꽃을 따면 안 돼요.
B: 아, 미안해요. 전 몰랐어요.

Conversation 시험대비 기본평가

01 다음 대화의 밑줄 친 부분의 의도로 알맞은 것은?

> A: <u>Is it okay to leave now?</u>
> B: Sure.

① 도움 요청하기　　② 허가 여부 묻기
③ 불만 표현하기　　④ 확인 요청하기
⑤ 불만에 응답하기

02 다음 대화의 빈칸에 알맞은 것은?

> A: May I go to a music concert on Saturday?
> B: _____ Let's go together.

① Thanks.　　② Sure.
③ Of course not.　　④ Yes, we do.
⑤ Help yourself.

[03~04] 다음 대화의 밑줄 친 부분과 바꾸어 쓸 수 있는 것을 고르시오.

03

> A: <u>Is it okay to</u> take pictures here?
> B: No, you're not supposed to do that.

① Would you like to　　② Am I allowed to
③ Where can you　　④ When can I
⑤ Do you want to

04

> A: Can I swim in this river?
> B: Oh, no. <u>You're not allowed to do that.</u>

① You may do that.
② You don't have to do that.
③ You don't need to do that.
④ I'm not sure if you can do that.
⑤ You're not supposed to do that.

[01~05] 다음 대화를 읽고, 물음에 답하시오.

G: _____ⓐ_____ put a poster on the bulletin board, Mr. Cha?

M: A poster? (①)

G: Here. It's a poster about World Oceans Day. (②)

M: Let me see. It's a great poster. Did you make it?

G: My club members made it together. I think people should care more ___ⓑ___ our oceans. (③)

M: I agree. (④)

G: Then can I put it on the door?

M: ___ⓒ___ Go ahead. (⑤)

01 위 대화의 ①~⑤ 중 다음 문장이 들어갈 알맞은 곳은?

> Well, we don't have space right now.

①   ②   ③   ④   ⑤

02 위 대화의 빈칸 ⓐ에 알맞은 것은?

① When do you
② Is it okay to
③ How about you
④ Is it okay if you
⑤ Do you know if I

03 위 대화의 빈칸 ⓑ에 알맞은 것은?

① to   ② of
③ for   ④ about
⑤ after

04 위 대화의 빈칸 ⓒ에 알맞지 않은 것은?

① Sure.   ② Certainly.
③ Why not?   ④ Of course.
⑤ Maybe next time.

서답형

05 위 대화를 읽고, 다음 질문에 영어로 답하시오.

Q: What is the poster about?

A: _____

[06~07] 다음 대화를 읽고, 물음에 답하시오.

A: ⓐYou're not supposed to study during breaks.

B: What's wrong with that?

A: It's a new class rule. You ___ⓑ___ do that.

B: Okay. I'll remember the rule.

06 위 대화의 밑줄 친 ⓐ와 바꿔 쓸 수 있는 것은?

① You should
② You don't want to
③ You would like to
④ You're not allowed to
⑤ You might want to

07 위 대화의 빈칸 ⓑ에 문맥상 알맞은 것은?

① will   ② can
③ may   ④ should
⑤ shouldn't

[08~12] 다음 대화를 읽고, 물음에 답하시오.

> G: What are you doing, Minsu?
> B: I'm throwing ___ⓐ___ unused medicine. (①)
> G: Well, ⓑyou're not supposed to do that.
> B: Why not? (②)
> G: It can pollute the water. It can also ___ⓒ___ people and animals in danger. (③)
> B: I see. (④)
> G: You must take it to a drugstore. They'll take care of it. (⑤)
> B: Oh, I didn't know that. I'll be more careful.

08 위 대화의 ①~⑤ 중 다음 문장이 들어갈 알맞은 곳은?

> Then what should I do?

① ② ③ ④ ⑤

서답형

09 위 대화의 빈칸 ⓐ에 '~을 버리고 있다'는 의미가 되도록 알맞은 말을 쓰시오.

➡ _____

10 위 대화의 밑줄 친 ⓑ의 의도로 알맞은 것은?

① 권유   ② 사과   ③ 수락
④ 금지   ⑤ 허가

11 위 대화의 빈칸 ⓒ에 알맞은 것은?

① set   ② put
③ gain   ④ keep
⑤ lose

서답형

12 위 대화를 읽고, 다음 질문에 우리말로 답하시오.

> Q: Why shouldn't we throw away unused medicine?
>
> A: _____
> _____

[13~15] 다음 대화를 읽고, 물음에 답하시오.

> G: Dad, ⓐis it okay to go out with my friends this Saturday?
> M: What are your plans?
> G: Well, my favorite singer is going to have a concert at Olympic Park.
> M: Okay, but come home ___ⓑ___ 9 o'clock.
> G: ⓒNo problem. The concert will be over by about 8:00.

서답형

13 위 대화의 밑줄 친 ⓐ를 다음과 같이 바꿔 쓸 때 빈칸에 알맞은 말을 쓰시오.

> is it OK _____ I go out with my friends this Saturday?

14 위 대화의 빈칸 ⓑ에 문맥상 알맞은 것은?

① to   ② by
③ after   ④ until
⑤ between

15 위 대화의 밑줄 친 ⓒ와 바꿔 쓸 수 있는 것은?

① No way.   ② Why not?
③ Certainly not.   ④ Not at all.
⑤ Don't mention it.

01 다음 괄호 안의 단어를 바르게 배열하여 대화를 완성하시오.

A: _____ swim here?
   (okay / is / to / it)
B: No, _____ swim here.
   (not / to / supposed / you're)

02 다음 대화의 밑줄 친 표현과 바꿔 쓸 수 있는 것을 쓰시오.
(2가지 이상)

A: Is it okay to eat chocolate, Dad?
B: Sure, but don't eat too much.

➡ _____

03 다음 괄호 안의 단어를 이용하여 대화를 완성하시오.

A: Dad, is it okay if I go to the movies with my boyfriend tonight?
B: No. _____.
   (allow / that)

04 다음 대화의 순서를 바르게 배열하시오.

(A) What's wrong with that?
(B) Okay. I'll remember the rule.
(C) It's a new class rule. You shouldn't do that.
(D) You're not supposed to study during breaks.

➡ _____

[05~09] 다음 대화를 읽고, 물음에 답하시오.

G: Wow! I love this place, Dad.
M: Oh, I forgot something. I didn't bring our toothbrushes.
G: I saw a store ⓐ our way here.
M: Okay. ⓑI'll go get some toothbrushes.
G: Sure. It's getting dark. You should drive carefully.
M: Don't worry.
G: Dad, is it okay ⓒ cook some *ramyeon*?
M: Of course. But you're ⓓ throw away any leftovers.
G: I know that. I really care about the environment.

05 위 대화의 빈칸 ⓐ에 알맞은 단어를 쓰시오.

➡ _____

06 위 대화의 밑줄 친 ⓑ를 우리말로 쓰시오.

➡ _____

07 위 대화의 빈칸 ⓒ에 알맞은 단어를 쓰시오.

➡ _____

08 위 대화의 빈칸 ⓓ에 문맥상 알맞은 표현을 쓰시오. (3단어)

➡ _____

09 What does the girl care about? Answer in English.

➡ _____

Grammar

① 수동태

- The shirt **was designed** by my father. 그 셔츠는 나의 아버지에 의해 디자인되었다.
- *The Scream* **was painted** by Vincent van Gogh. '비명'은 Vincent van Gogh에 의해 그려졌다.
- This house **was built** by my grandfather. 이 집은 우리 할아버지에 의해 지어졌다.

■ 수동태는 주어가 어떤 동작의 대상이 되어 그 동작을 당하는 것으로, 「be동사+과거분사+by+행위자(목적격)」의 형태로 쓰며, '~되다, ~당하다'라고 해석한다. 행위자가 일반 사람들인 경우, 「by+행위자」는 생략할 수 있다.

■ 능동태를 수동태로 바꾸는 방법
1. 능동태의 목적어를 수동태의 주어로 바꾼다. (필요한 경우 주격의 형태로 바꾼다.)
2. 능동태의 동사를 「be+과거분사」의 형태로 바꾼다. (주어와 동사의 수와 인칭에 일치한다.)
3. 능동태의 주어를 「by+목적격」의 형태로 바꾼다.

- He ate the apple. 그는 그 사과를 먹었다.
  → The apple was eaten by him.

■ 조동사가 있는 수동태
「조동사+be+과거분사」의 형태로 쓴다.
- The elevator **can be fixed** by Alex. 승강기는 Alex에 의해 수리될 수 있다.

■ 수동태 문장의 부정문과 의문문
부정문: 「주어+be동사+not+과거분사+by+목적격」
- This picture **was not drawn** by Jason. 이 그림은 Jason에 의해 그려지지 않았다.

의문문: 「Be동사+주어+과거분사+by+목적격 ~?」
- **Was** our car **washed** by your mom? 우리 차가 네 엄마에 의해 세차되었니?

■ 수동태의 관용 표현
be made of: ~로 만들어지다 (물리적 변화) / be made from: ~로 만들어지다 (화학적 변화)
be filled with: ~로 가득하다 / be interested in: ~에 관심이 있다 / be covered with: ~로 덮여 있다 /
be pleased with: ~에 기뻐하다 / be known to: ~에게 알려져 있다 / be known for: ~로 알려지다

핵심 Check

1. 다음 주어진 문장을 수동태 문장으로 바꿔 쓰시오.

(1) Brian broke the window.

➡ _____

(2) Mrs. Smith helps many poor kids.

➡ _____

(3) The police officer stopped the cars.

➡ _____

② as ~ as ...

> • I want to be **as** creative **as** Leonardo da Vinci. 나는 레오나르도 다 빈치처럼 창의적이기를 원한다.
>
> • Jade studies **as** hard **as** Kevin. Jade는 Kevin만큼 열심히 공부한다.
>
> • Saving money is **as** important **as** making money. 돈을 저축하는 것은 돈을 버는 것만큼 중요하다.

■ **as ~ as ...**
'as+원급+as ...'의 형태로 '~와 똑같이 …한[하게]'의 뜻을 나타낸다. 이것은 비교되는 두 개[사람]의 정도가 같은 경우에 쓰이는 표현이다.

• I am **as** tall **as** Kate. 나는 Kate만큼 키가 크다.

비교 대상의 정도가 완전히 같을 때는 as ~ as 앞에 just를 붙이고, 거의 같을 때는 as ~ as 앞에 nearly나 about, almost를 붙인다.

• This dictionary is **just as** good **as** that. 이 사전은 저 사전과 아주 똑같이 좋다.

• He plays tennis **almost[nearly] as** well **as** Tom. 그는 Tom과 거의 같은 정도로 테니스를 잘 친다.

■ **as+원급+as+사람+can[could]**
'가능한 한 ~하게'의 뜻으로 as ~ as ... 구문의 관용적인 표현이다. 같은 뜻으로 'as+원급+as possible'의 구문을 쓰기도 한다.

• He swam **as** fast **as** he **could**. = He swam **as** fast **as possible**. 그는 가능한 한 빨리 수영을 했다.

■ **동등 비교의 부정형**
'not as[so]+형용사[부사]의 원급+as'의 형태로 '~만큼 …하지 못한'의 의미이다. 비교급으로 바꿔 쓸 수도 있다.

• Jane is **not as** tall **as** Tommy. = Tommy is **taller than** Jane. Tommy는 Jane보다 더 키가 크다.

■ **배수 표현**
'…의 몇 배만큼 ~한'이라고 배수 표현을 나타낼 경우 '숫자+times+as+형용사/부사+as' 또는 '배수사 +as+형용사/부사+as'의 표현을 사용한다.

• This building is **three times as** high **as** that building. 이 건물은 저 건물보다 3배만큼 높다.

핵심 Check

2. 다음 괄호 안의 말을 알맞은 순서로 배열하시오.

(1) You are (as, your, as, father, tall)
➡ You are _____.

(2) The red pencil is (the, as, not, yellow, as, long, one).
➡ The red pencil is _____.

(3) Is your camera (as, mine, new, as)?
➡ Is your camera _____?

01 다음 동사의 과거형과 과거분사형을 쓰시오.

     (1) break _____ _____   (2) bring _____ _____

     (3) keep _____ _____   (4) see _____ _____

     (5) speak _____ _____   (6) teach _____ _____

     (7) write _____ _____   (8) steal _____ _____

     (9) make _____ _____   (10) know _____ _____

> break 깨뜨리다
> bring 가져오다
> steal 훔치다

02 다음 괄호 안에서 알맞은 것을 고르시오.

     (1) The chair was painted (by / with) his brother.

     (2) The telephone (is / was) invented by Bell.

     (3) This building was (build / built) by a famous architect.

     (4) Wine is made (from / of) grapes.

     (5) I was interested (at / in) sports.

     (6) The children (were / was) known to everyone.

     (7) They weren't satisfied (with / for) the result.

> invent 발명하다
> architect 건축가
> result 결과

03 다음 밑줄 친 부분을 바르게 고쳐 쓰시오.

     (1) I can as run fast as my father.

     ➡ _____

     (2) This is as not delicious as it looks.

     ➡ _____

     (3) Tokyo's population is as large as Seoul.

     ➡ _____

     (4) Your bag is as heavy as me.

     ➡ _____

     (5) The second question was more difficult as the first question.

     ➡ _____

> delicious 맛있는

01 다음 괄호 안의 동사를 알맞은 형태로 바꾼 것은?

> This delicious cake (make) by Sujin.

① makes   ② made
③ was made   ④ make
⑤ was making

02 다음 중 동사의 과거분사형이 잘못된 것은?

① give – given   ② ride – ridden
③ catch – catched   ④ speak – spoken
⑤ throw – thrown

03 다음 문장의 빈칸에 괄호 안의 말을 알맞은 형으로 바꿔 쓰시오.

(1) Is this dog _____ than your dog? (big)
(2) January is as _____ as December. (long)
(3) I am the _____ girl in the world. (happy)

04 다음 괄호 안의 동사를 알맞게 변형하여 쓰시오.

> Hangeul _____ _____ by King Sejong in 1443. (invent)

05 다음 문장을 수동태로 바르게 바꾼 것은?

> He didn't write this book.

① This book is not written by him.
② This book wasn't written by him.
③ This book didn't be write by him.
④ This book didn't be written by him.
⑤ This book wasn't be written by him.

06 다음 두 문장의 의미가 같도록 할 때 빈칸에 알맞은 것은?

> This room is the same size _____ that one.
> = This room is as large as that one.

① as   ② so
③ of   ④ for
⑤ with

07 다음 문장의 빈칸에 알맞은 것은?

> English _____ all over the world by people.

① speaks   ② spoke
③ is spoken   ④ is speaking
⑤ is to speak

08 다음 두 문장의 의미가 같도록 빈칸에 알맞은 쓰시오.

> Mr. Johnson can fix any machine in the town.
> = Any machine in the town can _____ _____ by Mr. Johnson.

09 다음 문장의 빈칸에 알맞은 것은?

> Jack is _____ old as my big brother.

① as
② so
③ than
④ very
⑤ much

10 (중요) 다음 중 어법상 어색한 것은?

① The treasure island was found by Loopi.
② Frank is called Potato by his friends.
③ My new iPhone was broken by someone.
④ *The Mona Lisa* was painted by Leonardo da Vinci.
⑤ The kitchen was cleaned by she.

11 [서답형] 다음 문장의 빈칸에 공통으로 알맞은 말을 쓰시오.

> • Cheese is _____ from milk.
> • This box is _____ of wood.

12 [서답형] 다음 두 문장이 같은 뜻이 되도록 빈칸에 알맞은 말을 쓰시오.

(1) February is colder than March.
　= March isn't as _____ as February.
(2) It wasn't as hot in Busan as in Taegu.
　= It was _____ in Taegu _____ in Busan.

13 다음 문장의 빈칸에 알맞은 것은?

> According to the news, all the schools will _____ tomorrow.

① be closed
② closing
③ closed
④ have closed
⑤ being closed

14 (중요) 다음 중 밑줄 친 부분의 쓰임이 나머지 넷과 <u>다른</u> 것은?

① She <u>was</u> hit by a bus.
② I <u>was</u> annoyed because I missed the bus.
③ I <u>was</u> given some cake by Mary.
④ Soyeon <u>was</u> praised by Mr. Brown.
⑤ These trees <u>were</u> brought from another city by the mayor.

15 (중요) 다음 빈칸에 들어갈 말이 바르게 짝지어진 것은?

> • You may eat as much _____ you like.
> • This picture is _____ beautiful than mine.

① as – much
② as – more
③ so – few
④ as – little
⑤ so – much

16 [서답형] 다음 문장에서 어법상 어색한 곳을 찾아 고쳐 쓰시오.

> Korean history should is taught to every student.

_____ ➡ _____

17 다음 중 밑줄 친 부분이 어법상 어색한 문장은?

① The huge rock in the field was <u>moved</u> by a crane.
② My wallet was <u>stolen</u> in the classroom yesterday.
③ This work should be <u>finished</u> by him.
④ English is <u>used</u> in the UK.
⑤ The survivor was <u>founded</u> under the bridge.

18 다음 중 밑줄 친 부분의 쓰임이 나머지 넷과 다른 것은?

① They were <u>as</u> busy as bees.
② Tom is not <u>as</u> honest as John.
③ Please come home <u>as</u> quickly as possible.
④ This house is twice <u>as</u> large as that.
⑤ He came up <u>as</u> she was speaking.

19 다음 문장을 수동태로 올바르게 바꾼 것은?

Who painted these wall paintings?

① Who these wall paintings were painted?
② Whom these wall paintings painted?
③ Who these wall paintings are painted?
④ By whom were these wall paintings painted?
⑤ By whom these wall paintings paint?

서답형 20 다음 주어진 단어를 이용하여 우리말을 영어로 옮기시오.

이 냉장고는 그에 의해 고쳐질 수 있다.
(refrigerator, fix)

➡ _____

서답형 21 다음 문장의 괄호 안에서 알맞은 것을 고르시오.

(1) Our teacher is as (old / older / oldest) as my father.
(2) I am (young / younger / youngest) than he.
(3) That boy is the (short / shorter / shortest) in our class.
(4) China is as (large / larger / largest) as the United States.
(5) Ann was the smartest (in / of / at) all the students.
(6) Jack finished his homework as early as he (was / did / could).

22 다음 중 어법상 어색한 것은?

① It is not as easy as you think.
② John doesn't work as hard as George do.
③ I don't have so much money as you do.
④ Let me have your answer as soon as possible.
⑤ I don't have as many friends as you do.

01 다음 〈보기〉의 단어를 알맞게 고쳐서 문장을 완성하시오.

> ┤ 보기 ├
> appear   break   sell   write

(1) The window _____ by Mike.

(2) This letter _____ by Sarah.

(3) The first steam engine _____ in Scotland.

(4) All kinds of things _____ in this convenient store.

02 다음 빈칸에 공통으로 알맞은 말을 쓰시오.

> • Radium _____ discovered by Madame Curie.
> • A pair of shoes _____ stolen yesterday.

03 다음 빈칸에 알맞은 말을 〈보기〉에서 골라 쓰시오.

> ┤ 보기 ├
> early   young   twice   just

(1) Today is _____ as cold as yesterday.

(2) He's not as _____ as he used to be.

(3) This box is _____ as large as that one.

(4) He doesn't get up as _____ as his brother.

04 다음 문장에서 어법상 어색한 곳을 찾아 바르게 고쳐 쓰시오.

(1) The cartoons were drawing by them.

   _____ ➡ _____

(2) The airplane is invented by the Wright brothers.

   _____ ➡ _____

(3) The company was found in 1976 by Mr. Kim.

   _____ ➡ _____

(4) This room does not used on weekends.

   _____ ➡ _____

(5) Did these pictures taken by your father?

   _____ ➡ _____

05 다음 두 문장의 뜻이 같도록 빈칸에 알맞은 말을 쓰시오.

(1) Mike can't run as fast as Nancy.

   = Nancy can run _____ _____ Mike.

(2) I don't have _____ much money _____ you.

   ➡ I have less money than you.

(3) Your sister and I are the same age.

   ➡ I'm _____ _____ as your sister.

(4) The girls came as soon as they could.

   ➡ The girls came as soon as _____.

06 다음 문장을 수동태의 문장으로 바꾸어 쓰시오.

(1) Chinese people first invented paper money around the 10th century.

➡ _____

_____

(2) People in the United States speak English.

➡ _____

(3) Tom took these pictures yesterday.

➡ _____

(4) Koreans used shells and rice as money in the past.

➡ _____

_____

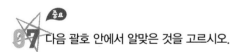

07 다음 괄호 안에서 알맞은 것을 고르시오.

(1) My car was (stolen / stole) last night.
(2) I was (hit / hitted) by a drunken driver's car.
(3) Joker was (catch / caught) by Batman.
(4) The window was (broke / broken) by Mike.
(5) The card key was (found / founded) under the table.
(6) The room was filled (with / by) many people.
(7) The singer is known (by / to) everybody.

08 다음 두 문장을 as ~ as를 써서 〈보기〉와 같이 한 문장으로 나타내시오.

┌─ 보기 ─
│ Jack has six dogs. Katc also has six
│ dogs.
│ ➡ Jack has as many dogs as Kate has.
└

(1) Ella has nine hats. I also have nine hats.

➡ _____

(2) This new tool is useful. The old one is useful, too.

➡ _____

(3) Tom drank a glass of wine. He also drank a glass of water.

➡ _____

09 다음 주어진 문장을 어법에 맞게 고쳐 쓰시오.

(1) 종이 상자들은 그들에 의해 옮겨졌다.
(carry, by)

➡ _____

(2) 나는 그녀에게서 그 책을 받았다.
(I, give, by)

➡ _____

10 다음 문장을 as ~ as 구문으로 바꿔 쓰시오.

(1) Jimin is shorter than Taemin.

➡ _____

(2) Jane is less heavy than Kirk.

➡ _____

Is It a Light Problem?

01 <u>Look at</u> this beautiful painting. It <u>was created</u> by <u>the famous</u>
　　~을 보아라　　　　　　　　　　　　　　　　be동사+과거분사(수동태)

Dutch artist Vincent van Gogh in 1889. In Van Gogh's time,
the famous Dutch artist와 Vincent van Gogh는 동격 관계

almost everyone <u>could</u> look up and <u>see</u> a wonderful starry night
　　　　　　　　can의 과거형　　　　　look과 함께 could에 연결

sky. Now, <u>how many</u> of us are <u>as lucky as</u> Van Gogh? <u>In fact,</u>
　　　　　얼마나 많은 사람들　　　　as+원급+as　　　사실 (= as a matter of fact)

many people <u>in today's world</u> cannot enjoy a starry night sky.
　　　　　　　　　형용사구

This is so because of light pollution.
앞 문장의 내용을 받는 지시대명사

02 <u>Most of us</u> <u>are familiar with</u> air, water, and land pollution. We
　　우리들 중의 대부분　~에 익숙하다

know that <u>they</u> are serious problems, and we <u>are taking</u> action <u>to</u>
　　　　　= air, water, and land pollution　　　　　현재진행형

<u>solve</u> them. But did you know <u>that</u> light can also <u>cause pollution?</u>
목적을 나타내는 부사적 용법　　　　　　　명사절을 이끄는 접속사　　　　　오염을 일으키다

Light pollution – too much light <u>in the wrong place</u> <u>at the wrong</u>
　　　　　　　　　　　　　　　　　형용사구　　　　　　　형용사구

time – is almost everywhere around the world. It can <u>have serious</u>
　　　있다–완전자동사　　　　　　　　　　　　　　　~에 심각한 영향을 끼치다

<u>effects on</u> humans and wildlife.

---

painting 그림
create 창조하다, 만들다
artist 미술가, 예술가
almost 거의
starry 별이 총총한
in fact 사실
light 빛, 광선
because of ~ 때문에
pollution 오염
most of ~의 대부분
be familiar with ~에 익숙하다, ~을 잘 알다
land 땅, 육지
serious 심각한
take action 조치를 취하다
cause 일으키다
wrong 잘못된, 틀린
everywhere 도처에
effect 영향
human 인간
wildlife 야생동물

 확인문제

● 다음 문장이 본문의 내용과 일치하면 T, 일치하지 <u>않으면</u> F를 쓰시오.

1　Vincent van Gogh was a famous Dutch artist. ☐

2　In Van Gogh's time, almost everyone could see a wonderful starry night sky. ☐

3　Many people in today's world can see a starry night sky. ☐

4　Most of us are familiar with light pollution. ☐

5　Air, water, and land pollution are serious problems. ☐

03 According to a recent report, about 89% of the world's population
   약   주어
lives under skies that are not dark enough at night. Especially in big
동사   부사구   주격 관계대명사–skies가 선행사   특히
cities, people often cannot see a starry night. They can also suffer
           빈도부사–조동사 앞에 위치   ~으로 고통을 받다
from sleep problems because the natural rhythm of day and night is
                                                            형용사구
disturbed by artificial light.
be동사+과거분사(수동태)

04 Wildlife is threatened by light pollution, too. Birds that migrate or
            be동사+과거분사(수동태)   주격 관계대명사–Birds가 선행사
hunt at night find their way by natural light, but light in big cities
at+noon. night. midnight   ~에 의해   형용사구
can cause them to wander off course. Every year millions of birds
    cause A to부정사: A가 ~하게 하다   수백만의
die after hitting buildings that have bright lights. Sea turtles cannot
    after+동명사   주격 관계대명사–buildings가 선행사
easily find a place to lay eggs since beaches are too bright at night.
easy의 부사형   to부정사의 형용사적 용법 ~이기 때문에(=because)
Also, many baby sea turtles die because artificial light draws them
                                     ~이기 때문에   그들이 ~에서 멀어지게 하다
away from the ocean.

05 Clearly, light pollution is as serious as other forms of pollution. We
   문장 수식 부사   as+원급+as   other+복수명사
have to find ways to solve the problem. If we do not, we may see
 = must   to부정사의 형용사적 용법   ~할지도 모른다
stars only in our dreams or paintings.
단지, ~만–부사구 in our dreams or paitings를 수식하는 부사

according to ~에 의하면
recent 최근의
population 인구
especially 특히
suffer from ~으로 고통을 받다
natural 자연적인
rhythm 리듬
disturb 방해하다
artificial 인공적인
threaten 위협하다
migrate 이주하다
hunt 사냥하다
cause 야기하다
wander off 벗어나다
course 코스, 경로
million 백만
turtle 거북
easily 쉽게
lay (알을) 낳다
beach 해변
draw 이끌다
ocean 대양
form 형태
dream 꿈

📎 **확인문제**

● 다음 문장이 본문의 내용과 일치하면 T, 일치하지 않으면 F를 쓰시오.

1 People in big cities can enjoy a starry night. ☐

2 Light pollution can cause sleep problems. ☐

3 Light pollution is also harmful to wildlife. ☐

4 Beaches are so bright at night, so sea turtles can find a place to lay eggs. ☐

5 Light pollution isn't as serious as other forms of pollution. ☐

● 우리말을 참고하여 빈칸에 알맞은 말을 쓰시오.

1 _____ at this beautiful _____ .

2 It was _____ by the famous Dutch _____ Vincent van Gogh in 1889.

3 In Van Gogh's _____, almost everyone could _____ up and see a wonderful _____ night sky.

4 Now, how _____ of us are as _____ as Van Gogh?

5 In _____, many people in today's _____ cannot enjoy a starry night _____ .

6 This is so _____ of light _____ .

7 Most of us are _____ with air, water, and _____ pollution.

8 We know _____ they are serious _____, and we are taking _____ to solve them.

9 But did you _____ that light can also _____ pollution?

10 _____ pollution—too much light in the _____ place at the wrong time—is almost _____ around the world.

11 It can have serious _____ on humans and _____ .

---

1 이 아름다운 그림을 보세요.

2 그것은 1889년에 유명한 네덜란드 미술가 빈센트 반 고흐에 의해 만들어졌습니다.

3 반 고흐의 시대에는 거의 모든 사람들이 위를 쳐다보고 멋진 별이 빛나는 밤하늘을 볼 수 있었습니다.

4 이제, 우리들 중 얼마나 많은 사람이 반 고흐만큼 운이 있을까요?

5 사실, 오늘날 세계의 많은 사람들은 별이 빛나는 밤하늘을 즐길 수 없습니다.

6 이것은 빛의 오염 때문에 그렇습니다.

7 우리들 중 대부분은 공기, 물, 토양 오염에 익숙합니다.

8 우리는 그것들이 심각한 문제라는 것을 알고 있으며, 그것들을 해결하기 위해 조치를 취하고 있습니다.

9 하지만 여러분은 빛이 오염도 일으킬 수 있다는 것을 알고 있었나요?

10 빛의 오염—잘못된 시간에 잘못된 장소에서의 너무 많은 빛—은 전 세계의 거의 모든 곳에 있습니다.

11 그것은 인간과 야생동물에게 심각한 영향을 미칠 수 있습니다.

12 According to a recent _____, about 89% of the world's _____ lives under skies that are not dark _____ at night.

13 _____ in big cities, people often cannot _____ a starry night.

14 They can also _____ from sleep problems _____ the natural rhythm of day and night is _____ by artificial light.

15 Wildlife is _____ by light pollution, too.

16 Birds that _____ or hunt at night find their way by _____ light, but light in big cities can _____ them to wander off course.

17 Every year _____ of birds die after _____ buildings that have bright lights.

18 Sea turtles cannot _____ find a place to lay eggs _____ beaches are too _____ at night.

19 Also, many baby sea turtles _____ because artificial light _____ them away from the _____.

20 _____, light pollution is as _____ as other forms of pollution.

21 We have to _____ ways to _____ the problem.

22 If we do not, we _____ see stars _____ in our dreams or paintings.

12 최근 보고서에 따르면, 세계 인구의 약 89%가 밤에 충분히 어둡지 않은 하늘 아래서 살고 있습니다.

13 특히 대도시에서는 별이 빛나는 밤을 종종 볼 수 없습니다.

14 그들은 또한 인공적인 빛에 의해 낮과 밤의 자연적인 리듬이 방해를 받기 때문에 수면 문제로 고통을 겪을 수도 있습니다.

15 야생동물도 빛의 오염으로 위협받고 있습니다.

16 밤에 이동하거나 사냥하는 새들은 자연광을 통해 길을 찾지만, 대도시의 빛은 길을 벗어나도록 할 수 있습니다.

17 매년 수백만 마리의 새들이 밝은 불빛이 있는 건물에 부딪치고서 죽습니다.

18 바다거북들은 밤에 해변이 너무 밝기 때문에 알을 낳을 장소를 쉽게 찾을 수 없습니다.

19 또한, 많은 아기 바다거북들은 인공 빛이 그들을 바다에서 멀어지게 하기 때문에 죽습니다.

20 분명히, 빛 오염은 다른 형태의 오염만큼이나 심각합니다.

21 우리는 그 문제를 해결할 방법을 찾아야 합니다.

22 만약 우리가 하지 않으면, 우리는 우리의 꿈이나 그림에서만 별을 볼 수 있을지 모릅니다.

• 우리말을 참고하여 본문을 영작하시오.

1 ▶ 이 아름다운 그림을 보세요.

➡ _____

2 ▶ 그것은 1889년에 유명한 네덜란드 미술가 빈센트 반 고흐에 의해 만들어졌습니다.

➡ _____

3 ▶ 반 고흐의 시대에는 거의 모든 사람들이 위를 쳐다보고 멋진 별이 빛나는 밤하늘을 볼 수 있었습니다.

➡ _____

4 ▶ 이제, 우리들 중 얼마나 많은 사람이 반 고흐만큼 운이 있을까요?

➡ _____

5 ▶ 사실, 오늘날 세계의 많은 사람들은 별이 빛나는 밤하늘을 즐길 수 없습니다.

➡ _____

6 ▶ 이것은 빛의 오염 때문에 그렇습니다.

➡ _____

7 ▶ 우리 대부분은 공기, 물, 토양 오염에 익숙합니다.

➡ _____

8 ▶ 우리는 그것들이 심각한 문제라는 것을 알고 있으며, 그것들을 해결하기 위해 조치를 취하고 있습니다.

➡ _____

9 ▶ 하지만 여러분은 빛이 오염도 일으킬 수 있다는 것을 알고 있었나요?

➡ _____

10 ▶ 빛의 오염—잘못된 시간에 잘못된 장소에서의 너무 많은 빛—은 전 세계의 거의 모든 곳에 있습니다.

➡ _____

_____

11 ▶ 그것은 인간과 야생동물에게 심각한 영향을 미칠 수 있습니다.

➡ _____

12 최근 보고서에 따르면, 세계 인구의 약 89%가 밤에 충분히 어둡지 않은 하늘 아래서 살고 있습니다.

➡ _____
_____

13 특히 대도시에서는 별이 빛나는 밤을 종종 볼 수 없습니다.

➡ _____

14 그들은 또한 인공적인 빛에 의해 낮과 밤의 자연적인 리듬이 방해를 받기 때문에 수면 문제로 고통을 겪을 수도 있습니다.

➡ _____
_____

15 야생동물도 빛의 오염으로 위협받고 있습니다.

➡ _____

16 밤에 이동하거나 사냥하는 새들은 자연광을 통해 길을 찾지만, 대도시의 빛은 길을 벗어나도록 할 수 있습니다.

➡ _____
_____

17 매년 수백만 마리의 새들이 밝은 불빛이 있는 건물에 부딪치고서 죽습니다.

➡ _____

18 바다거북들은 밤에 해변이 너무 밝기 때문에 알을 낳을 장소를 쉽게 찾을 수 없습니다.

➡ _____

19 또한, 많은 아기 바다거북들은 인공 빛이 그들을 바다에서 멀어지게 하기 때문에 죽습니다.

➡ _____

20 분명히, 빛 오염은 다른 형태의 오염만큼이나 심각합니다.

➡ _____

21 우리는 그 문제를 해결할 방법을 찾아야 합니다.

➡ _____

22 만약 우리가 하지 않으면, 우리는 우리의 꿈이나 그림에서만 별을 볼 수 있을지 모릅니다.

➡ _____

[01~04] 다음 글을 읽고, 물음에 답하시오.

Look at this beautiful painting. (①) It was created by the famous Dutch ⓐart Vincent van Gogh in 1889. (②) In Van Gogh's time, almost everyone could look up and see a wonderful starry night sky. (③) __ⓑ__ fact, many people in today's world cannot enjoy a starry night sky. (④) ⓒThis is so because of light pollution. (⑤)

01 위 글의 ①~⑤ 중 다음 주어진 문장이 들어갈 알맞은 곳은?

> Now, how many of us are as lucky as Van Gogh?

①   ②   ③   ④   ⑤

02 위 글의 밑줄 친 ⓐ를 알맞은 형으로 고치시오.

➡ _____

03 위 글의 빈칸 ⓑ에 알맞은 것은?

① In   ② On
③ At   ④ To
⑤ From

04 위 글의 밑줄 친 ⓒ가 가리키는 것을 우리말로 쓰시오.

➡ _____
_____

[05~07] 다음 글을 읽고, 물음에 답하시오.

Most of us are familiar __ⓐ__ air, water, and land pollution. We know that ⓑthey are serious problems, and we are taking action to solve them. But did you know that light can also cause pollution? Light pollution—too much light in the wrong place at the wrong time—is almost everywhere around the world. It can have serious effects on humans and wildlife.

05 위 글의 빈칸 ⓐ에 알맞은 것은?

① to   ② at
③ for   ④ with
⑤ from

06 위 글의 밑줄 친 ⓑ가 가리키는 것을 영어로 쓰시오.

➡ _____

07 위 글의 내용으로 보아 알 수 <u>없는</u> 것은?

① 우리는 대부분 공기 오염에 대해 알고 있다.
② 우리는 공기 오염, 물 오염, 토양 오염에 대처하고 있다.
③ 많은 사람들이 빛 오염에 대해 알고 있다.
④ 빛 오염은 잘못된 시간에 잘못된 장소에 빛이 너무 많이 생긴다.
⑤ 빛 오염은 인간과 야생 동물에 영향을 미친다.

[08~12] 다음 글을 읽고, 물음에 답하시오.

According to a recent report, about 89% of the world's population live under skies _____ⓐ_____ are not dark enough at night. Especially in big cities, people often cannot see a ⓑstar night. They can also suffer _____ⓒ_____ sleep problems because the natural rhythm of day and night is disturbed by _____ⓓ_____ light.

중요

08 위 글의 빈칸 ⓐ에 알맞은 것은? (2개)

① why   ② what
③ that   ④ where
⑤ which

서답형

09 위 글의 밑줄 친 ⓑ를 알맞은 어형으로 고치시오.

➡ _____

10 위 글의 빈칸 ⓒ에 알맞은 것은?

① in   ② from
③ over   ④ into
⑤ with

서답형

11 위 글의 빈칸 ⓓ에 natural의 반의어가 되는 단어를 쓰시오.

➡ _____

서답형

12 위 글에서 언급된 최근의 보도 내용을 우리말로 쓰시오.

➡ _____
_____

[13~17] 다음 글을 읽고, 물음에 답하시오.

Wildlife is _____ⓐ_____ by light pollution, too. Birds that migrate or hunt at night find their way by natural light, but light in big cities can _____ⓑ_____ them to wander off course. Every year millions of birds die after ⓒ hit buildings that have bright lights. Sea turtles cannot easily find a place to lay eggs _____ⓓ_____ beaches are too bright at night. Also, many baby sea turtles die because artificial light draws them away from the ocean.

13 위 글의 빈칸 ⓐ에 알맞은 것은?

① threaten   ② threatens
③ threatening   ④ threatened
⑤ to threaten

중요

14 위 글의 빈칸 ⓑ에 알맞은 것은?

① let   ② make
③ cause   ④ have
⑤ help

서답형

15 위 글의 밑줄 친 ⓒ를 알맞은 형으로 고치시오.

➡ _____

16 위 글의 빈칸 ⓓ에 알맞은 것은? (2개)

① if   ② since
③ though   ④ when
⑤ because

17 위 글의 내용으로 보아 대답할 수 <u>없는</u> 질문은?

① How do birds that migrate find their way?

② Why is light in big cities harmful to birds?

③ Why can't sea turtles find a place to lay eggs?

④ Why are beaches too bright?

⑤ Why do many baby sea turtles die?

[18~20] 다음 글을 읽고, 물음에 답하시오.

Clearly, light pollution is as serious ___ⓐ___ other forms of pollution. ⓑ우리는 그 문제를 해결하는 방법을 찾아야 한다. If we do not, we ⓒmay see stars only in our dreams or paintings.

18 위 글의 빈칸 ⓐ에 알맞은 것은?

① so   ② as
③ than   ④ like
⑤ more

19 위 글의 밑줄 친 ⓑ를 다음 주어진 말을 이용해서 영어로 옮기시오.

have, find, ways, solve, problem

➡ _____

20 위 글의 밑줄 친 ⓒ와 용법이 같은 것은?

① You <u>may</u> come in if you wish.

② <u>May</u> she rest in peace!

③ The rumor <u>may</u> be false.

④ <u>May</u> I take a picture here?

⑤ You <u>may</u> stay at this hotel for a week.

[21~24] 다음 글을 읽고, 물음에 답하시오.

Look ___ⓐ___ this beautiful painting. It was created ___ⓑ___ the famous Dutch artist Vincent van Gogh in 1889. In Van Gogh's time, almost everyone could look ___ⓒ___ and see a wonderful starry night sky. ⓓNow, how many of us are as lucky as Van Gogh? ⓔIn fact, many people in today's world cannot enjoy a starry night sky. This is so because of light pollution.

21 위 글의 빈칸 ⓐ와 ⓒ에 알맞은 것으로 짝지어진 것은?

① at – up   ② in – on
③ at – over   ④ for – on
⑤ for – over

22 위 글의 빈칸 ⓑ에 알맞은 전치사를 쓰시오.

➡ _____

23 위 글의 밑줄 친 ⓓ가 의미하는 것을 우리말로 간단히 쓰시오.

➡ _____

_____

24 위 글의 밑줄 친 ⓔ와 같은 뜻이 되도록 바꿔 쓸 때 빈칸에 알맞은 것은?

_____ a matter of fact

① To   ② In
③ As   ④ Of
⑤ With

[25~31] 다음 글을 읽고, 물음에 답하시오.

Most of us are familiar with air, water, and land pollution. We know that they are serious problems, and we are ___ⓐ___ action to solve them. But did you know that light can also ___ⓑ___ pollution? Light pollution—too much light in the wrong place at the wrong time– is almost everywhere around the world. ⓒ It can have serious effects on humans and wildlife.

According ___ⓓ___ a recent report, about 89% of the world's population lives under skies that are not dark enough at night. Especially in big cities, people often cannot see a starry night. They can also suffer from sleep problems ___ⓔ___ the natural rhythm of day and night is ⓕdisturb by artificial light.

25 위 글의 빈칸 ⓐ에 알맞은 것은?

① doing   ② making
③ taking   ④ getting
⑤ giving

26 위 글의 빈칸 ⓑ에 알맞은 것은?

① take   ② cause
③ turn   ④ become
⑤ appear

서답형
27 위 글의 밑줄 친 ⓒ가 가리키는 것을 영어로 쓰시오.

➡ _____

28 위 글의 빈칸 ⓓ에 알맞은 것은?

① to   ② at
③ for   ④ up
⑤ with

29 위 글의 빈칸 ⓔ에 알맞은 것은?

① when   ② that
③ if   ④ though
⑤ because

서답형
30 위 글의 밑줄 친 ⓕ를 알맞은 어형으로 고치시오.

➡ _____

31 위 글의 내용으로 보아 대답할 수 <u>없는</u> 질문은?

① What are most of us familiar with?
② Why are air, water, and land pollution serious problems?
③ What is light pollution?
④ What can light pollution have serious effects on?
⑤ Why can't people in big cities see a starry night?

[01~04] 다음 글을 읽고, 물음에 답하시오.

Wildlife is ⓐthreaten by light pollution, too. Birds that migrate or hunt at night find their way by natural light, ⓑ light in big cities can cause them to wander off course. ⓒEvery year million of birds die after hitting buildings that have bright lights. Sea turtles cannot easily find a place to lay eggs since beaches are too bright at night. Also, many baby sea turtles die ⓓ artificial light draws them away from the ocean.

01 위 글의 밑줄 친 ⓐ를 알맞은 어형으로 고치시오.

➡ _____

02 위 글의 빈칸 ⓑ에 알맞은 접속사를 쓰시오.

➡ _____

03 위 글의 밑줄 친 ⓒ에서 어법상 어색한 것을 고치시오.

_____ ➡ _____

04 위 글의 빈칸 ⓓ에 알맞은 접속사를 쓰시오.

➡ _____

[05~08] 다음 글을 읽고, 물음에 답하시오.

Lucas lives in Mon Repos, a small town in Queensland, Australia. ⓐ November to late March, sea turtles visit the town and lay eggs on the beach. Lucas ⓑ at the turtle center on weekends. ⓒHis work starts when turtles arrive after dark. He walks around the beach and says to people, "Please turn off the light, and be quiet." After work, Lucas feels proud because turtles are protected.

05 위 글의 빈칸 ⓐ에 알맞은 전치사를 쓰시오.

➡ _____

06 위 글의 빈칸 ⓑ에 다음 정의에 해당하는 말을 쓰시오. 필요하면 어형 변화를 하시오.

offer to do something without being forced to do it

➡ _____

07 위 글의 밑줄 친 ⓒ를 우리말로 옮기시오.

➡ _____

08 Why do sea turtles visit a small town in Queensland, Australia? Answer in English.

➡ _____

[09~12] 다음 글을 읽고, 물음에 답하시오.

Look at this beautiful painting. It was ⓐcrcatc by the famous Dutch artist Vincent van Gogh in 1889. In Van Gogh's time, ⓑ거의 모든 사람이 위를 쳐다보고 멋진 별이 총총한 밤하늘을 볼 수 있었다. Now, how many of us are as lucky as Van Gogh? ____ⓒ____ fact, many people in today's world cannot enjoy a starry night sky. This is so because of light pollution.

09 위 글의 밑줄 친 ⓐ를 알맞은 어형으로 고치시오.

➡ _____

10 위 글의 밑줄 친 ⓑ를 주어진 단어를 이용하여 영어로 옮기시오. 필요하면 어형 변화를 하시오.

almost, everyone, can, up, wonderful, star, sky

➡ _____

_____

11 위 글의 빈칸 ⓒ에 알맞은 전치사를 쓰시오.

➡ _____

12 위 글의 내용과 일치하도록 다음 문장의 빈칸에 알맞은 말을 쓰시오.

Actually, many people in today's world cannot _____ a starry night sky because _____ light pollution.

[13~17] 다음 글을 읽고, 물음에 답하시오.

ⓐMost of us are familiar with air, water, and land pollution. We know ____ⓑ____ they are serious problems, and we are taking action to ⓒsolution them. But did you know that light can also cause pollution? Light pollution–too much light in the wrong place at the wrong time–is almost everywhere around the world. It can have serious effects on humans and ____ⓓ____.

13 위 글의 밑줄 친 ⓐ를 우리말로 옮기시오.

➡ _____

14 위 글의 빈칸 ⓑ에 알맞은 접속사를 쓰시오.

➡ _____

15 위 글의 밑줄 친 ⓒ를 알맞은 형으로 고치시오.

➡ _____

16 위 글의 빈칸 ⓓ에 다음 정의에 해당하는 말을 쓰시오.

the animals that live in the wild

➡ _____

17 What is light pollution? Answer in Korean.

➡ _____

해석

My Speaking Portfolio - Step 3

"Welcome to Hanul Park. Please listen carefully and follow the rules. First,
~에 온 걸 환영하다   규칙을 따르다

you're not supposed to walk pets without a leash. And don't make a fire or
너는 ~해서는 안 돼.(=you're not allowed[permitted] to ~)   부정명령문: Don't+동사원형 ~(~하지 마라)

cook in the park."

구문해설 • carefully: 주의 깊게 • leash: (개 등을 매어 두는) 가죽 끈[줄] • make a fire: 불을 피우다

"하늘 공원에 오신 걸 환영합니다. 주의 깊게 듣고 규칙을 따르세요. 첫 번째, 목줄 없이 애완동물을 산책시켜서는 안 됩니다. 그리고 공원에서 불을 피우거나 요리를 하지 마세요."

My Writing Portfolio - Step 1

African penguin

• Home: southern Africa

• Food: fish

• Size: grows up to be 60-70 cm
        자라다

• Life span: 10-30 years
  수명

• Why are they in danger?: Sometimes they suffer from sea pollution. Also,
= African penguins   위험에 처한   ~로 고통 받다

people catch too many fish, and African penguins don't have enough food.

구문해설 • southern: 남쪽에 위치한 • fish: 생선 • sometimes: 때때로 • pollution: 오염
• also: 또한 • enough: 충분한

아프리카 펭귄

• 서식지: 남아프리카
• 먹이: 생선
• 크기: 60~70센티미터까지 자란다
• 수명: 10~30년
• 왜 그들은 위험에 처해 있는가?: 때때로 그들은 해양 오염으로 고통을 받는다. 또한, 사람들이 너무 많은 물고기를 잡아서 아프리카 펭귄들은 충분한 먹이가 없다.

Have Fun Together

1. Excuse me. You're not supposed to make a fire and cook here.
                  너는 ~해서는 안 된다   불을 피우다

2. In this park, you shouldn't feed wild animals. They can get sick, you know.
                  ~해서는 안 된다   아프다   알다시피

3. Please look at the sign. It says you're not supposed to touch the birds.
          ~을 보다   = The sign

4. Will you please take your trash home? You shouldn't leave it in the
                  take ~ home: ~을 집으로 가져가다
   mountains. That's the rule here.
              앞 문장을 받는 지시대명사

5. Excuse me. You're not supposed to pick flowers or fruits.
                      ~해서는 안 된다

6. I understand it's hot, but swimming isn't allowed in this national park.
                  날씨를 나타내는 비인칭 주어

7. Will you turn down the volume please? You're not supposed to play music
                      ~을 줄이다
   loudly.

8. Excuse me. You're not supposed to fish here.

구문해설 • feed: 먹이를 주다 • sign: 표지판 • touch: 만지다 • trash: 쓰레기
• leave: ~을 남겨 두다 • rule: 규칙 • allow: 허락하다 • loudly: 시끄럽게 • fish: 낚시하다

1. 실례합니다. 여기서 불을 피우고 요리하면 안 돼요.
2. 이 공원에서는 야생 동물들에게 먹이를 주면 안 돼요. 여러분도 알다시피, 그들은 아플 수 있어요.
3. 표지판을 보세요. 새들을 만지면 안 된다고 쓰여 있어요.
4. 쓰레기 좀 집에 가져가 줄래요? 산에 버려두면 안 돼요. 그게 바로 여기 규칙이에요.
5. 실례합니다. 꽃이나 과일을 따면 안 돼요.
6. 더운 건 알지만, 이 국립공원에서는 수영이 허용되지 않아요.
7. 소리 좀 줄여주시겠어요? 음악을 크게 틀면 안 돼요.
8. 실례합니다. 여기서 낚시하면 안 돼요.

영역별 핵심문제

01 다음 중 짝지어진 단어의 관계가 나머지 넷과 <u>다른</u> 것은?

① wrong : right ② bright : dark
③ heavy : light ④ hungry : full
⑤ allow : permit

02 다음 빈칸에 공통으로 알맞은 것은?

> • Let's run _____ at once.
> • Don't throw _____ trash here.

① on ② off
③ from ④ away
⑤ with

03 다음 우리말과 같도록 빈칸에 알맞은 말을 쓰시오.

> 그들은 환경에 관심을 가지지 않는다.
> ➡ They don't _____ _____ the
> environment.

04 다음 짝지어진 단어의 관계가 같도록 빈칸에 알맞은 말을 쓰시오.

> easy : difficult = artificial : _____

05 다음 우리말과 같도록 빈칸에 알맞은 말을 주어진 철자로 시작하여 쓰시오.

> 겨울에 많은 새들이 더 따뜻한 곳으로 이동한다.
> ➡ In winter, many birds m_____ to
> warmer places.

06 다음 빈칸에 들어갈 말로 적절하지 <u>않은</u> 것은?

> • Please _____ the rules.
> • He didn't _____ his toothbrushes.
> • She'll _____ a poster on the bulletin
> board.
> • You're not supposed to _____ flowers.

① bring ② put
③ feed ④ pick
⑤ follow

07 다음 영영풀이에 해당하는 단어로 알맞은 것은?

> food that has not been finished at a meal
> and that is often served at another meal

① dish ② leftover
③ taste ④ leash
⑤ dessert

08 다음 대화의 밑줄 친 부분과 바꿔 쓸 수 있는 것은?

> A: Is it okay to eat chocolate?
> B: Sure, but don't eat too much.

① you can eat too much
② you don't have to eat too much
③ you won't eat too much
④ you shouldn't eat too much
⑤ you'd better eat too much

09 다음 대화의 빈칸에 알맞은 말은?

> A: _____
> B: Sure. You can do that.

① Can you bring your friends home?
② Are you bringing friends home?
③ Is it okay if I bring friends home?
④ Would you like to bring friends home?
⑤ Do you want to bring your friends home?

10 다음 대화의 빈칸에 들어갈 수 <u>없는</u> 것은?

> A: _____ I use your phone?
> B: I'm afraid not. I'm waiting for an important call, and my battery's almost dead.

① Can   ② May
③ Is it okay if   ④ Is it alright if
⑤ Do you mind if

[11~13] 다음 대화를 읽고, 물음에 답하시오.

> G: _____ⓐ_____ I put a poster on the bulletin board, Mr. Cha?
> M: A poster?
> G: Here. It's a poster about World Oceans Day.
> M: Let me see. It's a great poster. Did you make it?
> G: My club members made it together. I think people ___ⓑ___ care more about our oceans.
> M: I agree. Well, we don't have space right now.
> G: Then ___ⓒ___ I put it on the door?
> M: Sure. Go ahead.

11 위 대화의 빈칸 ⓐ에 알맞은 것은?

① Is it okay if
② Are you sure if
③ Do you wonder if
④ Where do you think if
⑤ Why do you think if

12 위 대화의 빈칸 ⓑ와 ⓒ에 알맞은 말이 바르게 짝지어진 것은?

① will – may   ② can – could
③ should – can   ④ won't – would
⑤ shouldn't – should

13 위 대화를 읽고, 답할 수 <u>없는</u> 질문은?

① Where does the girl want to put the poster?
② What is the poster about?
③ Who made the poster?
④ When is World Oceans Day?
⑤ Where will the girl put the poster?

Grammar

14 다음 동사의 과거분사형이 잘못 연결된 것은?

① break – broken ② take – took

③ read – read ④ write – written

⑤ think – thought

15 다음 빈칸에 들어갈 알맞은 단어를 고르면?

> I _____ born in Seoul.

① am ② was

③ is ④ were

⑤ are

16 다음 주어진 어구를 이용하여 우리말을 영어로 옮기시오.

> 그는 Tom만큼 테니스를 잘 친다. (as ~ as)

➡ _____

17 다음 빈칸에 들어갈 말이 나머지 넷과 다른 하나는?

① The dog is loved _____ them.

② I was given a book _____ him.

③ This letter was written _____ Bill.

④ Her eyes were filled _____ tears.

⑤ The pizza was cooked _____ my mom.

18 다음 밑줄 친 부분의 쓰임이 바르지 않은 것은?

① All kinds of things were used as money.

② The bag was found by him.

③ This work should be done by tomorrow.

④ Portuguese is used in Brazil.

⑤ Jake was appeared after school.

19 다음 중 어법상 어색한 문장은?

① My house is not so large as yours.

② Jenny's mother ran as fast as she could.

③ He is as a great statesman as ever lived.

④ Are you as good at English as her?

⑤ The air is polluted as badly as the rivers.

20 다음 중 밑줄 친 부분을 생략해도 의미 변화가 없는 것은?

① Canned food was invented by Appert.

② Apple Inc. was founded by Steve Jobs in 1974.

③ The question was asked in the classroom by her.

④ The island was discovered by an English explorer, James Cook.

⑤ German is spoken by people in Germany and Austria.

21 다음 주어진 단어를 이용하여 우리말을 영어로 옮기시오.

> 이 냉장고는 그에 의해 고쳐질 수 있다.
> (refrigerator, fix)

➡ _____

22 다음 두 문장의 의미가 같도록 할 때 빈칸에 알맞은 것은?

> This room is just the same size _____ that one.
> = This room is just as large as that one.

① as   ② so
③ of   ④ for
⑤ with

23 다음 우리말과 일치하도록 주어진 단어를 바르게 배열하시오.

> 모든 종류의 물건들이 돈으로 사용되었다.
> (things / as / all / money / used / were / kinds / of)

➡ _____

24 다음 우리말과 같은 뜻이 되도록 할 때, 빈칸에 알맞은 것은?

> 꿀은 일벌에 의해 만들어진다.
> = Honey _____ by worker bees.

① makes   ② made
③ is made   ④ are made
⑤ is making

Reading

[25~29] 다음 글을 읽고, 물음에 답하시오.

(①) According to a recent report, about 89% of the world's population lives under skies ____ⓐ____ are not dark enough at night. (②) They can also suffer from sleep problems because the natural rhythm of day and night is disturbed by artificial light. (③) Wildlife is ____ⓑ____ by light pollution, too. (④) Birds that migrate or hunt at night find their way ⓒby natural light, but light in big cities can cause them to wander off course. (⑤)

25 위 글의 ①~⑤ 중 다음 주어진 문장이 들어갈 알맞은 곳은?

> Especially in big cities, people often cannot see a starry night.

①   ②   ③   ④   ⑤

26 위 글의 빈칸 ⓐ에 알맞은 말을 쓰시오.

➡ _____

27 위 글의 빈칸 ⓑ에 알맞은 것은?

① saved   ② removed
③ helped   ④ threatened
⑤ preserved

28 위 글의 밑줄 친 ⓒ와 같은 용법으로 쓰인 것은?

① The telephone is <u>by</u> the window.
② I will contact you <u>by</u> letter.
③ Can you finish the work <u>by</u> five o'clock?
④ We rented the car <u>by</u> the day.
⑤ He walked <u>by</u> me without speaking.

29 위 글의 내용과 일치하지 <u>않는</u> 것은?

① 세계의 많은 지역에서 밤에 하늘이 충분히 어둡지 않다.
② 대도시에서는 밤에 별을 잘 볼 수 없다.
③ 인공의 빛은 수면 장애를 일으킬 수 있다.
④ 야생 동물도 빛 오염에 영향을 받는다.
⑤ 새는 길을 찾는 데 자연의 빛과 인공의 빛을 둘 다 이용한다.

[30~34] 다음 글을 읽고, 물음에 답하시오.

Lucas lives in Mon Repos, a small ___ⓐ___ in Queensland, Australia. (①) ___ⓑ___ November to late March, sea turtles visit the town and lay eggs on the beach. (②) His work starts when turtles arrive after dark. (③) He walks around the beach and says to people, "Please turn ___ⓒ___ the light, and be quiet." (④) After work, Lucas feels proud because turtles are protected. (⑤)

30 위 글의 ①~⑤ 중 다음 주어진 문장이 들어갈 알맞은 곳은?

Lucas volunteers at the turtle center on weekends.

①   ②   ③   ④   ⑤

31 위 글의 빈칸 ⓐ에 다음 정의에 해당하는 단어를 쓰시오.

a place with many streets and buildings, where people live and work, which are larger than villages

➡ _____

32 위 글의 빈칸 ⓑ에 알맞은 것은?

① Of   ② At
③ From   ④ With
⑤ Among

33 위 글의 빈칸 ⓒ에 알맞은 것은?

① off   ② at
③ on   ④ from
⑤ with

34 위 글의 내용으로 보아 대답할 수 <u>없는</u> 질문은?

① Where does Lucas live?
② How many sea turtles visit the town?
③ Where do sea turtles lay eggs?
④ When does Lucas's work start?
⑤ Why does Lucas feel proud?

01 출제율 95%

다음 〈보기〉와 같이 변화하는 단어가 <u>아닌</u> 것은?

> ┤ 보기 ├
> luck → lucky

① cloud   ② wind

③ thirst   ④ mess

⑤ harm

02 출제율 90%

다음 우리말과 같도록 빈칸에 알맞은 단어를 주어진 철자로 시작하여 쓰시오.

> 아프리카 펭귄들은 충분한 음식을 먹지 못한다.
> ➡ African penguins don't have e_____
> food.

03 출제율 90%

다음 중 영영풀이가 <u>잘못된</u> 것은?

① artificial: not natural or real

② allow: to let someone do something

③ wildlife: an animal that people keep mainly for pleasure

④ create: to make or produce something

⑤ lay: to produce an egg outside of the body

04 출제율 100%

다음 빈칸에 공통으로 알맞은 단어를 쓰시오. (대 · 소문자 무시)

> • _____ fact, I want to have a pretty rabbit.
> • Driving too fast puts people _____ danger.

➡ _____

05 출제율 90%

다음 빈칸에 공통으로 알맞은 것은?

> • I'll take care _____ that right away.
> • She is not going out because _____ the rain.

① of   ② with

③ in   ④ for

⑤ about

06 출제율 85%

다음 대화의 빈칸에 알맞은 것은?

> A: It's raining. _____
> B: Okay. If it rains, I'll stay inside.

① You will go outside.

② You shouldn't go outside.

③ You would go outside.

④ You might not go outside.

⑤ You can go outside.

07 출제율 95%

다음 짝지어진 대화 중 <u>어색한</u> 것은?

① A: May I turn on the heater?
   B: Sure. Go ahead.

② A: Is it okay to go out and play?
   B: I'm sorry, but it's too late.

③ A: Is it okay if I use your cellphone?
   B: Certainly. I didn't bring it today.

④ A: Am I allowed to open the window?
   B: I'm afraid not. It's too hot outside.

⑤ A: Do you mind if I call you later?
   B: Not at all.

08 다음 대화의 빈칸에 알맞지 <u>않은</u> 것은?

> A: _____ go out and play?
> B: Yes, you can.

① May I   ② Can I
③ Is it okay to   ④ Is it OK to
⑤ Do you mind if I

[09~11] 다음 대화를 읽고, 물음에 답하시오.

> G: Dad, is it okay ⓐ go out with my friends this Saturday?
> M: What are your plans?
> G: Well, my favorite singer is going ⓑ have a concert at Olympic Park.
> M: Okay, but come home by 9 o'clock.
> G: ___ⓒ___ The concert will be over by about 8:00.

09 위 대화의 빈칸 ⓐ와 ⓑ에 공통으로 알맞은 것을 쓰시오.

➡ _____

10 위 대화의 빈칸 ⓒ에 들어갈 말로 적절하지 <u>않은</u> 것은?

① Sure.   ② Why not?
③ Of course.   ④ No problem.
⑤ Certainly not.

11 위 대화를 읽고, 다음 질문에 영어로 답하시오.

> Q: What time will the concert be over?
> A: _____

12 다음 문장의 빈칸에 알맞은 것은?

> The light bulb was invented _____ Thomas Edison.

① of   ② by
③ with   ④ from
⑤ for

13 다음 밑줄 친 부분의 쓰임이 〈보기〉와 <u>다른</u> 것은?

> ┌ 보기 ┐
> The letter <u>was</u> written by a nurse.

① The mirror <u>was</u> broken by James.
② *Harry Potter* <u>was</u> written by J. K. Rowling.
③ My English textbook <u>was</u> stolen yesterday.
④ I <u>was</u> disappointed to hear the news.
⑤ The work should <u>be</u> finished by tomorrow.

14 다음 우리말과 일치하도록 주어진 단어를 바르게 배열하시오.

> 그는 예전만큼 많이 그녀를 미워하지 않는다.
> He doesn't hate her (as / used / he / as / much / to).

➡ _____

15 다음 문장을 능동태로 바꾸시오.

> By whom were shells and rice used as money?

➡ _____

16 다음 중 어법상 어색한 문장은? (출제율 85%)

① Michael's sister made him happy.
② These letters was written by my dad.
③ Every store will be closed next week.
④ These cookies were baked by Jane.
⑤ *Romeo and Juliet* was written by Shakespeare.

17 다음 빈칸에 들어갈 말이 바르게 짝지어진 것은? (출제율 95%)

> • You may buy as many books _____ you like.
> • This tool is _____ more useful than mine.

① as – much
② as – very
③ so – few
④ as – little
⑤ so – much

18 다음을 수동태 문장으로 바르게 바꾼 것은? (출제율 90%)

> I made this cake for my friend.

① This cake was made for my friend by me.
② This cake is made by me for my friend.
③ My friend was made a cake by me.
④ My friend is made a cake by me.
⑤ This cake made for my friend by me.

19 다음 중 밑줄 친 부분의 쓰임이 나머지와 다른 하나는? (출제율 95%)

① The room was cleaned <u>by</u> me.
② Can you come <u>by</u> seven this afternoon?
③ The work was finished <u>by</u> Kelly.
④ Was this table painted <u>by</u> her?
⑤ The dog will be loved <u>by</u> its owner.

[20~22] 다음 글을 읽고, 물음에 답하시오.

> African penguin
> • Home: southern Africa
> • Food: fish
> • Size: grows up to be 60-70 cm
> • Life span: 10-30 years
> • Why are they in danger?: Sometimes they suffer ⓐ sea pollution. Also, people catch too many ⓑ_____, and African penguins don't have enough food.

20 위 글의 빈칸 ⓐ에 알맞은 것은? (출제율 100%)

① in
② of
③ from
④ for
⑤ with

21 위 글의 빈칸 ⓑ에 다음 정의에 해당하는 단어를 쓰시오. (출제율 85%)

> a creature that lives in water and has a tail and fins

➡ _____

22 Where do African penguins live? Answer in English. (출제율 90%)

➡ _____

[23~29] 다음 글을 읽고, 물음에 답하시오.

Wildlife is threatened ___ⓐ___ light pollution, too. Birds that migrate or hunt at night find their way ___ⓑ___ natural light, but light in big cities can cause them ___ⓒ___ off course. ⓓEvery year millions of birds die after hit buildings that have bright lights. Sea turtles cannot easily find a place ⓔto lay eggs since beaches are too bright at night. Also, many baby sea turtles die ⓕbecause artificial light draws them away from the ocean.

ⓖClearly, light pollution is as serious as other forms of pollution. We have to find ways to solve the problem. If we do not, we may see stars only in our dreams or paintings.

23 위 글의 빈칸 ⓐ와 ⓑ에 공통으로 알맞은 것은?

① at   ② to
③ of   ④ by
⑤ from

24 위 글의 빈칸 ⓒ에 알맞은 것은?

① wander   ② wandering
③ wandered   ④ to wandering
⑤ to wander

25 위 글의 밑줄 친 ⓓ에서 어법상 어색한 것을 고치시오.

_____ ➡ _____

26 위 글의 밑줄 친 ⓔ와 같은 용법으로 쓰인 것은?

① They want to be friends with us.
② There is nothing to worry about.
③ Kathy came to Korea to be a K-pop singer.
④ She was pleased to hear of my success.
⑤ It is our duty to obey laws.

27 위 글의 밑줄 친 ⓕ 대신 쓸 수 있는 것은? (2개)

① that   ② if
③ as   ④ when
⑤ since

28 위 글의 밑줄 친 ⓖ와 같은 뜻이 되도록 다음 문장의 빈칸에 알맞은 말을 쓰시오.

_____ is _____ that light pollution is as serious as other forms of pollution.

29 위 글의 내용으로 보아 대답할 수 없는 질문은?

① What does light pollution threaten?
② Do birds that migrate at night use natural light?
③ Why do millions of birds die every year?
④ Why are beaches too bright at night?
⑤ Why do we have to find ways to solve the light pollution problem?

01 다음 괄호 안에 주어진 단어들을 배열하여 대화를 완성하시오.

A: Is it okay to take a picture?
B: No, _____ do that.
(permitted / not / to / you're)

➡ _____

02 다음 괄호 안에 주어진 단어를 이용하여 우리말을 영어로 옮기시오.

이 포도 주스를 먹어도 되나요?
(okay / if / grape)

➡ _____

03 다음 대화의 밑줄 친 말과 바꿔 쓸 수 있는 표현을 2개 이상 쓰시오.

A: Is it okay to pick some flowers?
B: No, you're not supposed to do that.

➡ _____
_____

04 자연스러운 대화가 되도록 (A)~(D)의 순서를 바르게 배열하시오.

(A) What sign?
(B) Oh, I'm sorry. I didn't know that.
(C) Hey, look at the sign!
(D) The one over there. You're not supposed to pick flowers here.

➡ _____

05 다음 우리말과 일치하도록 괄호 안에 주어진 단어들을 바르게 배열하시오.

(1) 내 자전거는 Tom에 의해 고쳐졌다.
(bicycle, Tom, my, by, fixed, was)

➡ _____

(2) 우리 학교는 1976년에 설립되었다.
(1976, founded, school, was, our, in)

➡ _____

06 다음 〈조건〉에 맞게 괄호 안의 어구를 이용하여 우리말을 영어로 옮기시오.

┌ 조건 ┐
1. 주어진 단어를 모두 이용할 것.
2. 필요시 어형 변화를 할 것.
3. as ~ as ...를 쓸 것.
4. 대·소문자 및 구두점에 유의할 것.

(1) Meg는 너만큼 노래를 잘 부른다.
(sing, well)
➡ _____

(2) 이 거리는 저 거리와 아주 똑같은 넓이이다.
(street, just, wide, that one)
➡ _____

(3) 서울 타워는 이 탑보다 약 세 배 높다.
(Seoul Tower, about, time, as)
➡ _____
_____

(4) 나는 나의 언니만큼 요리를 잘하지 못한다.
(can, cook, well, my sister)
➡ _____

07 다음 문장을 주어진 조건에 맞게 바꿔 쓰시오.

(1) Everybody likes this song.

수동태 부정문:

_____

수동태 의문문:

_____

(2) Alice used my computer.

수동태 부정문:

_____

수동태 의문문:

_____

[08~11] 다음 글을 읽고, 물음에 답하시오.

　Lucas lives in Mon Repos, a small town in Queensland, Australia. From November to late March, sea turtles visit the town and ⓐ(lie, lay) eggs on the beach. Lucas volunteers at the turtle center ___ⓑ___ weekends. ⓒ그의 일은 어두워진 후 거북들이 도착하면 시작된다. He walks around the beach and says to people, "Please turn off the light, and be ___ⓓ___." After work, Lucas feels proud because turtles are protected.

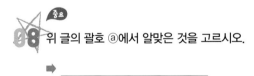

08 위 글의 괄호 ⓐ에서 알맞은 것을 고르시오.

➡ _____

09 위 글의 빈칸 ⓑ에 알맞은 말을 쓰시오.

➡ _____

10 위 글의 밑줄 친 ⓒ를 주어진 말을 써서 영어로 옮기시오.

| (work, starts, when, arrive, dark) |

➡ _____

11 위 글의 빈칸 ⓓ에 다음 정의에 해당하는 단어를 주어진 글자로 시작하여 쓰시오.

| making very little noise |

➡ q_____

[12~14] 다음 글을 읽고, 물음에 답하시오.

　Look at this beautiful ⓐpaint. It was created by the famous Dutch artist Vincent van Gogh in 1889. In Van Gogh's time, almost everyone could look up and see a wonderful starry night sky. ⓑNow, how many of us are as lucky as Van Gogh? In fact, many people in today's world cannot enjoy a starry night sky. This is so ⓒ(because, because of) light pollution.

12 위 글의 밑줄 친 ⓐ를 알맞은 어형으로 고치시오.

➡ _____

13 위 글의 밑줄 친 ⓑ가 의미하는 것을 우리말로 간단히 쓰시오.

➡ _____

14 위 글의 괄호 ⓒ에서 알맞은 것을 고르시오.

➡ _____

01 다음 질문에 각자의 상황에 맞게 적절한 응답을 써 보시오.

> Q: Is it okay if I turn on the TV?
> A: _____

02 다음 〈보기〉와 같이 질문에 적절한 답을 쓰시오.

> Q: Who wrote *Harry Potter*? [J. K. Rowling]
> A: *Harry Potter* was written by J. K. Rowling.

(1) Who directed *Zootopia*? [Byron Howard]
➡ _____

(2) Who painted *The Scream*? [Edward Munch]
➡ _____

(3) Who wrote *Anne of Green Gables*? [Lucy Maud Montgomery]
➡ _____

(4) Who made iPhone? [Steve Jobs]
➡ _____

(5) Who painted *The Starry Night*? [Vincent van Gogh]
➡ _____

03 다음 〈보기〉와 같이 동등비교 구문(as ~ as / not as ~ as)을 이용하여 자신의 입장에서 문장을 만드시오. (4 문장)

> 보기
> I am as tall as Junho.

(1) _____
(2) _____
(3) _____
(4) _____

단원별 모의고사

01 다음 중 단어의 성격이 나머지 넷과 <u>다른</u> 것은?

① thirsty　　　② windy

③ cloudy　　　④ messy

⑤ beauty

02 다음 우리말에 맞도록 빈칸에 알맞은 것은?

> 그 음악 소리 좀 줄여 주시겠어요?
> ➡ Would you _____ down the music?

① get　　　② put

③ make　　　④ turn

⑤ take

03 다음 영영풀이에 해당하는 단어를 쓰시오.

> full of stars

➡ _____

04 다음 빈칸에 알맞은 말이 바르게 짝지어진 것은?

> • He is not familiar _____ this area.
> • According _____ a report, that is not true.

① of – with　　　② about – by

③ with – in　　　④ on – of

⑤ with – to

05 다음 중 밑줄 친 부분의 뜻풀이가 <u>잘못된</u> 것은?

① <u>Look up at</u> the night sky.
~을 쳐다보다

② School will <u>be over</u> at three.
시작하다

③ <u>Millions of</u> people bought the book.
수백만의

④ His story began to <u>wander off</u> the topic.
~에서 벗어나다

⑤ He wants to <u>take action</u> to solve the problem. 조치를 취하다

06 다음 대화의 빈칸에 알맞은 것은?

> A: Is it okay if I turn on the TV?
> B: _____ I'm doing my homework.

① Of course.

② I don't mind at all.

③ No problem.

④ Sure, go ahead.

⑤ I'm afraid not.

07 다음 대화의 밑줄 친 표현과 바꾸어 쓸 수 있는 것은?

> A: <u>You're not supposed to</u> pick flowers here.
> B: Oh, I'm sorry. I didn't know that.

① You should

② You don't want to

③ You would like to

④ You're not permitted to

⑤ You might want to

08 다음 중 의도하는 바가 나머지와 <u>다른</u> 하나는?

① Is it OK if I take these pills?
② Can you tell me where you found it?
③ Is it okay to join you later?
④ May I take a picture with you?
⑤ Am I allowed to smoke in the hall?

09 다음 대화의 빈칸에 알맞지 <u>않은</u> 것은?

> A: Would you mind if I close the window?
> B: _____ I feel a little cold.

① Not at all.   ② Yes, I do.
③ No, I don't.   ④ Certainly not.
⑤ Of course not.

[10~11] 다음 대화를 읽고, 물음에 답하시오.

> W: Hey, look at the sign!
> B: What sign?
> W: The one over there. ⓐ<u>You're not supposed to pick</u> flowers here.
> B: Oh, I'm sorry. I didn't know ⓑ<u>that</u>.

10 위 대화의 밑줄 친 ⓐ와 바꿔 쓸 수 <u>없는</u> 것은?

① You must not pick
② You don't have to pick
③ You shouldn't pick
④ You're not permitted to pick
⑤ You're not allowed to pick

11 위 대화의 밑줄 친 ⓑ가 가리키는 것을 우리말로 쓰시오.

➡ _____

[12~14] 다음 문장의 빈칸에 알맞은 것을 고르시오.

12
> A bookstore is a shop where books are _____.

① sold   ② selling
③ buy   ④ sell
⑤ buying

13
> Books must be chosen as _____ as friends are.

① care   ② caring
③ cared   ④ careful
⑤ carefully

14
> If you _____ reading books, you may go to the library.

① interested at   ② interested in
③ be interested at   ④ are interested in
⑤ are interesting in

15 다음 두 문장이 같은 뜻이 되도록 빈칸에 알맞은 말은?

> They often invite us for dinner.
> = We are often _____ for dinner.

① invite   ② invited
③ invites   ④ be invited
⑤ will be invited

16 다음 두 문장의 뜻이 같도록 빈칸에 알맞은 말을 쓰시오.

> I don't have _____ much money _____ you.
> – I have less money than you.

[17~18] 다음 밑줄 친 단어를 어법상 알맞은 형태로 쓴 것을 고르시오.

17

> The World Cup is <u>hold</u> every four years.

① hold
② holded
③ holding
④ holds
⑤ held

18

> *Romeo and Juliet* <u>wrote</u> by Shakespeare.

① is written
② written
③ was written
④ writes
⑤ were written

[19~20] 다음 중 어법상 알맞지 <u>않은</u> 것을 고르시오.

19 ① Kate doesn't speak Korean as well as Mike do.
② The movie is not as interesting as you think.
③ I don't work so hard as you do.
④ Let me have your answer as soon as possible.
⑤ I don't have as much money as my brother does.

20 ① He wasn't invited to the party.
② Was that book written by James?
③ The novel was wrote by her.
④ I'm loved by him.
⑤ Those cookies were made by my aunt.

21 다음 두 문장을 한 문장으로 바꿔 쓸 때 빈칸에 알맞은 말을 쓰시오.

> • The job of a flight attendant is not easy.
> • The job of a flight attendant looks easy.

> ➡ The job of a flight attendant is _____ as _____ as it looks.

22 다음 문장의 빈칸에 알맞은 것으로 짝지어진 것은?

> • The mountain is covered _____ snow.
> • She is known _____ her sense of humor.

① with – for
② with – to
③ of – for
④ by – to
⑤ by – for

[23~25] 다음 글을 읽고, 물음에 답하시오.

Most of us are __ⓐ__ with air, water, and land pollution. We know that they are serious problems, and we are taking action __ⓑ__ them. But did you know that light can also cause pollution? Light pollution—too much light in the wrong place at the wrong time—is almost everywhere around the world. It can have serious effects on humans and wildlife.

23 위 글의 빈칸 ⓐ에 다음 정의에 해당하는 단어를 쓰시오.

> recognizing someone or something or knowing them well

➡ _____

24 위 글의 빈칸 ⓑ에 알맞은 것은?

① solve   ② solving
③ to solving   ④ to solve
⑤ for solving

25 Can light also cause pollution? Answer in English.

➡ _____

[26~32] 다음 글을 읽고, 물음에 답하시오.

(①) Birds that migrate or hunt at night find their way by ⓐnature light, ⓑ light in big cities can cause them to wander off course. (②) Every year millions of birds die after hitting buildings ⓒthat have bright lights. (③) ⓓSea turtles cannot easily find a place to lay eggs since beaches are too bright at night. (④) Also, many baby sea turtles die because ⓔ light draws them away from the ocean. (⑤)

26 위 글의 ①~⑤ 중 다음 주어진 문장이 들어갈 알맞은 곳은?

> Wildlife is threatened by light pollution, too.

①   ②   ③   ④   ⑤

27 위 글의 밑줄 친 ⓐ를 알맞은 형으로 고치시오.

➡ _____

28 위 글의 빈칸 ⓑ에 알맞은 것은?

① so   ② and
③ but   ④ for
⑤ though

29 위 글의 밑줄 친 ⓒ 대신 쓸 수 있는 것은?

① who   ② when
③ what   ④ where
⑤ which

30 위 글의 밑줄 친 ⓓ를 우리말로 옮기시오.

➡ _____
_____

31 위 글의 빈칸 ⓔ에 다음 정의에 해당하는 단어를 영어로 쓰시오.

> not occurring naturally and created by human beings, for example using science or technology

➡ _____

32 What causes birds that migrate or hunt at night to wander off course? Answer in English.

➡ _____

Reading for Fun 2
Humorous Stories

Laugh Out Loud

Words & Expressions

Key Words

- **allow**[əláu] 동 허락하다(= permit)
- **because**[bikɔ́ːz] 접 ~때문에
- **buy**[bai] 동 사다(↔ sell)
- **call**[kɔːl] 동 ~라고 부르다, 전화하다
- **clock**[klak] 명 (벽에 걸거나 실내에 두는) 시계
- **comic book** 만화책
- **continue**[kəntínjuː] 동 계속하다
- **corner**[kɔ́ːnər] 명 구석, 모퉁이
- **cost**[kɔːst] 동 (값·비용이) ~이다[들다]
- **crazy**[kréizi] 형 미친, 정신이상인(= mad)
- **decide**[disáid] 동 결정하다, 결심하다
- **different**[dífərənt] 형 다른(↔ same)
- **dish**[diʃ] 명 접시, 요리
- **early**[ə́ːrli] 부 일찍(↔ late)
- **everything**[evriθiŋ] 대 모든 것
- **excuse**[ikskjúːz] 명 변명, 핑계 거리
- **expensive**[ikspénsiv] 형 값비싼(↔ cheap)
- **explain**[ikspléin] 동 설명하다
- **flat**[flæt] 형 바람이 빠진, 펑크 난
- **global warming** 지구 온난화
- **hit**[hit] 동 치다, 때리다
- **invite**[inváit] 동 초대하다
- **jump rope** 줄넘기하다
- **late**[leit] 부 늦게(↔ early)
- **loud**[laud] 형 시끄러운(↔ quiet)
- **metal**[métl] 명 금속
- **noise**[nɔiz] 명 소리(=sound), 소음
- **owner**[óunər] 명 주인
- **parrot**[pǽrət] 명 앵무새
- **plan**[plein] 동 계획하다, 의도하다
- **point**[pɔint] 명 점수
- **professor**[prəfésər] 명 교수
- **proudly**[práudli] 부 자랑스럽게
- **reply**[riplái] 동 대답하다(= answer)
- **respond**[rispánd] 동 대답[응답]하다
- **shop**[ʃap] 명 가게
- **shout**[ʃaut] 동 외치다, 소리치다
- **special**[spéʃəl] 형 특별한(↔ general)
- **suddenly**[sʌ́dnli] 부 갑자기(= all of a sudden)
- **surprised**[sərpráizd] 형 놀란
- **university**[jùːnəvə́ːrsəti] 명 대학
- **wall**[wɔːl] 명 벽

Key Expressions

- **a piece of cake** 식은 죽 먹기
- **at night** 밤에
- **be late for** ~에 늦다
- **be proud of** ~을 자랑으로 여기다
- **come back** 돌아오다
- **get up late** 늦잠을 자다
- **go to bed** 자다
- **laugh out loud** 큰 소리로 웃다
- **make it to** ~에 이르다, ~에 도착하다
- **on Saturday** 토요일에
- **on the other side of** ~의 반대편에(는)
- **one evening** 어느 날 저녁
- **play the piano** 피아노를 연주하다
- **take a test** 시험을 보다

Word Power

※ 형용사와 부사 두 가지로 쓰이는 단어

□ **early** 형 이른 부 일찍
□ **enough** 형 충분한 부 충분히
□ **fast** 형 빠른 부 빨리
□ **hard** 형 열심히 하는 부 열심히

□ **high** 형 높은 부 높이
□ **late** 형 늦은 부 늦게
□ **low** 형 낮은 부 낮게
□ **near** 형 가까운 부 가까이

※ 감정을 나타내는 분사형 형용사 -ing(~한 감정을 느끼게 하는) / -ed(~한 감정을 느끼는)

□ **amazing** (놀라운) – **amazed** (놀란)
□ **boring** (지루한) – **bored** (지루해하는)
□ **exciting** (흥미진진한) – **excited** (흥분한)
□ **interesting** (흥미로운) – **interested** (흥미 있어 하는)

□ **satisfying** (만족감을 주는) – **satisfied** (만족하는)
□ **shocking** (충격적인) – **shocked** (충격을 받은)
□ **surprising** (놀라운) – **surprised** (놀란)
□ **tiring** (피곤하게 만드는) – **tired** (피곤한)

English Dictionary

□ **continue** 계속하다
→ to do something without stopping
어떤 일을 멈추지 않고 하다

□ **cost** (값·비용이) ~이다[들다]
→ to have an amount of money as a price
가격으로 일비의 금액이니

□ **crazy** 미친
→ unable to think in a clear or sensible way
명료하거나 분별 있게 생각할 수 없는

□ **dish** 접시
→ a shallow container that you cook or serve food in
요리하거나 음식을 제공하는 데 쓰는 얕은 그릇

□ **excuse** 변명, 핑계 거리
→ a reason that you give to explain a mistake, bad behavior, etc.
실수, 그릇된 행동 따위의 구실로 대는 이유

□ **expensive** 값비싼
→ costing a lot of money
돈이 많이 드는

□ **explain** 설명하다
→ to make something clear or easy to understand
무엇인가를 명료하게 또는 쉽게 이해하도록 해 주다

□ **flat** 펑크 난
→ not having enough air
충분한 공기가 없는

□ **invite** 초대하다
→ to ask someone to come to a party, wedding, meal, etc.
누군가에게 파티, 결혼식, 식사 등에 오라고 부탁하다

□ **noise** 소음
→ a loud or unpleasant sound
시끄럽거나 불쾌한 소리

□ **owner** 주인
→ a person or group that owns something
어떤 것을 소유한 사람이나 집단

□ **professor** 교수
→ a teacher of the highest rank at a college or university
대학에서의 최고 직위의 선생

□ **respond** 응답하다
→ to say or write something as an answer to a question or request
질문이나 요청에 대한 응답으로 어떤 것을 말하거나 쓰다

□ **shop** 가게, 상점
→ a building or part of a building where things are sold
물건들을 파는 건물이나 건물의 일부

□ **shout** 외치다, 소리치다
→ to say something very loudly
뭔가를 아주 크게 말하다

□ **suddenly** 갑자기
→ very quickly in usually an unexpected way
대개 뜻밖에 아주 빨리

□ **university** 대학
→ an institution at the highest level of education where you can study for a degree or do research
학위나 연구를 위해 공부할 수 있는 최고 수준의 교육 기관

Reading

Laugh Out Loud
큰 소리로 웃어라

1 A Clock That Talks

Dean invited his friends to his room one evening. He was proud
어느 날 저녁   ~을 자랑스러워했다
of everything in his room: a nice bed, many comic books, and a new
        형용사구
computer. In the corner, he also had a very big metal dish. A friend
                                                        접시
asked, "What's that big dish?" "Oh, that's my special clock. It talks,"
Dean replied proudly. "If you hit the dish, you'll know the time." Then
              접속사(~하면)
he hit the dish with his hand. It made a really loud noise. Suddenly, his
        ~으로   갑자기(=All of a sudden)
sister who was on the other side of the wall shouted, "Are you crazy?
주격 관계대명사(선행사: his sister)   ~의 반대편에
It's eleven o'clock at night. Time to go to bed!"
                                        자다

2 A Flat Tire

Jessie and Nicole are university friends. They visited Jessie's
                                        = Jessie and Nicole
grandma in Florida on Saturday. They planned to come back early on
                    토요일에   ~할 계획을 했다   돌아오다   (부) 일찍
Monday because they had a big test that afternoon. But they got up late
        월 (~이기 때문에) have a test: 시험이 있다   늦잠을 자다
and could not make it to the test. They needed a good excuse for being
                ~에 이르다, ~에 도착하다   be late: 늦다
late, so they decided to tell the professor that their car got a flat tire.
그래서   ~하기로 결정했다   타이어에 펑크가 났다

invite 초대하다	
corner 구석, 모퉁이	
metal 금속	
dish 접시	
special 특별한	
reply 대답하다	
proudly 자랑스럽게	
hit 치다, 때리다	
loud 시끄러운	
noise 소리, 소음	
shout 외치다, 소리치다	
crazy 미친, 정신이상인	
go to bed 자다	
because ~때문에	
flat 바람이 빠진, 펑크 난	
university 대학	
plan 계획하다, 의도하다	
late 늦게	
excuse 변명	
decide 결정하다	
professor 교수	

 확인문제

● 다음 문장이 본문의 내용과 일치하면 T, 일치하지 않으면 F를 쓰시오.

1 Dean invited his friends to his room one evening. ☐

2 There was a clock in Dean's room. ☐

3 The very big metal dish was Dean's sister's. ☐

4 Dean's sister was on the other side of the wall. ☐

5 Jessie and Nicole visited Jessie's grandma in Florida on Saturday. ☐

6 They got up early on Monday because they had a big test that afternoon. ☐

The professor agreed that it was just bad luck and allowed them to take
the test on Wednesday. When they came to take the test on Wednesday
morning, the professor put Jessie and Nicole in different rooms. As
they sat down, they read the first question.

For 5 points, explain global warming.

It was a piece of cake to them. Then, the test continued.

For 95 points, answer the question: Which tire?

3 A Special Parrot

One day Abril went to a pet shop to buy a parrot. "How much is this
blue one?" she asked.

"It costs $2,000," said the pet shop owner.

"Why is it so expensive?" asked Abril.

"This parrot is a very special one. It can play the piano!"

"What about the green one?" she asked.

"It costs $5,000 because it can play the piano, paint pictures, and jump
rope."

"Then what about the red one?" Abril asked. The owner responded that
it costs $10,000. She was surprised and asked, "What does it do?"

"I don't know," said the owner, "but the other two birds call it
'teacher.'"

allow 허락하다
different 다른
explain 설명하다
continue 계속하다
buy 사다
cost (값 · 비용이) ~이다[들다]
owner 주인
expensive 비싼
jump rope 줄넘기하다
respond 응답하다
surprised 놀란

확인문제

● 다음 문장이 본문의 내용과 일치하면 T, 일치하지 않으면 F를 쓰시오.

1 Jessie and Nicole told the professor that their car had gotten a flat tire. ☐

2 The professor believed what they had said. ☐

3 Abril wanted to buy a parrot. ☐

4 The blue parrot wasn't so expensive. ☐

5 The green parrot could play the piano, paint pictures, and jump rope. ☐

6 The red parrot was the cheapest of the three. ☐

● 우리말을 참고하여 빈칸에 알맞은 말을 쓰시오.

1 A _____ That _____

2 Dean _____ his friends _____ his room _____ _____.

3 He _____ _____ _____ everything _____ his room: a nice bed, many _____ _____, and a new computer.

4 _____ the corner, he also _____ a very big _____ _____.

5 A friend _____, "_____ that big dish?"

6 "Oh, that's my _____ clock. It _____." Dean replied _____.

7 "_____ you _____ the dish, you'll know _____ _____."

8 Then he _____ the dish _____ his hand.

9 It _____ a really _____ noise.

10 _____, his sister who was _____ _____ _____ _____ of the wall _____, "Are you _____?"

11 _____ eleven o'clock _____ night. Time to _____ _____ _____!"

12 A _____ Tire

13 Jessie and Nicole are _____ friends.

14 They visited Jessie's grandma _____ Florida _____ Saturday.

15 They planned to _____ _____ _____ on Monday _____ they had a big test that afternoon.

16 But they _____ _____ _____ and could not _____ it to the test.

17 They needed a good excuse for _____ _____, so they _____ _____ _____ the professor that their car _____ a flat _____.

1	말하는 시계
2	어느 날 저녁 Dean은 친구들을 자기 방으로 초대했다.
3	그는 방에 있는 모든 것 즉, 멋진 침대, 많은 만화책들, 그리고 새 컴퓨터를 자랑스러워했다.
4	구석에 그는 커다란 금속 접시도 가지고 있었다.
5	한 친구가 "저 큰 접시는 뭐니?"라고 물었다.
6	"아, 저건 내 특별한 시계야. 그건 말을 해." Dean이 자랑스럽게 대답했다.
7	"접시를 치면, 시간을 알게 될 거야."
8	그러고 나서 그는 손으로 접시를 쳤다.
9	그것은 정말 큰 소리를 냈다.
10	갑자기 벽 반대편에 있던 그의 누나가 소리쳤다. "너 미쳤니?"
11	밤 11시야. 잘 시간이야!"
12	펑크 난 타이어
13	Jessie와 Nicole은 대학 친구이다.
14	그들은 토요일에 플로리다에 계시는 Jessie의 할머니를 방문했다.
15	그들은 월요일 오후에 큰 시험이 있기 때문에 그날 일찍 돌아올 계획이었다.
16	하지만 그들은 늦게 일어나서 시험에 맞춰 올 수 없었다.
17	그들은 지각한 것에 대한 좋은 핑계 거리가 필요해서 교수에게 차의 타이어에 펑크가 났다고 말하기로 결정했다.

18 The professor agreed _____ it was just _____ and _____ them _____ take the test _____ Wednesday.

19 _____ they came _____ _____ the test _____ Wednesday morning, the professor _____ Jessie and Nicole in _____ rooms.

20 _____ they _____ _____, they read the first question.

21 For 5 points, explain _____ _____.

22 It was _____ _____ _____ _____ to them. Then, the test _____.

23 For 95 points, _____ the question:

24 _____ tire?

25 A _____ Parrot

26 _____ _____ Abril went to a pet shop _____ _____ a parrot.

27 "_____ _____ is this blue _____?" she asked.

28 "It _____ $2,000," said the _____ _____ owner.

29 "_____ is it so _____?" asked Abril.

30 "This parrot is a very _____ _____. It can _____ _____ _____!"

31 "_____ _____ the green one?" she asked.

32 "It costs $5,000 _____ it can play the piano, paint pictures, and _____ _____."

33 "Then _____ _____ the red one?" Abril asked.

34 The owner _____ that it _____ $10,000.

35 She was _____ and asked, "What _____ it _____?"

36 "I don't know," _____ the owner, "but the _____ two birds _____ it 'teacher.'"

18 교수는 그것이 단지 불운이라는 것에 동의했고 수요일에 그들이 시험을 볼 수 있도록 허락했다.

19 수요일 아침에 그들이 시험을 보러 왔을 때, 교수는 Jessie와 Nicole을 다른 방에 들어가게 했다.

20 그들은 앉아서 첫 번째 문제를 읽었다.

21 5점짜리, 지구 온난화를 설명하시오.

22 그것은 그들에게 식은 죽 먹기였다. 그러고 나서, 시험은 계속되었다.

23 95점짜리, 질문에 답하시오.

24 어느 타이어였는가?

25 특별한 앵무새

26 어느 날 Abril은 앵무새를 사러 애완동물 가게에 갔다.

27 "이 파란 앵무새는 얼마죠?" 그녀가 물었다.

28 "이것은 2,000달러예요." 애완동물 가게 주인이 말했다.

29 "왜 그렇게 비싸죠?" Abril이 물었다.

30 "이것은 아주 특별한 앵무새입니다. 피아노를 칠 수 있어요!"

31 "초록색 앵무새는요?" 그녀가 물었다.

32 "이것은 피아노를 치고, 그림을 그리고, 줄넘기를 할 수 있기 때문에 5,000달러입니다."

33 "그럼 빨간 앵무새는요?" Abril이 물었다.

34 주인은 10,000달러라고 대답했다.

35 그녀는 놀라서 물었다. "그것은 뭘 할 수 있죠?"

36 "모르겠어요, 하지만 다른 두 새들이 그것을 '선생님'이라고 불러요."라고 주인이 말했다.

● 우리말을 참고하여 본문을 영작하시오.

1 말하는 시계
➡ _____

2 어느 날 저녁 Dean은 친구들을 자기 방으로 초대했다.
➡ _____

3 그는 방에 있는 모든 것 즉, 멋진 침대, 많은 만화책들, 그리고 새 컴퓨터를 자랑스러워했다.
➡ _____

4 구석에 그는 커다란 금속 접시도 가지고 있었다.
➡ _____

5 한 친구가 "저 큰 접시는 뭐니?"라고 물었다.
➡ _____

6 "아, 저건 내 특별한 시계야. 그건 말을 해." Dean이 자랑스럽게 대답했다.
➡ _____

7 "접시를 치면, 시간을 알게 될 거야."
➡ _____

8 그러고 나서 그는 손으로 접시를 쳤다.
➡ _____

9 그것은 정말 큰 소리를 냈다.
➡ _____

10 갑자기 벽 반대편에 있던 그의 누나가 소리쳤다. "너 미쳤니?"
➡ _____

11 밤 11시야. 잘 시간이야!"
➡ _____

12 펑크 난 타이어
➡ _____

13 Jessie와 Nicole은 대학 친구이다.
➡ _____

14 그들은 토요일에 플로리다에 계시는 Jessie의 할머니를 방문했다.
➡ _____

15 그들은 월요일 오후에 큰 시험이 있기 때문에 그날 일찍 돌아올 계획이었다.
➡ _____

16 하지만 그들은 늦게 일어나서 시험에 맞춰 올 수 없었다.
➡ _____

17 그들은 지각한 것에 대한 좋은 핑계 거리가 필요해서 교수에게 차의 타이어에 펑크가 났다고 말하기로 결정했다.
➡ _____

18 교수는 그것이 단지 불운이라는 것에 동의했고 수요일에 그들이 시험을 볼 수 있도록 허락했다.
➡ _____

19 수요일 아침에 그들이 시험을 보러 왔을 때, 교수는 Jessie와 Nicole을 다른 방에 들어가게 했다.
➡ _____

20 그들은 앉아서 첫 번째 문제를 읽었다.
➡ _____

21 5점짜리, 지구 온난화를 설명하시오.
➡ _____

22 그것은 그들에게 식은 죽 먹기였다. 그러고 나서, 시험은 계속되었다.
➡ _____

23 95점짜리, 질문에 답하시오.
➡ _____

24 어느 타이어였는가?
➡ _____

25 특별한 앵무새
➡ _____

26 어느 날 Abril은 앵무새를 사러 애완동물 가게에 갔다.
➡ _____

27 "이 파란 앵무새는 얼마죠?" 그녀가 물었다.
➡ _____

28 "이것은 2,000달러예요," 애완동물 가게 주인이 말했다.
➡ _____

29 "왜 그렇게 비싸죠?" Abril이 물었다.
➡ _____

30 "이것은 아주 특별한 앵무새입니다. 피아노를 칠 수 있어요!"
➡ _____

31 "초록색 앵무새는요?" 그녀가 물었다.
➡ _____

32 "이것은 피아노를 치고, 그림을 그리고, 줄넘기를 할 수 있기 때문에 5,000달러입니다."
➡ _____

33 "그럼 빨간 앵무새는요?" Abril이 물었다.
➡ _____

34 주인은 10,000달러라고 대답했다.
➡ _____

35 그녀는 놀라서 물었다. "그것은 뭘 할 수 있죠?"
➡ _____

36 "모르겠어요, 하지만 다른 두 새들이 그것을 '선생님'이라고 불러요."라고 주인이 말했다.
➡ _____

01 다음 빈칸에 알맞은 말을 〈보기〉에서 골라 쓰시오.

> ┤ 보기 ├
> special   excuse   surprised   global

(1) She was _____ to see the sight.

(2) Today, _____ warming is a serious problem.

(3) They needed a good _____ for being late.

(4) Actors wear _____ clothes for the play.

02 다음 주어진 우리말에 맞게 빈칸에 알맞은 말을 쓰시오.

(1) 그것은 그들에게 식은 죽 먹기이다.
⇒ It is _____ _____ _____ cake to them.

(2) 나는 매일 아침 늦잠을 잔다.
⇒ I _____ _____ _____ every morning.

(3) Dean은 어느 날 저녁 그의 집으로 친구들을 초대했다.
⇒ Dean invited his friends to his house _____ _____.

03 다음 영영풀이에 해당하는 단어를 〈보기〉에서 찾아 쓰시오.

> ┤ 보기 ├
> invite   shout   owner   flat

(1) _____ : not having enough air

(2) _____ : to say something very loudly

(3) _____ : a person that owns something

(4) _____ : to ask someone to come to a party, wedding, meal, etc.

04 다음 주어진 단어를 이용하여 우리말을 영어로 옮기시오.

(1) 태풍이 오고 있으므로 너는 나가지 않는 게 좋겠다. (a typhoon, had better, because)
➡ _____
_____

(2) 그는 내가 가진 유일한 친구이다. (the only friend, have)
➡ _____

05 다음 두 문장이 같은 뜻이 되도록 빈칸에 알맞은 말을 쓰시오.

(1) My mother let me go to the concert.
➡ My mother allowed me _____ _____ to the concert.

(2) He made us sweep the floor.
➡ He forced us _____ _____ the floor.

06 다음 빈칸에 알맞은 말을 〈보기〉에서 골라 쓰시오. (문장의 앞에 오는 경우 대문자로 쓰시오.)

> ┤ 보기 ├
> though   when   if

(1) _____ you don't leave now, you will miss the last train.

(2) We had a big party _____ Sarah came home.

(3) _____ it was very warm, she didn't take off her coat.

Dean invited his friends to his room one evening. He was proud _____ⓐ_____ everything in his room: a nice bed, many comic books, and a new computer. ⓑIn the corner, he also had a very big metal dish. A friend asked, "What's that big dish?" "Oh, that's my _____ⓒ_____ clock. It talks," Dean replied proudly, "If you hit the dish, you'll know the time." Then he hit the dish with his hand. It made a really loud noise. Suddenly, his sister ⓓwho was on the other side of the wall shouted, "Are you crazy? It's eleven o'clock at night. Time to go to bed!"

07 위 글의 빈칸 ⓐ에 알맞은 전치사를 쓰시오.

➡ _____

08 위 글의 밑줄 친 ⓑ와 같은 뜻이 되도록 다음 문장의 빈칸에 알맞은 말을 쓰시오.

In the corner, _____ _____ also a very big metal dish.

09 위 글의 빈칸 ⓒ에 다음 정의에 해당하는 단어를 주어진 단어로 시작하여 쓰시오.

better or more important than someone or something

➡ s_____

10 위 글의 밑줄 친 ⓒ 대신 쓸 수 있는 관계대명사를 쓰시오.

➡ _____

11 Where was Dean's sister? Answer in English.

➡ _____

One day Abril went to a pet shop to buy a parrot. "How much is this blue ⓐone?" she asked.

"It costs $2,000," said the pet shop owner.

"Why is it so expensive?" asked Abril.

"This parrot is a very special one. It can play the piano!"

"What _____ⓑ_____ the green one?" she asked.

"It costs $5,000 because it can play the piano, paint pictures, and jump rope."

"Then what _____ⓒ_____ the red one?" Abril asked. The owner responded _____ⓓ_____ it costs $10,000. She was ⓔsurprise and asked,

"What does it do?"

"I don't know," said the owner, "but the other two birds call it 'teacher.'"

12 위 글의 밑줄 친 ⓐ가 가리키는 것을 영어로 쓰시오.

➡ _____

13 위 글의 빈칸 ⓑ와 ⓒ에 공통으로 알맞은 말을 쓰시오.

➡ _____

14 위 글의 빈칸 ⓓ에 알맞은 말을 쓰시오.

➡ _____

15 위 글의 밑줄 친 ⓔ를 알맞은 형으로 고치시오.

➡ _____

16 What can the blue parrot do? Answer in English.

➡ _____

01 출제율 90%

다음 중 짝지어진 단어의 관계가 나머지 넷과 <u>다른</u> 것은?

① sell : buy
② special : general
③ ask : answer
④ allow : permit
⑤ expensive : cheap

02 출제율 90%

다음 영영풀이에 해당하는 단어로 알맞은 것은?

> to make something clear or easy to understand

① invite
② choose
③ explain
④ excuse
⑤ respond

03 출제율 85%

다음 빈칸에 공통으로 알맞은 것은?

> • The woman is changing a _____ tire.
> • There are many buildings with _____ roofs.

① round
② flat
③ sharp
④ smooth
⑤ thick

04 출제율 95%

다음 우리말에 맞게 빈칸에 알맞은 말을 쓰시오.

> 그는 자기 아들을 자랑스러워한다.
> ➡ He _____ _____ _____ his son.

05 출제율 90%

다음 영영풀이에 해당하는 단어를 주어진 철자로 시작하여 쓰시오.

> a reason that you give to explain a mistake, bad behavior, etc.

➡ e_____

06 출제율 100%

다음 빈칸에 알맞은 말이 바르게 짝지어진 것은?

> • He lives _____ the other side of the street.
> • People all laughed _____ loud at his joke.

① at – in
② on – out
③ in – of
④ with – over
⑤ from – on

07 출제율 95%

다음 짝지어진 단어의 관계가 같도록 빈칸에 알맞은 말을 쓰시오.

> different : _____ = noisy : quiet

08 출제율 90%

다음 빈칸에 들어갈 말로 적절하지 <u>않은</u> 것은?

> • How much does it _____?
> • He _____ the nail with the hammer.
> • He's going to _____ a test.
> • We _____ this land the Island of the Sun.

① call
② cost
③ hit
④ take
⑤ allow

09 다음 빈칸에 공통으로 알맞은 말을 쓰시오.

> • He had no time _____ eat lunch.
> • We are looking for a person _____ live in this house.

10 다음 중 밑줄 친 부분의 쓰임이 나머지 넷과 <u>다른</u> 것은?

① He is always the first boy <u>to come</u>.
② He has nothing <u>to write</u> with.
③ He went to England <u>to study</u> English.
④ There are a lot of things for him <u>to do</u>.
⑤ He was looking for an apartment <u>to live</u> in.

11 다음 〈보기〉와 문장 구조가 <u>다른</u> 하나는?

> ┤ 보기 ├
> My little brother always makes me upset.

① People call him Lion King.
② I made my son a police officer.
③ He heard the girl play the flute.
④ Jake gave me some sandwich.
⑤ They saw an alien kidnapping a farmer.

12 다음 문장의 빈칸에 알맞은 것은?

> I had to carry the heavy box in one hand and an umbrella in _____.

① other
② the other
③ others
④ another
⑤ the others

13 다음 중 어법상 <u>어색한</u> 것은?

① The teacher told Jake to be friendly.
② My brother always makes me laugh.
③ People call him Uncle Bob.
④ They saw a woman to play soccer.
⑤ The news made the students excited.

14 다음 문장의 빈칸에 알맞은 것은?

> Do you know the boy _____ is running after a dog?

① what
② who
③ whom
④ which
⑤ whose

15 다음 문장의 빈칸에 알맞은 것은?

> Why don't you eat some gimbap _____ you're hungry?

① and
② but
③ if
④ where
⑤ because

16 다음 밑줄 친 ①~⑤ 중 어법상 <u>어색한</u> 것은?

> My father ①<u>will buy</u> ②<u>me a computer</u> ③<u>if</u> I ④<u>will get</u> a perfect score ⑤<u>in the</u> <u>final exam</u>.

① ② ③ ④ ⑤

[17~21] 다음 글을 읽고, 물음에 답하시오.

Jessie and Nicole are university friends. They visited Jessie's grandma in Florida on Saturday. They planned to come back early on Monday ⓐ they had a big test that afternoon. But they got up late and could not ⓑ it to the test. They needed a good excuse for ⓒbe late, so they decided to tell the professor that their car got a flat tire.

The professor agreed that it was just bad luck and ⓓallowed them to take the test on Wednesday. When they came to take the test on Wednesday morning, the professor put Jessie and Nicole in different rooms. As they sat down, they read the first question.

For 5 points, explain global warming.
It was a piece of cake to them. Then, the test continued.

For 95 points, answer the question: Which tire?

17 위 글의 빈칸 ⓐ에 알맞은 것은? (2개)

① if　　　　② as
③ though　　④ when
⑤ because

18 위 글의 빈칸 ⓑ에 알맞은 것은?

① be　　　　② do
③ make　　　④ get
⑤ take

19 위 글의 밑줄 친 ⓒ를 알맞은 어형으로 고치시오.

➡ _____

20 위 글의 밑줄 친 ⓓ와 같은 뜻이 되도록 다음 문장의 빈칸에 알맞은 말을 쓰시오.

_____ them _____ the test

21 위 글의 내용으로 보아 알 수 없는 것은?

① Jessie and Nicole visited Jessie's grandma.
② They got up late on Monday.
③ They told a lie to the professor.
④ The professor wasn't a generous man.
⑤ The answer to the question for 95 points was very easy.

[22~26] 다음 글을 읽고, 물음에 답하시오.

Dean invited his friends to his room one evening. ⓐHe was proud of everything in his room: a nice bed, many comic books, and a new computer. In the corner, he also had a very big metal dish. A friend asked, "What's that big dish?" "Oh, that's my special clock. It talks," Dean replied ⓑproud, "　ⓒ　 you hit the dish, you'll know the time." Then he hit the dish with his hand. It made a really loud noise. ⓓSuddenly, his sister who was on the other side of the wall shouted, "Are you crazy? It's eleven o'clock at night. Time to go to bed!"

22 위 글의 밑줄 친 ⓐ와 같은 뜻이 되도록 빈칸에 알맞은 것은?

He took pride _____ everything in his room:

① in　　　　② at
③ to　　　　④ for
⑤ with

출제율 85%
23 위 글의 밑줄 친 ⓑ를 알맞은 어형으로 고치시오.

➡ _____

출제율 90%
24 위 글의 빈칸 ⓒ에 알맞은 것은?

① Till   ② After

③ If   ④ Though

⑤ While

출제율 95%
25 위 글의 밑줄 친 ⓓ와 같은 뜻이 되도록 다음 어구의 빈칸에 알맞은 말을 쓰시오.

All _____ a sudden

출제율 100%
26 위 글의 분위기로 가장 알맞은 것은?

① urgent   ② sad

③ lonely   ④ peaceful

⑤ humorous

[27~31] 다음 글을 읽고, 물음에 답하시오.

One day Abril went to a pet shop to buy a parrot. "How much is this blue one?" she asked.

"It costs $2,000," said the pet shop owner.

"Why is it so ___ⓐ___?" asked Abril.

"This parrot is a very special one. It can play the piano!"

"What about the green one?" she asked.

"It costs $5,000 ⓑbecause it can play the piano, paint pictures, and jump rope."

"Then what about the red one?" Abril asked. The owner responded that it costs $10,000. She was surprised and asked, "What does it do?"

"I don't know," said the ⓒown, "ⓓbut the other two birds call it 'teacher.'"

출제율 95%
27 위 글의 빈칸 ⓐ에 알맞은 것은?

① low   ② high

③ cheap   ④ expensive

⑤ valuable

출제율 90%
28 위 글의 밑줄 친 ⓑ와 바꿔 쓸 수 있는 것은?

① as   ② if

③ when   ④ though

⑤ while

출제율 85%
29 위 글의 밑줄 친 ⓒ를 알맞은 어형으로 고치시오.

➡ _____

출제율 90%
30 위 글의 밑줄 친 ⓓ와 문형이 같은 것은?

① My uncle planted some trees in the garden.

② The child looked very hungry.

③ Birds fly in the sky.

④ They called her Little Princess.

⑤ Kirk sent her a birthday present last week.

출제율 95%
31 위 글의 내용으로 보아 대답할 수 없는 질문은?

① Why did Abril go to a pet shop?

② How much was the blue parrot?

③ What can the green parrot do?

④ How much was the green parrot?

⑤ What can the red parrot do?

[32~35] 다음 글을 읽고, 물음에 답하시오.

(①) Jessie and Nicole are university friends. (②) They visited Jessie's grandma in Florida on Saturday. (③) They planned ⓐto come back early on Monday because they had a big test that afternoon. (④) They needed a good excuse ⓒ____ being late, ⓓ____ they decided to tell the professor that their car got a flat tire. (⑤)

32 위 글의 ①~⑤ 중 다음 주어진 문장이 들어갈 알맞은 위치는? (출제율 90%)

> But they got up late and could not make it to the test.

①   ②   ③   ④   ⑤

33 위 글의 밑줄 친 ⓐ와 같은 용법으로 쓰인 것은? (출제율 95%)

① Jane made a promise to help us.
② He went to a bookstore to buy a book.
③ They sent some people to live on the planet.
④ The boys decided to go swimming in the pool.
⑤ I awoke to find myself lying on the floor.

34 위 글의 빈칸 ⓒ에 알맞은 것은? (출제율 90%)

① at   ② for
③ to   ④ with
⑤ from

35 위 글의 빈칸 ⓓ에 알맞은 것은? (출제율 100%)

① so   ② for
③ or   ④ but
⑤ as

[36~38] 다음 글을 읽고, 물음에 답하시오.

The professor agreed that it was just bad luck and allowed them ⓐ____ the test on Wednesday. When they came to take the test on Wednesday morning, the professor put Jessie and Nicole in ⓑ____ rooms. As they sat down, they read the first question.

For 5 points, explain global warming. ⓒIt was a piece of cake to them. Then, the test continued.

For 95 points, answer the question: Which tire?

36 위 글의 빈칸 ⓐ에 알맞은 것은? (출제율 100%)

① take   ② took
③ taking   ④ to take
⑤ to taking

37 위 글의 빈칸 ⓑ에 알맞은 것은? (출제율 90%)

① same   ② silent
③ near   ④ strange
⑤ different

38 위 글의 밑줄 친 ⓒ를 우리말로 옮기시오. (출제율 95%)

➡ _____

Lesson 5

Understanding Others

🎙 의사소통 기능

- 희망이나 바람 표현하기
  A: I have an important exam tomorrow.
  B: I hope you'll do well on the exam.

- 외모 묘사하기
  A: What does he look like?
  B: He has brown hair and brown eyes.

🎙 언어 형식

- want/ask/tell + 목적어 + to부정사
  Parents **want their children to be** honest.

- 접속사 before, after
  Before she has breakfast, Dora puts on her uniform.

Words & Expressions

Key Words

- **accuse** [əkjúːz] 동 고발하다, 비난하다
- **activity** [æktívəti] 명 활동
- **ago** [əgóu] 부 전에
- **allowance** [əláuəns] 명 용돈
- **annoucement** [ənáunsmənt] 명 발표, 공표
- **anytime** [énitàim] 부 언제든지, 언제나
- **appearance** [əpíərəns] 명 외모
- **arrest** [ərést] 동 체포하다
- **attack** [ətǽk] 동 공격하다
- **attitude** [ǽtitjùːd] 명 태도, 자세
- **avoid** [əvɔ́id] 동 피하다
- **back** [bæk] 명 등, 뒤
- **beard** [biərd] 명 턱수염
- **behind** [biháind] 전 ~ 뒤에
- **bullying** [búliiŋ] 명 약자 괴롭히기
- **carry** [kǽri] 동 휴대하다, 지니다
- **character** [kǽriktər] 명 등장인물, 캐릭터
- **choice** [tʃɔis] 명 선택
- **choose** [tʃuːz] 동 선택하다, 고르다
- **confident** [kánfədənt] 형 자신감 있는
- **curly** [kə́ːrli] 형 곱슬곱슬한
- **difficulty** [dífikʌlti] 명 어려움
- **enter** [éntər] 동 들어가다, 참가[출전]하다
- **face** [feis] 동 직면하다, (힘든 상황에) 처하다
- **free** [friː] 동 석방하다
- **freedom** [fríːdəm] 명 자유
- **friendly** [fréndli] 형 다정한, 친절한
- **guilty** [gílti] 형 유죄의

- **hide**(-hid-hidden) [haid] 동 숨기다
- **judge** [dʒʌdʒ] 명 판사 동 판단하다
- **lucky** [lʌ́ki] 형 운이 좋은
- **mind** [maind] 동 신경 쓰다, 꺼리다
- **missing** [mísiŋ] 형 실종된, 행방불명된
- **Mongolia** [mɑŋɡóuliə] 명 몽골
- **monthly** [mʌ́nθli] 형 매월의, 한 달에 한 번의
- **neighbor** [néibər] 명 이웃
- **ordinary** [ɔ́ːrdənèri] 형 평범한
- **pass** [pæs] 동 통과하다, 지나가다
- **ponytail** [póunitèil] 명 포니테일(말꼬리 모양으로 묶은 머리)
- **popular** [pápjulər] 형 인기 있는, 대중적인
- **president** [prézədənt] 명 회장
- **prison** [prízn] 명 감옥
- **promise** [prámis] 명 공약, 약속
- **protect** [prətékt] 동 보호하다
- **receive** [risíːv] 동 받다
- **right** [rait] 명 권리
- **score** [skɔːr] 동 득점하다
- **shout** [ʃaut] 동 소리치다, 외치다
- **shy** [ʃai] 형 부끄럼을 많이 타는, 수줍어하는
- **throw**(-threw-thrown) [θrou] 동 던지다
- **truth** [truːθ] 명 진실
- **victim** [víktim] 명 희생자
- **vote** [vout] 동 투표하다
- **whisper** [hwíspər] 동 속삭이다
- **worried** [wə́ːrid] 형 걱정하는

Key Expressions

- **accuse A of B** B 때문에 A를 고발하다
- **agree with+사람** ~에게 동의하다
- **a little** 약간, 조금
- **be afraid of** ~ ~을 두려워하다
- **be for** ~ ~을 지지하다, ~을 찬성하다
- **be good at** ~ ~을 잘하다
- **bulletin board** 게시판
- **calm down** 진정하다
- **care for** ~ ~을 돌보다
- **cut off** ~ ~을 자르다

- **do well on** ~ ~을 잘하다, 잘 보다
- **fight off** ~ ~을 싸워 물리치다
- **go 동사원형+ing** ~하러 가다
- **look different from** ~ ~와 다르게 보이다
- **look like** ~ ~처럼 보이다
- **set 목적어 free** ~을 석방하다
- **so far** 지금까지
- **thanks to** ~ ~ 덕분에
- **vote for** ~ ~을 뽑다, ~에게 투표하다
- **would like to+동사원형** ~하고 싶다

Word Power

※ 여러 가지 품사로 쓰이는 단어

- □ **cause** (명) 원인 (동) 야기하다
- □ **fall** (명) 가을 (동) 떨어지다
- □ **change** (명) 잔돈, 변화 (동) 변하다
- □ **train** (명) 기차 (동) 훈련하다
- □ **kind** (명) 종류 (형) 친절한

- □ **face** (명) 얼굴 (동) 직면하다, 마주하다
- □ **judge** (명) 판사 (동) 판단하다
- □ **play** (명) 연극 (동) 놀다, 경기하다
- □ **mean** (동) 의미하다 (형) 못된, 비열한
- □ **like** (동) 좋아하다 (전) ~와 같은

※ 서로 반대되는 뜻을 가진 단어

- □ **ordinary** (평범한) ↔ **extraordinary** (비범한)
- □ **friendly** (친절한) ↔ **unfriendly**(불친절한)
- □ **guilty** (유죄의) ↔ **innocent** (무죄의)

- □ **difficulty** (어려움) ↔ **ease** (쉬움)
- □ **avoid** (피하다) ↔ **face** (직면하다)
- □ **popular** (인기 있는) ↔ **unpopular** (인기 없는)

※ 다양한 접미사를 붙여 동사가 명사로 바뀌는 단어

- □ **allow** (주다, 지급하다) – **allowance** (용돈)
- □ **assist** (도와주다) – **assistance** (도움, 원조)
- □ **free** (자유롭게 하다) – **freedom** (자유)

- □ **appear** (보이다) – **appearance** (외모)
- □ **judge** (판단하다) – **judgement** (판단)
- □ **act** (행동하다) – **action** (행동)

English Dictionary

- □ **allowance** 용돈
  → an amount of money that parents give to a child each week
  부모가 매주 아이에게 주는 돈

- □ **arrest** 체포하다
  → to take the person away to ask them about a crime that they might have committed
  저질렀을지도 모르는 범죄에 대해 심문하기 위해 사람을 데려가다

- □ **attack** 공격하다
  → to use violence to hurt or damage someone
  폭력을 사용하여 사람을 다치게 하거나 피해를 주다

- □ **attitude** 태도
  → how you think or feel about something
  어떤 것에 대해 생각하고 느끼는 방식

- □ **avoid** 피하다
  → to stay away from a person or place
  사람이나 장소로부터 멀리하다

- □ **bullying** 괴롭히기
  → an action to try to frighten someone who is smaller or weaker
  더 작거나 약한 사람을 겁주려고 하는 행위

- □ **cause** 야기하다
  → to make something happen
  어떤 일이 일어나도록 만들다

- □ **change** 잔돈
  → the money you get back when you pay more money than something costs
  어떤 것의 비용보다 더 많은 돈을 지불했을 때 돌려받는 돈

- □ **choose** 선택하다, 고르다
  → to decide which thing you want
  어느 것을 원하는지 결정하다

- □ **confidence** 자신감
  → the belief that you are able to do things well or be successful
  일을 잘하거나 성공할 수 있다는 믿음

- □ **neighbor** 이웃
  → someone who lives near you
  당신 근처에 사는 사람

- □ **protect** 보호하다
  → to keep someone or something safe from something dangerous or bad
  위험하거나 나쁜 것으로부터 어떤 사람이나 사물을 지키다

- □ **victim** 피해자, 희생자
  → someone who has been hurt or killed
  다치거나 살해된 사람

- □ **whisper** 속삭이다
  → to speak very quietly so that other people cannot hear
  다른 사람들이 들을 수 없도록 매우 조용히 말하다

서답형

01 다음 짝지어진 두 단어의 관계가 같도록 주어진 철자로 시작하는 단어를 쓰시오.

> friendly : unfriendly
> – extraordinary : o_____

서답형

02 다음 글의 빈칸에 영영 풀이에 맞는 알맞은 형태의 단어를 쓰시오.

> • We'll go out and look for him. Also, we'll make an _____ about a missing child.
> <영영 풀이> something that someone says officially, giving new information about something

➡ _____

03 다음 중 밑줄 친 단어의 우리말 뜻이 <u>잘못된</u> 것은?

① All my classmates are very <u>friendly</u>. 다정한
② I'll <u>vote for</u> Jang Jimin. ~에게 투표하다
③ <u>Bullying</u> is a big problem in many schools. 괴롭히기
④ When you <u>face</u> difficulties, just call me. 직면하다
⑤ They <u>whispered</u> behind his back, "What is he trying to hide?" 외쳤다

중요

[04~05] 다음 영영 풀이에 해당하는 단어를 고르시오.

04
> to keep someone or something safe from something dangerous or bad

① avoid   ② protect
③ choose   ④ change
⑤ cause

05
> an amount of money that parents give to a child each week

① victim   ② attitude
③ choice   ④ judge
⑤ allowance

서답형

06 다음 우리말에 맞게 주어진 철자로 시작하는 단어를 쓰시오.

> 그들은 그에게 턱수염을 그만 기르라고 말했다. Joseph은 신경 쓰지 않았다.
> ➡ They told him to stop growing a beard. Joseph did not m_____.

➡ _____

07 다음 빈칸에 들어갈 말로 알맞은 것은?

> People did not like a long beard very much. So they _____ the man with a beard.

① whispered   ② believed
③ avoided   ④ cared
⑤ freed

중요

08 다음 빈칸에 들어갈 단어가 알맞게 짝지어진 것은?

> Joseph was a big man, and he was able to fight them _____. But the men called the police and _____ him of attacking them. Poor Joseph was arrested.

① on – caused
② of – set
③ off – caused
④ off – accused
⑤ of – accused

01 다음 문장의 밑줄 친 단어를 알맞은 형태로 바꾸어 쓰시오.

(1) We should not judge people by their underline{appear}.

(2) He just wanted the underline{free} to have his beard.

➡ (1) _____ (2) _____

02 다음 영영 풀이에 해당하는 단어를 쓰시오.

(1) • to make something different
   • the money you get back when you pay more money than something costs

(2) • to teach a person or an animal how to do something
   • a number of cars connected together on a railway

➡ (1) _____ (2) _____

03 다음 문장에 공통으로 들어갈 단어를 쓰시오.

(1) • He said to the _____, "I'm the victim here."
   • We should not _____ people by the way they look.

(2) • You _____ the girl from Mongolia?
   • The police officer was not kind. He was _____ to her.

➡ (1) _____ (2) _____

04 다음 빈칸에 들어갈 말을 〈보기〉에서 찾아 쓰시오. (필요하면 변형하여 쓰시오.)

┌─ 보기 ────────────────────┐
thanks to, care for, do well on, calm down
└──────────────────────────┘

(1) I hope you'll _____ the exam.

(2) 42-year-old Joseph Palmer was an ordinary person. He had a job and _____ his family.

(3) He was freed _____ his son's letters.

05 다음 우리말과 같은 표현이 되도록 괄호 안의 지시대로 문장의 빈칸을 채우시오.

(1) 매사추세츠에 있는 작은 도시로 이사한 후에 그는 어려움에 직면하기 시작했다.
   ➡ After he moved to a small town in Massachusetts, he began to _____ _____. (복수형을 쓸 것.)

(2) Joseph은 다른 사람들과 달라 보였다.
   ➡ Joseph _____ _____ _____ other people. (look을 이용할 것.)

(3) 사람들은 Joseph이 단지 자신과 자신의 턱수염을 지키려다 감옥에 갇혔다는 것을 알게 되었다. (동명사를 이용할 것)
   ➡ People learned that Joseph was _____ _____ just for _____ himself and his beard.

1 희망이나 바람 표현하기

A I have an important exam tomorrow. 나는 내일 중요한 시험이 있어.

B I hope you'll do well on the exam. 네가 시험을 잘 보길 바라.

- 'I hope ~.'는 '나는 ~을 희망한다.'라는 뜻으로 자신의 소망을 나타낼 때 쓰는 표현이며 뒤에는 to부정사, 'that+주어+동사'가 온다. 경우에 따라 hope 대신 want 또는 wish를 사용할 수 있다.

희망이나 바람을 표현하기

- I hope to be a famous singer. 나는 유명한 가수가 되길 희망해.
  = I want to be a famous singer.
  = I'd like to be a famous singer.
- I hope to be a basketball player. 나는 농구선수가 되기를 희망한다.
- I want to be a famous writer. 나는 유명한 작가가 되고 싶다.

핵심 Check

1. 다음 대화의 빈칸에 알맞은 말을 고르시오.

A: Are you going to watch a movie?

B: Yes, _____

① I hope you'll find him soon.
② I hope to watch an action movie.
③ you will watch a movie tonight.
④ you go to the movies once a month.
⑤ I hope to be a famous actor.

2. 다음 대화의 밑줄 친 부분의 의도로 알맞은 것은?

- I have an important exam tomorrow! I hope I will pass it.

① 바람 표현하기   ② 의도 묻기
③ 충고하기   ④ 안부 묻기
⑤ 칭찬하기

② 외모 묘사하기

A What does he look like? 그는 어떻게 생겼나요?

B He has brown hair and brown eyes. 그는 갈색 머리카락과 갈색 눈을 지녔어요.

■ 인물의 외모나 모습을 묘사할 경우, 체형을 설명할 때는 주로 be동사를 사용하며, 이목구비나 머리 모양을 묘사할 때는 have동사를 사용한다. 또한 모자, 안경, 옷 등의 착용 상태를 묘사할 때는 '주어 + be동사+wearing ~.'으로 표현한다.

■ 현재 진행 중인 동작을 생생하게 묘사할 때에는 'be동사의 현재형+동사원형-ing'의 현재진행형을 사용한다.

외모를 묘사하는 표현들

• **A:** What does he look like? 그는 어떻게 생겼니?

B: He's tall and he has curly hair. 그는 키가 크고, 머리가 곱슬이야.

• **A:** Sujin, where is your sister, Somin? 수진아, 너의 여동생 소민이 어디에 있니?

B: She's over there. She's wearing glasses. 그녀는 저기에 있어. 그녀는 안경을 쓰고 있어.

• **A:** What does he look like? 그는 어떻게 생겼나요?

B: He has brown hair and brown eyes. 그는 갈색 머리이고 갈색 눈을 지녔어요.

A: What is he wearing? 그는 무엇을 입고 있나요?

B: He is wearing a green shirt. 그는 초록색 셔츠를 입고 있어요.

핵심 Check

3. 다음 대화의 빈칸에 들어갈 말로 알맞은 것을 <u>모두</u> 고르시오.

A: What does she look like?

B: _____

① She is playing the guitar.

② She always wears black pants.

③ She has brown hair and is wearing glasses.

④ She is boring.

⑤ She's tall and has long straight hair.

4. 다음 우리말에 맞도록 빈칸에 알맞은 것을 쓰시오.

• 그녀의 개는 어떻게 생겼니?

➡ What does her dog _____ _____?

Communicate: Listen-Listen and Answer. Talk

G: Hi, I'm Gacha. I'm from Mongolia. ❶When I first came to Songji Middle School two months ago, I was so worried. I was a little shy, and ❷I wasn't good at Korean. However, I'm a lucky girl. All my classmates are nice and friendly. ❸I enjoy playing handball with them in P.E. class. I'm a good player. ❹They call me "Golden Hand." ❺There will be a sports day next week. ❻I hope my class will win in the handball event.

여: 안녕, 나는 Gacha라고 해. 나는 몽골에서 왔어. 두 달 전에 내가 처음 송지 중학교에 왔을 때, 나는 무척 걱정이 되었어. 나는 좀 수줍음을 탔고 한국어를 잘 못했어. 하지만 난 운이 좋은 아이야. 내 학급 친구들은 모두 멋지고 다정해. 나는 체육 시간에 친구들과 핸드볼 하는 것을 즐겨. 난 실력이 좋은 선수야. 친구들은 나를 '황금 손'이라고 불러. 다음 주에 운동회가 있을 거야. 난 우리 반이 핸드볼 대회에서 이기길 바라.

❶ When은 '~할 때'의 의미로 부사절을 이끄는 접속사이다. two months ago라는 과거 시점이 있어서 과거시제 came을 사용한다.
❷ be good at ~은 '~을 잘하다'라는 의미다.
❸ enjoy는 동명사를 목적어로 취하는 동사로 playing을 사용했다.
❹ 'call+목적어+목적보어'의 형태로 '~을 …라고 부르다'로 해석한다.
❺ next week이라는 미래 시점과 사용되어서 미래시제 will be를 사용했다.
❻ 'I hope (that)+주어+동사 ~'는 희망이나 바람을 나타내는 표현이다.

Check(√) True or False

(1) Gacha was worried and a little shy at first. T ☐ F ☐

(2) Though Gacha likes playing handball, she isn't good at playing handball. T ☐ F ☐

 Communicate: Listen-Listen and Answer. Dialog

B: Hi, Minsol. Is your class winning?

G: Of course. We have a great handball player.

B: ❶You mean the girl from Mongolia?

G: Yes, her name is Gacha.

B: I've heard a lot about her. But ❷what does she look like?

G: She's very tall and has a ponytail.

B: Oh, is she the girl ❸who scored the goal just now?

G: Yes, that's her seventh goal.

B: Wow, she's really great.

남: 안녕, 민솔아. 너희 반이 이기고 있니?
여: 물론이지. 우리는 훌륭한 핸드볼 선수가 있거든.
남: 몽골에서 온 여자아이 말하는 거니?
여: 응, 그녀의 이름은 Gacha야.
남: 그녀에 대해 많이 들었어. 그런데 그녀는 어떻게 생겼어?
여: 그녀는 키가 크고 말총머리를 하고 있어.
남: 아, 지금 막 골을 넣은 여자아이가 그녀니?
여: 맞아, 저건 그녀의 일곱 번째 골이야.
남: 와, 그녀는 정말 잘하는구나.

❶ 일반동사 의문문 'Do you mean ~?'에서 Do가 생략된 형태로 '~을 말하는 거니?'라는 의미다.
❷ 사람의 외모를 묻는 표현이다.
❸ 선행사(사람)를 수식할 때 관계대명사절을 이끄는 who를 사용한다.

Check(√) True or False

(3) Minsol's class is winning the handball game. T ☐ F ☐

(4) Gacha is very tall and has a ponytail. T ☐ F ☐

Communicate: Listen-Listen More

M: ❶What can I do for you?
G: I lost my younger brother.
M: Okay, ❷calm down. What's your brother's name?
G: His name is Wally Brown. He's five years old.
M: ❸What does he look like?
G: He has brown hair and brown eyes.
M: What is he wearing?
G: He is wearing a green shirt and black pants.
M: Can you tell me more?
G: Oh, he is carrying a red backpack.
M: All right. We'll go out and look for him. Also, we'll make an announcement about ❹a missing child.
G: Thank you so much. ❺I hope I'll find him soon.

❶ 상대방에게 도움을 주고자 할 때 사용하는 표현으로, '무엇을 도와줄까요?'라는 뜻이다.
❷ '진정해'라는 뜻이다.
❸ 사람의 외모를 묻는 표현이다.
❹ missing은 형용사로 '실종된, 행방불명된'의 뜻이다.
❺ 'I hope (that)+주어+동사 ~'는 희망이나 바람을 나타내는 표현이다.

Communicate: Speak 2-Talk in pairs

A: I have an important exam tomorrow!
B: ❶I hope you'll do well on the exam.
A: ❷I hope so, too. Thanks.

❶ 희망이나 바람을 나타내는 표현으로, do well on은 '~을 잘하다'라는 뜻이다.
❷ '나도 그러길 바라'라는 의미다.

Communicate: Speak 2-Talk in groups

A: What is your character's name?
B: His name is Buster.
A: ❶What does he look like?
B: ❷He has no hair.
A: Does he have big eyes?
B: Yes, he does.

❶ 사람의 외모를 묻는 표현이다.
❷ 사람의 이목구비나 머리 모양을 묘사할 때는 동사 have를 사용한다.

Communicate: Speak-Rap Time

A: I hope you'll do your best in the final game.
B: Thanks. ❶I wish you the same.
A: ❷What does your sister look like, Claire?
B: She's tall and has long straight hair.

❶ '나도 네가 그러길 바라.'라는 뜻이다.
❷ 사람의 외모를 묻는 표현이다.

My Speaking Portfolio

G: Look at the bulletin board. ❶There are posters for the next school president.
B: Yeah, I've already made my choice. ❷I'll vote for Jang Jimin.
G: You mean the boy with glasses? He looks smart, but I don't like his promises.
B: Then who will you choose?
G: Well, I am for number 1, Han Siwon. She wants to make our school a safe place.
B: She always has a ponytail, right?
G: Yes, and Hong Jiho seems okay.
B: ❸She looks friendly, but I don't like talent shows.

❶ 'There are+복수 명사' 형태로 '~가 있다'는 뜻이다.
❷ vote for ~는 '~에게 투표하다'라는 뜻이다.
❸ 'look+형용사' 형태로 '~처럼 보이다'라는 뜻이다.

Wrap Up

1.
B: I hear there is a new student in your class.
G: Yes. She's from Jejudo. Oh, she's over there!
B: ❶ Which one? What does she look like?
G: ❷She has curly hair and is wearing glasses.

2.
G: You look sad. What's wrong, Jongmin?
B: My sister broke her arm this morning.
G: What happened?
B: She fell off her bike.
G: That's too bad. ❸I hope she'll get better soon.

❶ '어느 아이니?'의 뜻이다.
❷ 사람의 외모를 표현하는 말로 머리 모양을 묘사할 때는 동사 have를 사용한다.
❸ 희망이나 바람을 나타내는 표현이다.

● 다음 우리말과 일치하도록 빈칸에 알맞은 말을 쓰시오.

Communicate: Listen-Listen and Answer. Talk

G: Hi, I'm Gacha. I'm _____ Mongolia. When I first came to Songji Middle School two months _____, I was so _____. I was a little _____, and I wasn't _____ at Korean. However, I'm a _____ girl. All my classmates are nice and _____. I enjoy _____ handball with them in P.E. class. I'm a good player. They _____ me "Golden Hand." There will be a sports day next week. _____ _____ my class will win in the handball event.

Communicate: Listen-Listen and Answer. Dialog

B: Hi, Minsol. Is your class _____?
G: Of course. We have a _____ handball player.
B: You _____ the girl from Mongolia?
G: Yes, her name is Gacha.
B: I've heard a lot about her. But _____ does she _____ _____?
G: She's very tall and _____ a _____.
B: Oh, is she the girl _____ _____ the goal just now?
G: Yes, that's her _____ goal.
B: Wow, she's really great.

Communicate: Listen-Listen More

M: _____ can I do for you?
G: I _____ my younger brother.
M: Okay, _____ _____. What's your brother's name?
G: His name is Wally Brown. He's five years old.
M: _____ does he _____ _____?
G: He _____ brown hair and brown eyes.
M: What is he _____?
G: He is _____ a green shirt and black pants.
M: Can you tell me more?
G: Oh, he is _____ a red backpack.
M: All right. We'll go out and _____ _____ him. Also, we'll make an _____ about a _____ child.
G: Thank you so much. _____ _____ I'll find him soon.

Communicate: Speak 2-Talk in pairs

A: I _____ an _____ exam tomorrow!
B: I hope you'll _____ _____ _____ the exam.
A: I hope _____, too. Thanks.

해석

여: 안녕, 나는 Gacha라고 해. 나는 몽골에서 왔어. 두 달 전에 내가 처음 송지 중학교에 왔을 때, 나는 무척 걱정이 되었어. 나는 좀 수줍음을 탔고 한국어를 잘 못했어. 하지만 난 운이 좋은 아이야. 내 학급 친구들은 모두 멋지고 다정해. 나는 체육 시간에 친구들과 핸드볼 하는 것을 즐겨. 난 실력이 좋은 선수야. 친구들은 나를 '황금 손'이라고 불러. 다음 주에 운동회가 있을 거야. 난 우리 반이 핸드볼 대회에서 이기길 바라.

남: 안녕, 민솔아. 너희 반이 이기고 있니?
여: 물론이지. 우리는 훌륭한 핸드볼 선수가 있거든.
남: 몽골에서 온 여자아이 말하니?
여: 응, 그녀의 이름은 Gacha야.
남: 그녀에 대해 많이 들었어. 그런데 그녀는 어떻게 생겼어?
여: 그녀는 키가 크고 말총머리를 하고 있어.
남: 아, 지금 막 골을 넣은 여자아이가 그녀니?
여: 맞아, 저건 그녀의 일곱 번째 골이야.
남: 와, 그녀는 정말 잘하는구나.

남: 무엇을 도와드릴까요?
여: 남동생을 잃어버렸어요.
남: 알겠어요, 진정하세요. 남동생 이름이 뭐죠?
여: 그의 이름은 Wally Brown이에요. 다섯 살이고요.
남: 어떻게 생겼나요?
여: 그는 갈색 머리이고 갈색 눈을 지녔어요.
남: 그는 무엇을 입고 있나요?
여: 그는 초록색 셔츠와 검은 바지를 입고 있어요.
남: 더 말해 줄 수 있나요?
여: 아, 그는 빨간 배낭을 메고 있어요.
남: 알겠어요. 우리가 나가서 그를 찾아볼게요. 또, 우리가 미아 방송을 할 겁니다.
여: 정말 감사합니다. 동생을 빨리 찾길 바라요.

A: 나는 내일 중요한 시험이 있어.
B: 네가 시험을 잘 보길 바라.
A: 나도 그러길 바라. 고마워.

Communicate: Speak 2-Talk in groups

A: _____ is your character's name?
B: His name is Buster.
A: _____ _____ he look _____?
B: He has _____ hair.
A: Does he _____ big eyes?
B: Yes, he does.

Communicate: Speak-Rap Time

(1) A: I lost my puppy this afternoon.
B: _____ _____ you'll _____ him soon.
(2) A: I hope you'll _____ your _____ in the final game.
B: Thanks. I wish you _____ _____.
(3) A: What does your sister _____ _____, Claire?
B: She's tall and has long _____ hair.
(4) A: Is your father _____ a blue cap?
B: Yeah. Now, he's _____ a map.

My Speaking Portfolio

G: Look at the _____ _____. There _____ posters for the next school president.
B: Yeah, I've already _____ my _____. I'll _____ _____ Jang Jimin.
G: You _____ the boy with glasses? He looks smart, but I don't like his _____.
B: Then who will you _____?
G: Well, I am for number 1, Han Siwon. She wants to make our school a safe place.
B: She always has a ponytail, right?
G: Yes, and Hong Jiho _____ _____.
B: She looks _____, but I don't like _____ _____.

Wrap Up

1. B: I hear there is a new student in your class.
G: Yes. She's from Jejudo. Oh, she's _____ _____!
B: _____ one? _____ _____ she _____ like?
G: She has _____ hair and is _____ glasses.
2. G: You look _____. What's _____, Jongmin?
B: My sister broke her arm this morning.
G: What _____?
B: She _____ _____ her bike.
G: _____ _____ _____. _____ she'll _____ soon.

해석

A: 네 캐릭터의 이름은 뭐니?
B: 그의 이름은 Buster야.
A: 그는 어떻게 생겼니?
B: 그는 머리카락이 없어.
A: 그는 눈이 크니?
B: 응, 맞아.

(1) A: 나는 오늘 오후에 내 강아지를 잃어버렸어.
B: 네가 그를 곧 찾기를 바랄게.
(2) A: 나는 네가 결선에서 최선을 다하길 바라.
B: 고마워. 나도 네가 그러길 바라.
(3) A: 네 언니는 어떻게 생겼니, Claire?
B: 그녀는 키가 크고 긴 생머리야.
(4) A: 네 아버지는 파란 모자를 쓰고 계시니?
B: 응. 지금 지도를 보고 계셔.

여: 이 게시판을 봐. 다음 학생회장의 포스터가 있어.
남: 응, 나는 이미 결정을 내렸어. 나는 장지민에게 투표할 거야.
여: 안경을 쓴 남자아이 얘기하는 거야? 그는 똑똑해 보이지만 나는 그의 공약이 마음에 들지 않아.
남: 그럼 넌 누굴 선택할 거야?
여: 음, 나는 1번 한시원을 지지해. 그녀는 우리 학교를 안전한 장소로 만들고 싶어 해.
남: 그녀는 항상 말총머리를 해, 그렇지?
여: 맞아, 그리고 홍지호도 괜찮아 보여.
남: 그녀는 친절해 보이지만, 나는 장기자랑이 싫어.

1. 남: 너희 반에 새로 온 학생이 있다고 들었어.
여: 응. 그녀는 제주도에서 왔어. 어, 그녀가 저기에 있어!
남: 어느 아이? 어떻게 생겼어?
여: 그녀는 곱슬머리이고 안경을 끼고 있어.
2. 여: 너 슬퍼 보여. 무슨 일이니, 종민아?
남: 여동생이 오늘 아침에 팔이 부러졌어.
여: 무슨 일이 있었는데?
남: 자전거에서 떨어졌어.
여: 안됐구나. 그녀가 곧 회복되기를 바라.

01 다음 우리말에 맞도록 빈칸에 알맞은 말을 쓰시오.

> A: 네 언니는 어떻게 생겼니, Claire?
> B: She's tall and has long straight hair.

➡ _____ does your sister _____ _____

02 다음 대화의 빈칸에 들어갈 말로 알맞은 것은?

> A: I lost my puppy this afternoon.
> B: _____

① She's tall and has long straight hair.
② I hope she'll get better soon.
③ I hope you'll find him soon.
④ He has brown hair and brown eyes.
⑤ He has no hair.

03 다음 대화의 빈칸에 들어갈 말로 가장 적절한 것은?

> A: I have an important exam tomorrow!
> B: I hope you'll _____ the exam.
> A: I hope so, too. Thanks.

① look like   ② do well on
③ care for   ④ look different from
⑤ get better

04 다음 대화의 밑줄 친 우리말에 맞게 주어진 단어를 알맞은 순서로 배열하시오.

> A: I hope you'll do your best in the final game.
> B: Thanks. <u>나도 네가 그러길 바라.</u>

(wish, you, I, the, same)

➡ _____

Conversation 시험대비 실력평가

[01~03] 다음 대화를 읽고 물음에 답하시오.

Ben: Hi, Minsol. Is your class winning?

Minsol: Of course. We have a great handball player.

Ben: ____(A)____ the girl from Mongolia?

Minsol: Yes, her name is Gacha.

Ben: I've heard a lot about her. But what does she look like?

Minsol: She's very tall and has a ponytail.

Ben: Oh, is she the girl (B)지금 막 골을 넣은?

Minsol: Yes, that's her seventh goal.

Ben: Wow, she's really great.

01 위 대화의 빈칸 (A)에 들어갈 말로 알맞은 것은?

① I mean
② She is
③ You mean
④ You know
⑤ Guess what

서답형

02 위 대화의 밑줄 친 (B)의 우리말에 맞게 주어진 단어를 알맞은 순서로 배열하시오.

the, scored, who, goal, just, now

➡ _____

03 위 대화의 내용과 일치하지 않는 것은?

① Minsol and Ben are watching a handball game.
② Gacha is from Mongolia.
③ Minsol and Gacha are in the same class.
④ Gacha is very tall and has a ponytail.
⑤ Ben doesn't know about Gacha.

[04~05] 다음 대화를 읽고 물음에 답하시오.

G: Look at the bulletin board. There are posters for ____(A)____.

B: Yeah, I've already made my choice. I'll vote for Jang Jimin.

G: You mean the boy with glasses? He looks smart, but I don't like his promises.

B: Then who will you choose?

G: Well, I am for number 1, Han Siwon. She wants to make our school a safe place.

B: (B)She always has a ponytail, right?

G: Yes, and Hong Jiho seems okay.

B: She looks friendly, but I don't like talent shows.

04 위 대화의 빈칸 (A)에 들어갈 말로 알맞은 것은?

① talent shows
② a safe school
③ the next school president
④ a beauty contest
⑤ class president election

중요

05 밑줄 친 (B)의 답을 얻을 수 있는 질문으로 알맞은 것은?

① What do you think of her?
② What does she look like?
③ How does she feel?
④ What is she looking for?
⑤ What does she like?

[06~07] 다음 대화를 읽고 물음에 답하시오.

B: My sister broke her arm this morning.

G: What happened?

B: She fell off her bike.

G: ____(A)____. (B) 그녀가 곧 회복되기를 바라.

06 위 대화의 빈칸 (A)에 알맞은 말을 주어진 단어를 이용하여 쓰시오.

서답형

> that, bad

서답형 ➡ _____

07 위 대화의 밑줄 친 (B)의 우리말에 맞게 주어진 단어를 알맞은 순서로 배열하시오.

> she'll, hope, better, I, get, soon

➡ _____

[08~09] 다음 대화를 읽고 물음에 답하시오.

M: What can I do for you?
G: I lost my younger brother.
M: Okay, calm down. What's your brother's name?
G: His name is Wally Brown. He's five years old.
M: _____(A)
G: He has brown hair and brown eyes.
M: What is he wearing?
G: He is wearing a green shirt and black pants.
M: _____(B)
G: Oh, he is carrying a red backpack.
M: All right. We'll go out and look for him. Also, we'll make an announcement about a missing child.
G: Thank you so much. I hope I'll find him soon.

서답형

08 위 대화의 빈칸 (A), (B)에 들어갈 말을 〈보기〉에서 찾아 쓰시오.

┌─ 보기 ┐
• You mean the boy with glasses?
• What does he look like?
• Can you tell me more?

➡ (A) _____
 (B) _____

09 위 대화를 읽고 질문에 답할 수 없는 것을 고르시오.

① What's the girl's brother's name?
② How old is the girl's brother?
③ What does the girl's brother look like?
④ Where's the girl's brother?
⑤ What will the man do after the dialog?

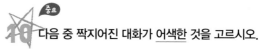

10 다음 중 짝지어진 대화가 어색한 것을 고르시오.

① A: You look sad. What's wrong, Jongmin?
 B: My sister broke her arm this morning.
② A: I fell off my bike.
 B: I'm glad to hear that. I hope you'll get better soon.
③ A: Is your father wearing a blue cap?
 B: Yeah. Now, he's reading a map.
④ A: What does he look like?
 B: He has no hair.
⑤ A: What does she look like?
 B: She's very tall and has a ponytail.

서답형

11 다음 대화를 읽고, 주어진 문장을 완성하시오.

B: I hear there is a new student in your class.
G: Yes. She's from Jejudo. Oh, she's over there!
B: Which one? What does she look like?
G: She has curly hair and is wearing glasses.

➡ The new student has _____ _____ and is wearing _____.

[01~02] 다음 대화를 읽고 물음에 답하시오.

B: Hi, Minsol. Is your class winning?
G: Of course. We have a great handball player.
B: You mean the girl from Mongolia?
G: Yes, her name is Gacha.
B: I've heard a lot about her. But ____(A)____?
G: She's very tall and has a ponytail.
B: Oh, is she the girl who scored the goal just now?
G: Yes, that's her seventh goal.
B: Wow, she's really great.

01 다음은 Minsol이 Gacha에 관해 언급한 글이다. 빈칸을 완성하시오.

➡ Gacha _____ _____ Mongolia. Gacha and I are in the _____ class. She has scored _____ goals so far.

 02 위 대화의 빈칸 (A)에 알맞은 말을 쓰시오.

➡ _____

[03~04] 다음 대화를 읽고 물음에 답하시오.

G: Look at the bulletin board. There are posters for the next school president.
B: Yeah, I've already made my choice. I'll __(A)__ Jang Jimin.
G: You mean the boy with ____(B)____? He looks smart, but I don't like his promises.
B: Then who will you choose?
G: Well, I am for number 1, Han Siwon. She wants to make our school a __(C)__.
B: She always has a __(D)__, right?
G: Yes, and Hong Jiho seems okay.
B: She looks friendly, but I don't like talent shows.

03 위 대화의 빈칸 (A)에 들어갈 표현을 주어진 영영 풀이를 참고하여 두 단어로 쓰시오.

> to choose someone in an election by making a mark on an official piece of paper

➡ _____

04 아래 그림을 참고하여 위 대화의 빈칸 (B)와 (D)에는 외모에 관한 단어를, (C)에는 공약에 관한 글을 쓰시오.

➡ (B) _____ (C) _____ (D) _____

05 다음 대화의 밑줄 친 우리말에 맞게 주어진 어휘를 알맞게 배열하시오.

M: What can I do for you?
G: I lost my younger brother.
M: Okay, calm down. What's your brother's name?
G: His name is Wally Brown. He's five years old.
M: What does he look like?
G: He has brown hair and brown eyes.
M: All right. We'll go out and look for him. Also, we'll <u>미아 방송을 할 겁니다.</u> (about, announcement, make, missing, a, an, child)
G: Thank you so much. I hope I'll find him soon.

➡ _____

교과서 Grammar

① want/ask/tell + 목적어 + to부정사

> • Parents **want** their children **to be** honest. 부모들은 그들의 아이들이 정직하기를 원한다.
> • They **told** him **to stop** growing a beard. 그들은 그에게 턱수염을 그만 기르라고 말했다.

■ 형태: want/ask/tell + 목적어 + to부정사

■ 의미: ~가 …하기를 바라다, ~에게 …하기를 요청하다, ~에게 …하라고 말하다

■ 동사 want, ask, tell 뒤에 목적어와 'to+동사원형'이 이어지면 '(목적어)가 ~하도록 원하다/요청하다/말하다'라는 의미를 나타낸다.

  • I **want** you **to finish** your homework first. 나는 네가 숙제를 먼저 끝내길 원한다.
  • Mom **told** me **to put** out the trash. 엄마는 나에게 쓰레기를 내놓으라고 말씀하셨다.

■ to부정사를 목적격보어로 취하는 동사에는 want, ask, tell 외에도 advise, allow, beg, cause, enable, encourage, expect, force, get, help, need, order, persuade, require, teach, would like 등이 있다.

  • They **advised** him **to leave** the place as soon as possible.
    그들은 그에게 가능한 한 빨리 그 장소를 떠나라고 조언했다.
  • Will you please **help** him **to clear[clear]** the table? 그가 식탁 치우는 거 거들어 줄래?

■ to부정사의 부정형은 'not[never]+to 동사원형'이다.

  • She **asked** me **not to say** anything. 그녀는 나에게 아무 말도 하지 말라고 요청했다.
  • The doctor **ordered** me **not to drink** alcohol. 의사는 나에게 술을 마시지 말라고 명령했다.

핵심 Check

1. 다음 우리말과 일치하도록 빈칸에 알맞은 말을 쓰시오. (철자가 주어진 것도 있음.)

(1) 우리는 그녀가 늦을 것이라고 예상했다.
  ➡ We _____ her _____ _____ late.

(2) 갑작스런 굉음 때문에 나는 펄쩍 뛰었다.
  ➡ A sudden noise c_____ me _____ j_____.

(3) 그들은 그에게 서류에 서명하도록 강요했다.
  ➡ They f_____ him _____ _____ the paper.

2 접속사 before, after

- **Before** she has breakfast, Dora puts on her uniform.
  아침을 먹기 전에 Dora는 교복을 입는다.

- **After** he was freed, Joseph traveled and told his story to lots of people.
  Joseph은 석방된 뒤에 순회를 하며 많은 사람들에게 자신의 이야기를 전했다.

- 형태: Before/After + 주어 + 동사 ~, 주어 + 동사 …

  주어 + 동사 … before/after + 주어 + 동사 ~.

- 의미: before: ~하기 전에 / after: ~한 후에

- before와 after는 두 개의 절을 연결해 주는 접속사로 어떤 일이 일어나기 전이나 후의 시간 관계를 나타낸다.
  - Please swing to the door **after** you entered. 들어오고 나서, 문 좀 닫아주세요.
  - Did she leave a message **before** she went? 그녀가 가기 전에 전갈을 남겼어요?

- 시간이나 조건의 부사절에서는 현재시제를 사용하여 미래를 나타낸다.
  - It will be long **before** we meet again. 한참 지나야 다시 만나게 되겠군요.
  - I'll start **after** he comes. 그가 온 후에 출발하겠다.
  - **If** it is warm tomorrow, we will drive in the country. 내일 날씨가 포근하면 시골로 드라이브 가자.

핵심 Check

2. 다음 괄호 안에서 알맞은 말을 고르시오.

(1) (Before / After) you leave the room, turn out the light.

(2) After she (comes / will come), we will go on a picnic.

(3) The road became wet (before / after) it rained.

➡ (1) _____ (2) _____ (3) _____

[01~02] 다음 문장의 빈칸에 들어갈 알맞은 말을 고르시오.

01

I asked him _____ off the TV.

① turn   ② turns   ③ turned
④ turning   ⑤ to turn

02

_____ Jacob went to bed, he washed his hands.

① Before   ② After   ③ While
④ During   ⑤ If

03 다음 중 가장 자연스러운 것은?

① Before I woke up, I ate a cup of coffee.
② Before I went to the library, I borrowed books at the library.
③ Do it after you forget.
④ Wendy understood the situation after she heard it from Sue.
⑤ After she went to bed, she took a shower.

04 다음 문장에서 어법상 어색한 것을 바르게 고쳐 다시 쓰시오.

(1) I want you clean the windows.

  ➡ _____

(2) Before I will have dinner, I will clean my room.

  ➡ _____

(3) He took my hand and asked me marrying him.

  ➡ _____

(4) Tell her buys a comfortable pair of shoes!

  ➡ _____

05 주어진 어휘를 이용하여 다음 우리말을 영작하시오.

Justin은 축구를 한 후에 과일을 먹었다. (had, soccer, some fruit)
(Justin으로 시작할 것)

  ➡ _____

01 다음 빈칸에 알맞은 것은?

> My parents want me _____ healthy food.

① eat   ② eats
③ ate   ④ eating
⑤ to eat

02 다음 빈칸에 들어갈 가장 알맞은 것은?

> • I turn off my phone. And then I pass the school gate.
> = _____ I pass the school gate, I turn off my phone.

① As   ② Before   ③ After
④ But   ⑤ When

03 다음 중 어법상 바르지 <u>않은</u> 것은?

> My homeroom teacher ①told ②me ③be ④on time ⑤for class.

①   ②   ③   ④   ⑤

04 다음 우리말을 영어로 바르게 옮긴 것은?

> 진수는 아침을 먹기 전에 양치질을 한다.

① Jinsu brushes his teeth when he has breakfast.
② Jinsu brushes his teeth while he has breakfast.
③ Jinsu brushes his teeth after he has breakfast.
④ Jinsu brushes his teeth before he has breakfast.
⑤ Jinsu brushes his teeth if he has breakfast.

서답형

05 다음 괄호 안에서 알맞은 말을 고르시오.

(1) He told me (came / to come) home before 9 o'clock.
(2) Harry wanted me (doing / to do) it at once.
(3) My mom (expects / hopes) me to be a teacher.
(4) She allowed her daughter (go / to go) to the K-pop concert.
(5) The class started (after / before) the teacher arrived.
(6) I wash my hands (before / after) I go to bed.

➡ (1) _____ (2) _____ (3) _____
(4) _____ (5) _____ (6) _____

06 다음 빈칸에 적절하지 <u>않은</u> 것은?

> I _____ her to take part in the party.

① watched   ② wanted   ③ told
④ persuaded   ⑤ expected

07 다음 중 어법상 바르지 <u>않은</u> 것은?

① He knew the truth already before we told him about it.
② After she will come tomorrow, we will go camping.
③ He arrived at the station after the train left.
④ Before he meets her, he is already in love with her.
⑤ He will call Kelly after he arrives there.

08 다음 중 두 문장의 의미가 <u>다른</u> 것은?

① Sean expected that his son would exercise to be healthy.
➡ Sean expected his son to exercise to be healthy.

② I got up before the sun rises.
➡ After the sun rose, I got up.

③ Anna told me that I must wear a long sleeve shirt at the campsite.
➡ Anna told me to wear a long sleeve shirt at the campsite.

④ Take a bath before you go to bed.
➡ Take a bath before going to bed.

⑤ The restaurant was crowded, but we found a table.
➡ Though the restaurant was crowded, we found a table.

09 다음 두 문장이 뜻이 같도록 빈칸에 들어갈 알맞은 말은?

> • Before you get into the swimming pool, do some exercises to warm up.
> = _____ you do some exercises to warm up, get into the swimming pool.

① Before ② After ③ As
④ When ⑤ While

서답형

10 괄호 안의 동사를 어법에 맞게 고쳐 쓰시오.

(1) The police asked him (tell) them the truth.

(2) Her parents encouraged her (study) hard.

(3) Please help me (push) the boat.

➡ (1) _____ (2) _____ (3) _____

11 두 문장의 의미가 같도록 빈칸에 알맞은 말을 쓰시오.

> Ms. Rose drank coffee after she finished cleaning the living room.
> = Ms. Rose finished cleaning the living room _____ she drank coffee.

➡ _____

12 다음 중 어법상 어색한 부분을 찾아 바르게 고친 것은?

> Yejun asked his mom play badminton with him that afternoon.

① asked → has asked
② his → him
③ play → to play
④ with → to
⑤ that → this

서답형

13 주어진 어휘를 바르게 배열하여 다음 우리말을 영어로 쓰시오.

(1) 그들은 테니스를 친 후에 쇼핑을 갔다. (they, they, went, played, shopping, tennis, after)

➡ _____

(2) 은지는 영화를 보기 전에 모자를 샀다. (Eunji, she, a hat, the movie, bought, watched, before)

➡ _____

(3) 선생님은 우리에게 체육관에 모이라고 말씀하셨다. (the teacher, the gym, us, gather, told, at, to)

➡ _____

(4) 지호는 도훈이에게 창문을 닦아 달라고 부탁했다. (Jiho, Dohun, the window, clean, asked, to)

➡ _____

14 다음 빈칸에 들어갈 동사 do의 형태가 다른 하나는?

① Jim wanted me _____ the dishes.
② She planned _____ some exercise regularly.
③ Our teacher asked us _____ our homework.
④ Did you expect him _____ his best?
⑤ Mom made us _____ it.

[15~16] 다음 중 어법상 옳은 것을 고르시오.

15 ① I read a book after I fell asleep last night.
② I brushed my teeth after I went to bed.
③ Before he eats food, he always washes his hands.
④ Before he bought the book, he read it.
⑤ Eric will go swimming when Sue will arrive.

16 ① The typhoon caused the old bridge to fall.
② They expect her participates in the ceremony.
③ Judy asked him make sandwiches.
④ Do you want me waking you up tomorrow morning?
⑤ The math teacher told us solving 10 problems every day.

17 다음 빈칸에 적절하지 않은 것은?

_____ he visits my office, I will call you immediately.

① When   ② After   ③ If
④ Even if   ⑤ As soon as

18 다음 빈칸에 알맞은 말이 바르게 짝지어진 것은?

When Yewon asked her dad _____ her bike, he told her _____ it.

① to fix – bringing
② to fix – to bring
③ fixing – to bring
④ fixing – bringing
⑤ fix – bring

서답형

19 다음 문장에서 어법상 어색한 부분을 바르게 고쳐 다시 쓰시오.

(1) She asked her brother helping her with her homework.
➡ _____

(2) Jim wanted her go shopping with him.
➡ _____

(3) They advised him left the place as soon as possible.
➡ _____

(4) After he rode his bike, Jason put on his helmet.
➡ _____

(5) She will be a good wife when she will get married.
➡ _____

01 다음 문장에서 어법상 <u>어색한</u> 부분을 바르게 고쳐 다시 쓰시오.

(1) Lucy's dad wants her is a police officer.

➡ _____

_____

(2) My mother asked me buy milk on my way home.

➡ _____

_____

(3) The teacher told the students bringing some water.

➡ _____

_____

(4) She got her two sons divided a cake exactly in half.

➡ _____

_____

(5) Her family environment forced her to not continue her studies.

➡ _____

_____

02 주어진 단어를 바르게 배열하여 다음 우리말을 영어로 쓰시오.

(1) 내가 결정을 내리자마자 너에게 내 마음을 알릴 것이다. (I로 시작할 것)
(I, my, will, let, you, know, mind, I, make, a, decision, as soon as)

➡ _____

_____

(2) Nancy는 오빠가 자기에게 라면을 끓여 주기를 원했다.
(Nancy, brother, ramyeon, her, her, cook, wanted, for, to)

➡ _____

_____

03 주어진 동사를 어법에 맞게 빈칸에 쓰시오.

(1) My best friend Jiho often asks me _____ him. (help)

(2) My dad doesn't allow me _____ out at night. (go)

(3) Marianne ordered him _____ with her. (stay)

(4) The manager warned him _____ any pictures there. (take, not)

(5) When Jenny _____, we will leave for Seoul. (come)

(6) The boys will go hiking after they _____ lunch. (have)

04 다음 우리말에 맞도록 빈칸에 알맞은 말을 쓰시오.

(1) Audrey는 숙제를 끝낸 후에 TV를 본다.
= Audrey _____ TV _____ she finishes her homework.

(2) 그는 수영하기 전에 준비 운동을 했다.
= _____ he swam, he _____ some warm-up exercises.

(3) 그가 돌아오면 저한테 전화해 달라고 부탁해 주시겠어요?
= Will you ask him _____ me when he _____ back?

(4) 그녀는 자기 딸에게 개에게 먹이를 주라고 말했다.
= She told her daughter _____ the dog.

05 적절한 접속사를 이용하여 〈보기〉에 주어진 문장과 연결하여 자연스러운 하나의 문장을 만드시오.

┌─── 보기 ───┐
- The students took a bus for one hour.
- They arrived at the museum.
- They went to the beach.
└────────────┘

(1) They bought their swimming suit.

➡ _____

_____

(2) They arrived at their destination.

➡ _____

_____

(3) They appreciated the works in the museum.

➡ _____

_____

06 다음은 Angelina의 일요일 일정표이다. 빈칸에 알맞은 말을 시간의 전후 관계가 표현된 완전한 영어 문장으로 쓰시오.

time	what to do
10:00	go to church
13:00	have lunch with her family
15:00	study math in her room
18:00	go to the movie with James

(1) Angelina will have lunch with her family

_____.

(2) Angelina will study math in her room

_____

_____.

(3) Angelina will go to the movie with James _____.

07 다음 문장을 읽고 빈칸에 알맞은 말을 쓰시오.

┌──────────────────────────────┐
Laura: I'm worried about my history grade.

Teacher: Study history a little harder. You can do it.
└──────────────────────────────┘

➡ The teacher encourages _____

_____ a little harder.

08 다음 문장에서 어법상 어색한 부분을 바르게 고쳐 쓰시오.

(1) Before the sun sets, they can see many stars.

_____ ➡ _____

(2) Turn off the light after you leave the room.

_____ ➡ _____

(3) The migrating birds will come back when spring will come next year.

_____ ➡ _____

(4) I would like you meeting a friend of mine.

_____ ➡ _____

09 주어진 단어를 활용하여 다음 우리말을 영어로 쓰시오.

(1) 나의 부모님은 항상 내게 학교에서 최선을 다하라고 말씀하신다. (always, best, in school)

➡ _____

(2) 건강했기 때문에 그는 그 계획을 수행할 수 있었다. (good health, carry out, enable)

➡ _____

(3) Yuri는 내일 아침을 먹은 후에 교복을 입을 것이다. (put, her uniform) (Yuri로 시작할 것)

➡ _____

Reading

교과서

The Right To Be Different

In many ways, 42-year-old Joseph Palmer was an ordinary
~~42-years-old(×)~~

person. He had a job and cared for his family. But in 1830, after he
접속사 after 뒤에 오는 절이 먼저 일어난 일, 주절은 after가 이끄는 절보다 나중에 일어난 일

moved to a small town in Massachusetts, he began to face difficulties.
~으로 이사했다   = facing

Joseph looked different from other people: he had a long beard. People
감각동사 look+형용사 보어: ~하게 보이다

did not like it very much.
a long beard

The town's people avoided the man with a beard. They did not want
피했다   = Joseph Palmer

to sit next to him. They even whispered behind his back, "What is he
want는 목적어로 to부정사를 취한다.   behind somebody's back: ~의 등 뒤에서

trying to hide?"
try+to부정사: ~을 하려고 노력하다

Some neighbors broke his windows. Others threw stones at him when
some …. others …: 어떤 것[사람]들은 …, 다른 것[사람]들은

he walked down the street. They told him to stop growing a beard.
tell+목적어+to부정사: (목적어)에게 ~하라고 말하다. stop은 동명사를 목적어로 취하는 동사

Joseph did not mind. He just wanted the freedom to have his beard.
the freedom을 꾸며 주는 형용사적 용법의 to부정사

right 권리
ordinary 평범한, 보통의
care for ~을 돌보다
face 직면하다, 대면하다
beard 수염, 턱수염
avoid 피하다
whisper 속삭이다, 속닥거리다
hide 숨기다
mind 신경 쓰다, 언짢아하다
freedom 자유

📎 **확인문제**

● 다음 문장이 본문의 내용과 일치하면 T, 일치하지 <u>않으면</u> F를 쓰시오.

1 Joseph Palmer had a job and cared for his family. ☐

2 Before he moved to a small town in Massachusetts, Joseph began to face
   difficulties. ☐

3 Joseph looked different from other people. ☐

4 People liked Joseph's long beard very much. ☐

5 Some neighbors broke Joseph's windows. ☐

6 Joseph just wanted the freedom to live alone. ☐

One day, four men attacked Joseph and threw him on the ground.
V1   V2   =Joseph

"We're going to cut off your beard!" they shouted. Joseph was a big
자르다

man, and he was able to fight them off. But the men called the police
목적어가 인칭대명사이므로 fight off them이 아니라 fight them off가 적절하다.

and accused him of attacking them. Poor Joseph was arrested. He said
accuse A of B: A를 때문에 고발하다   수동태

to the judge, "I'm the victim here." Sadly, no one believed a man with
문장 전체를 수식하는 부사   ~을 가진

a beard, and he went to prison for over a year. 일 년이 넘는 기간 동안
감옥에 갔다. / the가 없는 경우에는 건물의 본래 목적을 나타낸다. go to school(학교에 다니다)과 비슷한 맥락으로 이해할 수 있다.

Joseph's son, Thomas, wanted people to know the truth. He sent
want+목적어+to부정사: (목적어)가 ~하기를 원하다

letters to newspapers across the country. People learned that Joseph
send는 to를 사용하여 3형식으로 고친다.   명사절을 이끄는 접속사

was in prison just for protecting himself and his beard. Many people
him(×)

became angry about this, so the judge finally decided to set Joseph
= Joseph was in prison just for protecting himself and his beard.   decide는 목적어로 to부정사를 취한다.

free.

After he was freed, Joseph traveled and told his story to lots of
석방되다   = many

people. Slowly, people's attitudes toward beards changed. Before
접속사 before는 '~ 전에'라는 뜻. 주절은 before가 이끄는 절에 앞서 일어난 일을 나타낸다.

Joseph died, a man with a beard became the President of the United
턱수염을 가진 남자

States. His name was Abraham Lincoln. He made beards popular, but
= Abraham Lincoln

Joseph Palmer fought for the right to have them.
the right를 수식하는 형용사적 용법의 to부정사   = beards

---

attack 공격하다

fight off ~을 싸워 물리치다

accuse 고발하다, 기소하다

arrest 체포하다

judge 판사

victim 희생자

prison 감옥

truth 진실

set free 석방하다

attitude 태도

toward ~을 향한

president 대통령

 확인문제

● 다음 문장이 본문의 내용과 일치하면 T, 일치하지 <u>않으면</u> F를 쓰시오.

1   Joseph said to the judge, "I'm the victim here." ☐

2   The judge believed Joseph and set him free. ☐

3   Joseph's son sent letters to newspapers across the country. ☐

4   People learned that Joseph was in prison just for protecting his family. ☐

5   After he was freed, Joseph traveled and told his story to lots of people. ☐

6   Joseph died before Abraham Lincoln became the President of America. ☐

● 우리말을 참고하여 빈칸에 알맞은 말을 쓰시오.

1 The Right To _____ _____

2 In many ways, 42-year-old Joseph Palmer was _____ _____ _____.

3 He had a job and _____ _____ his family.

4 But in 1830, after he moved to a small town in Massachusetts, he began _____ _____ _____.

5 Joseph _____ _____ from other people: he had a long beard.

6 People _____ _____ _____ _____ very much.

7 The town's people avoided _____ _____ _____ _____ _____.

8 They did not want to _____ _____ _____ _____.

9 They even whispered _____ _____ _____, "What is he trying to hide?"

10 Some neighbors _____ _____ _____.

11 Others _____ _____ _____ him when he walked down the street.

12 They told him to _____ _____ a beard.

13 Joseph did not _____.

14 He just wanted the freedom _____ _____ his beard.

15 One day, four men _____ Joseph and _____ him on the ground.

1	다를 권리
2	여러 면에서 42살의 Joseph Palmer는 평범한 사람이었다.
3	그는 직업이 있었고 가족을 돌보았다.
4	하지만 1830년에 매사추세츠에 있는 작은 도시로 이사를 한 후에 그는 어려움에 직면하기 시작했다.
5	Joseph은 다른 사람들과 달라 보였다. 그는 기다란 턱수염을 기르고 있었다.
6	사람들은 그것을 별로 좋아하지 않았다.
7	마을 사람들은 턱수염을 가진 그 남자를 피했다.
8	그들은 그의 곁에 앉고 싶어 하지 않았다.
9	그들은 심지어 그의 등 뒤에서 "그가 무엇을 숨기려는 거지?"라고 속삭였다.
10	어떤 이웃들은 그의 창문을 깼다.
11	다른 사람들은 그가 길을 걸어 내려갈 때 그에게 돌을 던졌다.
12	그들은 그에게 턱수염을 그만 기르라고 말했다.
13	Joseph은 신경 쓰지 않았다.
14	그는 그저 자신의 턱수염을 기를 자유를 원했다.
15	어느 날, 네 명의 남자가 Joseph을 공격했고 그를 바닥에 던졌다.

16 "We're going to _____ _____ your beard!" they shouted.

17 Joseph was a big man, and he was able to _____ _____ _____.

18 But the men called the police and _____ _____ _____ attacking them.

19 Poor Joseph _____ _____.

20 He said to the judge, "I'm _____ _____ here."

21 Sadly, no one believed _____ _____ _____ _____ _____, and he _____ _____ _____ for over a year.

22 Joseph's son, Thomas, _____ people _____ _____ the truth.

23 He _____ letters _____ newspapers across the country.

24 People learned that Joseph _____ _____ _____ just for _____ _____ and his beard.

25 Many people _____ _____ about this, so the judge finally decided _____ _____ Joseph _____.

26 After he _____ _____, Joseph traveled and told his story to lots of people.

27 Slowly, people's _____ _____ _____ changed.

28 Before Joseph died, a man _____ _____ _____ became the President of the United States.

29 _____ _____ was Abraham Lincoln.

30 He made beards _____, but Joseph Palmer _____ _____ the right to have them.

16 "우리가 당신의 턱수염을 잘라 버리겠어!"라고 그들은 소리쳤다.

17 Joseph은 덩치가 큰 사람이었고, 그는 그들을 싸워 물리칠 수 있었다.

18 하지만 그 남자들은 경찰을 불렀고, 자신들을 공격한 것으로 그를 고발했다.

19 불쌍한 Joseph은 체포되었다.

20 그는 "저는 여기서 희생자입니다."라고 판사에게 말했다.

21 슬프게도, 아무도 턱수염을 가진 남자를 믿지 않았고, 그는 일 년이 넘는 기간 동안 감옥에 갔다.

22 Joseph의 아들인 Thomas는 사람들이 진실을 알기를 원했다.

23 그는 전국에 있는 신문사에 편지를 보냈다.

24 사람들은 Joseph이 단지 자신과 자신의 턱수염을 지키려다 감옥에 갇혔다는 것을 알게 되었다.

25 많은 사람들은 이에 대해 분개했고, 그래서 판사는 결국 Joseph을 석방하기로 결정했다.

26 Joseph은 석방된 뒤에 순회를 하며 많은 사람들에게 자신의 이야기를 전했다.

27 사람들의 턱수염에 대한 태도는 서서히 변해갔다.

28 Joseph이 죽기 전에, 턱수염을 가진 남자가 미국의 대통령이 되었다.

29 그의 이름은 Abraham Lincoln (에이브러햄 링컨)이었다.

30 그는 턱수염을 대중적으로 만들었지만, Joseph Palmer는 그것을 기를 권리를 위하여 싸웠다.

● 우리말을 참고하여 본문을 영작하시오.

1 다를 권리

➡ _____

2 여러 면에서 42살의 Joseph Palmer는 평범한 사람이었다.

➡ _____

3 그는 직업이 있었고 가족을 돌보았다.

➡ _____

4 하지만 1830년에 매사추세츠에 있는 작은 도시로 이사를 한 후에 그는 어려움에 직면하기 시작했다.

➡ _____

5 Joseph은 다른 사람들과 달라 보였다. 그는 기다란 턱수염을 기르고 있었다.

➡ _____

6 사람들은 그것을 별로 좋아하지 않았다.

➡ _____

7 마을 사람들은 턱수염을 가진 그 남자를 피했다.

➡ _____

8 그들은 그의 곁에 앉고 싶어 하지 않았다.

➡ _____

9 그들은 심지어 그의 등 뒤에서 "그가 무엇을 숨기려는 거지?"라고 속삭였다.

➡ _____

10 어떤 이웃들은 그의 창문을 깼다.

➡ _____

11 다른 사람들은 그가 길을 걸어 내려갈 때 그에게 돌을 던졌다.

➡ _____

12 그들은 그에게 턱수염을 그만 기르라고 말했다.

➡ _____

13 Joseph은 신경 쓰지 않았다.

➡ _____

14 그는 그저 자신의 턱수염을 기를 자유를 원했다.

➡ _____

15 어느 날, 네 명의 남자가 Joseph을 공격했고 그를 바닥에 던졌다.

➡ _____

16 "우리가 당신의 턱수염을 잘라 버리겠어!"라고 그들은 소리쳤다.

➡ _____

17 Joseph은 덩치가 큰 사람이었고, 그는 그들을 싸워 물리칠 수 있었다.

➡ _____

18 하지만 그 남자들은 경찰을 불렀고, 자신들을 공격한 것으로 그를 고발했다.

➡ _____

19 불쌍한 Joseph은 체포되었다.

➡ _____

20 그는 "저는 여기서 희생자입니다."라고 판사에게 말했다.

➡ _____

21 슬프게도, 아무도 턱수염을 가진 남자를 믿지 않았고, 그는 일 년이 넘는 기간 동안 감옥에 갔다.

➡ _____

22 Joseph의 아들인 Thomas는 사람들이 진실을 알기를 원했다.

➡ _____

23 그는 전국에 있는 신문사에 편지를 보냈다.

➡ _____

24 사람들은 Joseph이 단지 자신과 자신의 턱수염을 지키려다 감옥에 갇혔다는 것을 알게 되었다.

➡ _____

25 많은 사람들은 이에 대해 분개했고, 그래서 판사는 결국 Joseph을 석방하기로 결정했다.

➡ _____

26 Joseph은 석방된 뒤에 순회를 하며 많은 사람에게 자신의 이야기를 전했다.

➡ _____

27 사람들의 턱수염에 대한 태도는 서서히 변해갔다.

➡ _____

28 Joseph이 죽기 전에, 턱수염을 가진 남자가 미국의 대통령이 되었다.

➡ _____

29 그의 이름은 Abraham Lincoln(에이브러햄 링컨)이었다.

➡ _____

30 그는 턱수염을 대중적으로 만들었지만, Joseph Palmer는 그것을 기를 권리를 위하여 싸웠다.

➡ _____

[01~03] 다음 글을 읽고 물음에 답하시오.

In many ways, 42-year-old Joseph Palmer was an ordinary person. He had a job and ⓐ cared for his family. But in 1830, after he moved to a small town in Massachusetts, he began to face difficulties. Joseph looked different ⓑ other people: he had a long beard. People did not like it very much.

The town's people avoided the man ⓒ a beard. They did not want to sit next to him. They even whispered behind his back, "What is he trying to hide?"

01 위 글의 밑줄 친 ⓐcared for와 바꿔 쓸 수 있는 말을 모두 고르시오.

① cared about   ② looked after
③ looked for   ④ took off
⑤ took care of

02 위 글의 빈칸 ⓑ와 ⓒ에 들어갈 전치사가 바르게 짝지어진 것은?

① in – from   ② from – on
③ from – with   ④ for – on
⑤ for – with

03 Joseph Palmer에 대한 설명으로 옳지 <u>않은</u> 것을 고르시오.

① 그는 직업이 있었고 가족을 돌보았다.
② 매사추세츠주의 작은 도시로 이사를 한 후에 어려움에 직면하기 시작했다.
③ 그는 기다란 턱수염을 기르고 있었다.
④ 마을 사람들은 그를 피했고 그의 곁에 앉고 싶어 하지 않았다.
⑤ 그는 등 뒤에 무엇을 숨기고 있었다.

[04~06] 다음 글을 읽고 물음에 답하시오.

Some neighbors broke his windows. Others threw stones at him when he walked down the street. They told him ___ⓐ___ growing a beard. Joseph did not mind. He just wanted the freedom to have his beard.

One day, four men attacked Joseph and threw him on the ground. "We're going to cut off your beard!" they shouted. Joseph was a big man, and he was able to fight (A)[it / them] off. But the men called the police and accused him of attacking them. Poor Joseph was arrested. He said to the judge, ⓑ"I'm the victim here." (B)[Luckily / Sadly], no one believed a man with a beard, and he went to prison (C)[during / for] over a year.

서답형

04 위 글의 빈칸 ⓐ에 stop을 이용하여 알맞은 어구를 쓰시오.

➡ _____

서답형

05 위 글의 괄호 (A)~(C)에서 문맥이나 어법상 알맞은 낱말을 골라 쓰시오.

➡ (A) _____ (B) _____ (C) _____

06 밑줄 친 ⓑ를 통해 자신이 체포된 것에 대해 Joseph이 표현하고자 한 심경으로 가장 알맞은 것을 고르시오.

① bored   ② scared
③ unfair   ④ excited
⑤ ashamed

[07~10] 다음 글을 읽고 물음에 답하시오.

Joseph's son, Thomas, wanted people to know the truth. ⓐHe sent letters to newspapers across the country. People learned that Joseph was in prison just for protecting ⓑhimself and his beard. Many people became angry about this, so the judge Ⓐfinally decided to set Joseph free.

After he was freed, Joseph traveled and told ⓒhis story to lots of people. Slowly, people's attitudes toward beards changed. Before Joseph died, ⓓa man with a beard became the President of the United States. His name was Abraham Lincoln. ⓔHe made beards popular, but Joseph Palmer fought for the right Ⓑto have them.

07 위 글의 제목으로 알맞은 것을 고르시오.

① Inform People of the Truth
② Hard-Won Right to Have a Beard
③ The Pressure of Public Opinion
④ Notice the Attitudes toward Beards
⑤ Abraham Lincoln vs Joseph Palmer

08 위 글의 밑줄 친 ⓐ~ⓔ 중 가리키는 대상이 같은 것끼리 짝 지어진 것은?

① ⓐ – ⓑ   ② ⓐ – ⓒ
③ ⓑ – ⓒ   ④ ⓒ – ⓓ
⑤ ⓒ – ⓔ

09 위 글의 밑줄 친 Ⓐfinally와 의미가 다른 말을 모두 고르시오.

① immediately   ② at last
③ after all   ④ exactly
⑤ in the end

10 위 글의 밑줄 친 Ⓑto have와 to부정사의 용법이 다른 것을 모두 고르시오.

① Are there any questions for me to answer?
② It is important to do your homework.
③ She was surprised to see the sight.
④ I want a book to read during my vacation.
⑤ It's time to leave for New York.

[11~13] 다음 독서 기록장을 읽고 물음에 답하시오.

The Right to Be Different

A Story About Joseph Palmer
I read the story about Joseph Palmer last week. I really enjoyed it. I learned from the story that we should not judge people by their _____ⓐ_____. Students who talk about other people's _____ⓐ_____ must read the story. However, I have a question about it. Why did Joseph Palmer want to have a beard?

11 위 독서 기록장의 빈칸 ⓐ에 appear를 알맞은 형태로 쓰시오.

➡ _____

12 다음 질문에 대한 알맞은 대답을 주어진 말로 시작하여 쓰시오. (7 단어)

Q: To whom does the writer want to recommend this story?
A: The writer wants to recommend this story to _____.

➡ _____

13 위 독서 기록장에서 알 수 <u>없는</u> 것을 고르시오.

① 제목   ② 주인공

③ 교훈   ④ 구입 장소

⑤ 궁금한 점

[14~16] 다음 글을 읽고 물음에 답하시오.

ⓐ<u>In many ways, 42-year-old Joseph Palmer was an extraordinary person.</u> He had a job and cared for his family. But in 1830, after he moved to a small town in Massachusetts, he began to face difficulties. Joseph looked different from other people: he had a long beard. People did not like it very much.

The town's people avoided the man with a beard. They did not want to sit next to him. They even whispered ⓑ<u>그의 등 뒤에서</u>, "What is he trying ⓒ<u>to hide</u>?"

서답형

14 위 글의 밑줄 친 ⓐ에서 흐름상 어색한 부분을 찾아 고치시오.

➡ _____

서답형

15 위 글의 밑줄 친 ⓑ의 우리말에 맞게 3 단어로 영작하시오.

➡ _____

16 위 글의 밑줄 친 ⓒto hide와 to부정사의 용법이 다른 것을 모두 고르시오.

① Who is the best man <u>to do</u> the work?

② Her first mistake was <u>to tell</u> the information carelessly.

③ Tom decided <u>to wash</u> the dishes for his mom.

④ He got up early <u>to go</u> on a picnic.

⑤ It's not easy <u>to lose</u> weight in a short period of time.

[17~19] 다음 글을 읽고 물음에 답하시오.

    ⓐ _____ neighbors broke his windows. ⓑ _____ threw stones at him when he walked down the street. They told him to stop growing a beard. Joseph did not mind. He just wanted the freedom to have his beard.

One day, four men attacked Joseph and threw him on the ground. "We're going to cut off your beard!" they shouted. Joseph was a big man, and he was able to fight them off. But the men called the police and accused him of attacking them. Poor Joseph was arrested. He said to the judge, "I'm the victim here." Sadly, no one believed a man with a beard, and he went to prison for over a year.

17 위 글의 빈칸 ⓐ와 ⓑ에 들어갈 알맞은 말을 고르시오.

① Some – The other

② Others – The others

③ Some – Others

④ Some – Another

⑤ Others – Some

18 위 글에서 Joseph에 대한 이웃들의 태도에 어울리는 속담을 고르시오.

① It never rains but it pours.

② Every dog has his day.

③ A stitch in time saves nine.

④ Don't count your chickens before they are hatched.

⑤ A tall tree catches much wind.

19 위 글의 내용과 일치하지 <u>않는</u> 것은?

① 어떤 이웃들은 Joseph의 집 창문을 깼다.

② Joseph은 그저 자신의 턱수염을 기를 자유를 원했다.

③ 어느 날, 네 명의 남자가 Joseph을 공격했고 그를 바닥에 던졌다.

④ Joseph은 덩치가 큰 사람이었지만 네 명의 남자들을 싸워 물리칠 수 없었다.

⑤ Joseph은 일 년이 넘는 기간 동안 감옥에 갔다.

[20~22] 다음 글을 읽고 물음에 답하시오.

A Story About Steve Jobs

I read a story about Steve Jobs. I really enjoyed ___@___ his story. I learned from the story that we should think (A)[different / differently]. Young people who study for the future must read the story. However, I have a question about the story. How was his middle school life? I still remember his saying, "Stay (B)[hungry / hungrily]. Stay (C)[foolish / foolishly]."

20 위 글의 빈칸 @에 read를 알맞은 형태로 쓰시오.

➡ _____

21 위 글의 괄호 (A)~(C)에서 어법상 알맞은 낱말을 골라 쓰시오.

➡ (A) _____ (B) _____ (C) _____

22 위 글의 종류로 알맞은 것을 고르시오.

① article   ② book report

③ diary   ④ essay

⑤ biography

[23~25] 다음 글을 읽고 물음에 답하시오.

Joseph's son, Thomas, wanted people to know the truth. (①) He sent letters to newspapers across the country. (②) Many people became angry about this, so the judge finally decided to set Joseph free. (③)

After he was freed, Joseph traveled and told his story to lots of people. (④) Slowly, people's attitudes toward beards changed. (⑤) Before Joseph died, a man with a beard became the President of the United States. His name was Abraham Lincoln. He made beards popular, but Joseph Palmer fought for the @right to have them.

23 위 글의 흐름으로 보아, 주어진 문장이 들어가기에 가장 적절한 곳은?

People learned that Joseph was in prison just for protecting himself and his beard.

①   ②   ③   ④   ⑤

24 위 글에서 알 수 있는 Joseph Palmer의 성격으로 알맞은 것을 고르시오.

① funny   ② curious

③ generous   ④ creative

⑤ strong-willed

25 위 글의 밑줄 친 @right과 같은 의미로 쓰인 것을 고르시오.

① She had every <u>right</u> to be angry.

② Is this the <u>right</u> way to the beach?

③ Lee was standing <u>right</u> behind her.

④ Keep on the <u>right</u> side of the road.

⑤ Nothing goes <u>right</u> with me.

[01~03] 다음 글을 읽고 물음에 답하시오.

In many ways, (A)[42-year-old / 42-years-old] Joseph Palmer was an ordinary person. He had a job and cared for his family. But in 1830, after he moved to a small town in Massachusetts, he began to face difficulties. Joseph looked (B)[different / differently] from other people: he had a long beard. People did not like ⓐit very much.

The town's people avoided the man with a beard. They did not want (C)[sitting / to sit] next to him. They even whispered behind his back, "What is he trying to hide?"

01 위 글의 괄호 (A)~(C)에서 어법상 알맞은 낱말을 골라 쓰시오.

➡ (A) _____ (B) _____ (C) _____

02 위 글의 밑줄 친 ⓐit이 가리키는 것을 본문에서 찾아 쓰시오.

➡ _____

03 Joseph Palmer가 매사추세츠주의 작은 도시로 이사를 한 후에 직면했던 어려움 네 가지를 우리말로 쓰시오.

➡ (1) _____
   (2) _____
   (3) _____
   (4) _____

[04~05] 다음 글을 읽고 물음에 답하시오.

Some neighbors broke his windows. Others threw stones at him when he walked down the street. They told him to stop growing a beard. Joseph did not mind. He just wanted the freedom to have his beard.

One day, four men attacked Joseph and threw him on the ground. "We're going to cut off your beard!" they shouted. Joseph was a big man, and he was able to fight them off. But the men called the police and accused him of attacking them. Poor Joseph was arrested. He said to the judge, "I'm the victim here." Sadly, no one believed a man with a beard, and he went to prison for over a year.

04 다음 문장에서 위 글의 내용과 <u>다른</u> 부분을 고쳐 문장을 다시 쓰시오.

Joseph called the police and accused the four men of attacking him.

➡ _____
_____

05 have를 알맞은 형태로 변형하여, 다음 질문에 대한 대답을 쓰시오. (4 단어)

Q: When Joseph said to the judge, "I'm the victim here," why did no one believe him?
A: Because _____.

➡ _____

[06~08] 다음 글을 읽고 물음에 답하시오.

ⓐJoseph의 아들인 Thomas는 사람들이 진실을 알기를 원했다. He sent letters to newspapers across the country. People learned that Joseph was ①in prison just ②for protecting himself and his beard. Many people became angry ③about this, so the judge finally decided to set Joseph free.

After he was freed, Joseph traveled and told his story to lots of people. Slowly, people's attitudes ④toward beards changed. Before Joseph died, a man with a beard became the President of the United States. His name was Abraham Lincoln. ⓑHe made beards popular, but Joseph Palmer fought ⑤against the right to have them.

06 위 글의 밑줄 친 ⓐ의 우리말에 맞게 주어진 어휘를 이용하여 9 단어로 영작하시오.

> people, truth

➡ _____

_____

07 위 글의 밑줄 친 ①~⑤에서 전치사의 쓰임이 **틀린** 것을 찾아 고치시오.

_____ 번, ➡ _____

08 위 글의 밑줄 친 ⓑHe가 가리키는 것을 본문에서 찾아 쓰시오.

➡ _____

[09~13] 다음 글을 읽고 물음에 답하시오.

Some neighbors broke his windows. ⓐThe others threw stones at him when he walked down the street. They told him to stop ⓑ grow a beard. Joseph did not mind. He just wanted the freedom to have his beard.

One day, four men attacked Joseph and threw him on the ground. "We're going to cut off your beard!" they shouted. Joseph was a big man, and he was able to fight them off. But the men called the police and ⓒ자신들을 공격한 것으로 그를 고발했다. Poor Joseph was arrested. He said to the judge, "I'm the ___ⓓ___ here." Sadly, no one believed a man with a beard, and he went to prison for over a year.

09 위 글의 밑줄 친 ⓐ에서 어법상 틀린 것을 고치시오.

_____ ➡ _____

10 위 글의 밑줄 친 ⓑ를 알맞은 어형으로 고치시오.

➡ _____

11 위 글의 밑줄 친 ⓒ의 우리말에 맞게 한 단어를 보충하여, 주어진 어휘를 알맞게 배열하시오.

> attacking / them / him / accused

➡ _____

12 주어진 영영풀이를 참고하여 빈칸 ⓓ에 철자 v로 시작하는 단어를 쓰시오.

> someone who has been hurt or killed

➡ _____

13 다음 빈칸 (A)와 (B)에 알맞은 단어를 넣어 Joseph에 대한 소개를 완성하시오.

> Joseph just wanted the freedom to have his beard, but he went to prison for (A)_____ _____ _____ because of the prejudice of the neighbors about a man with (B)_____ _____.
>
> *prejudice: 편견

구석구석

My Speaking Portfolio

I will vote for Han Siwon. She looks confident and smart. She thinks school
 look+형용사 보어: ~하게 보이다
should be a safe place. I agree with her. I like her promises such as no more
~이어야 한다   ~와 같은
bullying. I hope Han Siwon becomes the next school president. I really want
      hope와 Han 사이에 접속사 that 생략   = will become
my school to be a safer place.
      want의 목적격보어로 쓰인 to부정사

구문해설 • vote for: ~을 뽑다, ~에게 투표하다 • agree with: ~에 동의하다
• bully: (약자를) 괴롭히다[왕따시키다], 협박하다

나는 한시원을 뽑을 겁니다. 그녀는 자신감 있고 똑똑해 보입니다. 그녀는 학교가 안전한 장소가 되어야 한다고 생각합니다. 저는 그녀에게 동의합니다. 나는 집단 괴롭힘 없애기 같은 공약들이 좋습니다. 나는 한시원이 다음 학생회장이 될 바랍니다. 나는 우리 학교가 더 안전한 장소가 되길 정말 바랍니다.

My Writing Portfolio: My Book Report

The Right to Be Different
형용사적 용법
A Story About Joseph Palmer

I read the story about Joseph Palmer last week. I really enjoyed it. I learned
                                                  the story about Joseph Palmer
from the story that we should not judge people by their appearance. Students
         접속사   그들의 외모로
who talk about other people's appearance must read the story. However, I have
주격 관계대명사   ~해야 한다   그러나
a question about it. Why did Joseph Palmer want to have a beard?
                                         want는 목적어로 to부정사를 취한다.

구문해설 • right 권리 • judge: (~로 미루어) 판단하다[여기다] • appearance: 외모
• however: 그러나 • beard: 턱수염

다를 권리
Joseph Palmer에 관한 이야기
나는 지난주에 Joseph Palmer에 관한 이야기를 읽었다. 나는 그게 정말 재미있었다. 나는 그 이야기로부터 우리는 사람들을 외모로 판단해서는 안 된다는 것을 배웠다. 다른 사람들의 외모에 관해 이야기하는 학생들은 이 이야기를 꼭 읽어야 한다. 하지만, 나는 그것에 관한 질문이 하나 있다. Joseph Palmer는 왜 턱수염을 기르고 싶었을까?

Words in Action

Welcome to the travel fair. Admission is free. What countries do you have in
                                                               ~을 마음에 두다
mind? If you want to visit South America, you can look around the booths on
      부사절을 이끄는 접속사로 '만약 ~ 한다면'의 의미   형용사구
the left. If you get hungry, you can have drinks and a light snack.
              get+형용사: ~해지다

구문해설 • fair 박람회 • admission 입장료 • free 무료의 • look around 둘러보다
• light 가벼운

여행 박람회에 오신 것을 환영합니다. 입장료는 무료입니다. 여러분은 어떤 나라들을 마음에 두고 있나요? 여러분이 남아메리카를 방문하고 싶다면, 왼쪽에 있는 부스들을 살펴볼 수 있습니다. 배가 고파진다면, 음료와 간단한 간식을 드실 수 있습니다.

영역별 핵심문제

Words & Expressions

01 다음 주어진 두 단어의 관계가 같도록 빈칸에 알맞은 단어를 쓰시오.

> act : action – appear : _____

02 다음 글의 빈칸 ⓐ와 ⓑ에 들어갈 단어가 바르게 짝지어진 것은?

> One day, four men _____ ⓐ ed Joseph and threw him on the ground. "We're going to _____ ⓑ your beard!" they shouted.

① avoid – protect   ② avoid – cut off
③ wait – protect   ④ attack – fight off
⑤ attack – cut off

03 다음 밑줄 친 부분의 뜻이 잘못된 것은?

① After he was freed, Joseph traveled. 석방되었다
② Joseph Palmer fought for the right to have beards. 권리
③ Joseph Palmer was an ordinary person. 평범한
④ He said to the judge, "I'm the victim here." 판단하다
⑤ Joseph looked different from other people. 다르게 보였다

04 다음 영영 풀이에 해당하는 것을 고르시오.

> • to make something happen
> • the reason that something happens

① cut   ② cause   ③ fall
④ change   ⑤ mean

05 다음 문장의 빈칸에 공통으로 들어갈 말을 쓰시오.

> • I do well in subjects _____ social studies and history.
> • He looks smart, but I don't _____ his promises.

06 빈칸에 주어진 단어를 알맞은 형태로 고쳐 쓰시오.

> • The men called the police and accused him of attacking them. Poor Joseph _____ (arrest).

➡ _____

Conversation

07 주어진 문장이 들어갈 위치로 알맞은 것은?

> But what does she look like?

B: Hi, Minsol. Is your class winning?
G: Of course. We have a great handball player. (①)
B: You mean the girl from Mongolia?
G: Yes, her name is Gacha. (②)
B: I've heard a lot about her. (③)
G: She's very tall and has a ponytail. (④)
B: Oh, is she the girl who scored the goal just now?
G: Yes, that's her seventh goal. (⑤)
B: Wow, she's really great.

①   ②   ③   ④   ⑤

08 다음 질문에 대한 답으로 적절하지 <u>않은</u> 것은?

> A: What does he look like?

① He has long straight hair.
② He has a big head.
③ He is very tall.
④ He's reading a map.
⑤ He has blond hair.

[09~10] 다음 대화를 읽고 물음에 답하시오.

> M: What can I do for you?
> G: I lost my younger brother.
> M: Okay, calm down. What's your brother's name?
> G: His name is Wally Brown. He's five years old.
> M: What does he look like?
> G: He has brown hair and brown eyes.
> M: What is he wearing?
> G: He is wearing a green shirt and black pants.
> M: Can you tell me more?
> G: Oh, he is carrying a red backpack.
> M: All right. We'll go out and look for him. Also, we'll make an announcement about a missing child.
> G: Thank you so much. _____(A)_____

09 위 대화의 빈칸 (A)에 들어갈 말로 적절한 것은?

① I hope you'll do well on the exam.
② I hope I'll find him soon.
③ I hope he'll enjoy an announcement about a missing child.
④ I hope so, too.
⑤ My cat is missing.

10 위 대화의 소녀의 남동생에 관한 정보로 일치하지 <u>않는</u> 것은?

① His name is Wally Brown.
② He's five years old.
③ He has brown hair and brown eyes.
④ He's wearing a green shirt and black pants.
⑤ He'll go out and look for a child.

11 다음 대화의 빈칸 (A)에 들어갈 말로 알맞은 것은?

> B: I hear there is a new student in your class.
> G: Yes. She's from Jejudo. Oh, she's over there!
> B: Which one? _____(A)_____
> G: She has curly hair and is wearing glasses.

① What does she look like?
② What is she looking for?
③ Where is she?
④ How do you know her?
⑤ Where is she going?

12 주어진 말에 이어질 대화의 순서로 알맞은 것은?

> You look sad. What's wrong, Jongmin?

> (A) What happened?
> (B) She fell off her bike.
> (C) My sister broke her arm this morning.
> (D) That's too bad. I hope she'll get better soon.

① (A) – (B) – (C) – (D)
② (B) – (A) – (C) – (D)
③ (C) – (A) – (B) – (D)
④ (C) – (B) – (A) – (D)
⑤ (D) – (A) – (B) – (C)

Grammar

13 다음 빈칸에 들어갈 말로 어법상 적절한 것을 <u>모두</u> 고르시오.

> _____ John gets a haircut, he will wash his hair.

① Before   ② Although   ③ If
④ After   ⑤ Because

14 지난 토요일에 Emily가 다음 그림 속의 1~3 순서대로 동물들을 보고 왔다. 내용에 맞게 빈칸을 알맞게 채우시오.

(1) Emily saw an elephant before _____
_____.
(2) Emily saw a giraffe _____ she saw a lion.
(3) Emily saw a lion _____.

15 다음 빈칸에 공통으로 들어갈 수 있는 것을 고르시오.

> • Wayne _____ her to take part in the party.
> • Harold _____ to know what was inside the box.

① asked   ② wanted
③ invited   ④ told
⑤ advised

16 다음 중 어법상 바르지 <u>않은</u> 것은?

① After they finished their homework, Miso and Mijin went out for dinner.
② He persuaded her coming to his party.
③ Before I get an allowance, I do a lot of house chores.
④ Did you make him paint the gate?
⑤ She forced him to give up smoking and drinking.

17 다음 문장을 주어진 단어로 시작하는 문장으로 바꾸어 쓰시오.

(1) Before we watched the movie, we ate ice cream.
➡ After _____
_____.

(2) After I pass the school gate, I untie my hair.
➡ Before _____
_____.

18 다음 문장에서 어법상 잘못된 부분을 바르게 고쳐 문장을 다시 쓰시오.

(1) I will take a photo of myself after I will get a haircut tomorrow.
➡ _____
_____

(2) Fiona wants Andrew doesn't come to the party.
➡ _____
_____

(3) The situation required me have strong belief.
➡ _____
_____

19 다음 빈칸에 들어갈 말로 알맞게 짝지어진 것은?

> • Vida warned her son _____ fast food.
> • Jerome asked me _____ the TV volume.

① not to eat – to turn down
② not eating – to turn down
③ not to eat – turning down
④ not eating – turning down
⑤ not eat – turn down

20 주어진 어휘를 이용하여 영작하시오. (8단어)

> 잠자리에 들기 전에 양치질을 해라. (brush, bed)

➡ _____

Reading

[21~22] 다음 글을 읽고 물음에 답하시오.

In many ways, 42-year-old Joseph Palmer was an ordinary person. He had a job and cared for his family. But in 1830, after he moved to a small town in Massachusetts, he began to ⓐface difficulties. Joseph looked different from other people: he had a long _____ⓑ_____. People did not like it very much.
The town's people avoided the man with a _____ⓑ_____. They did not want to sit next to him. They even whispered behind his back, "What is he trying to hide?"

21 위 글의 밑줄 친 ⓐface와 같은 의미로 쓰인 것을 고르시오.

① He buried his face in his hands.
② Look at the north face of the mountain.
③ He didn't face a financial crisis.
④ The face of the clock is covered with a simple glass cover.
⑤ Don't lose your face.

22 주어진 영영풀이를 참고하여 빈칸 ⓑ에 철자 b로 시작하는 단어를 쓰시오.

> the hair that grows on one's chin and cheeks

➡ _____

[23~25] 다음 글을 읽고 물음에 답하시오.

Some neighbors broke his windows. Others threw stones at him when he walked down the street. They told him to stop growing a beard. Joseph did not mind. He just wanted the freedom ⓐto have his beard.
One day, four men attacked Joseph and threw him on the ground. "We're going to cut off your beard!" they shouted. Joseph was a big man, and he was able to fight them off. But the men called the police and accused him of attacking them. Poor Joseph was arrested. He said to the judge, "I'm the victim here." Sadly, no one believed a man with a beard, and he went to prison for over a year.

23 위 글의 밑줄 친 ⓐto have와 to부정사의 용법이 같은 것을 모두 고르시오.

① Did you want to go there then?
② I have no house to live in.
③ She wants something cold to drink.
④ I'm happy to get the birthday present.
⑤ Jane had the kindness to help me.

24 위 글의 주제로 알맞은 것을 고르시오.

① various cases of bullying in our society
② the judge who sent the victim to prison
③ the importance of the good neighbors
④ unfair behavior towards a man with a beard
⑤ the way to grow a wonderful beard

25 위 글을 읽고 대답할 수 없는 질문은?

① When did some neighbors break Joseph's windows?

② Who told Joseph to stop growing a beard?

③ What did Joseph want?

④ What did Joseph say to the judge?

⑤ How long did Joseph go to prison?

[26~28] 다음 글을 읽고 물음에 답하시오.

Joseph's son, Thomas, wanted people to know the truth. He sent letters to newspapers across the country. People learned that Joseph was in prison just for protecting himself and his beard. Many people became angry about ⓐthis, so the judge finally decided to set Joseph free.

After he was freed, Joseph traveled and told his story to lots of people. Slowly, people's attitudes toward beards changed. Before Joseph died, a man with a beard became the President of the United States. His name was Abraham Lincoln. ⓑHe made beards popular, but Joseph Palmer fought for the right to have it.

26 위 글의 밑줄 친 ⓐthis가 가리키는 것을 본문에서 찾아 쓰시오.

➡ _____

_____

27 위 글의 밑줄 친 ⓑ에서 어법상 틀린 부분을 찾아 고치시오.

➡ _____

28 위 글의 내용과 일치하지 않는 것은?

① Joseph's son sent letters to newspapers across the country.

② Before Joseph traveled and told his story to lots of people, he was freed.

③ Joseph died after Abraham Lincoln became the President of the United States.

④ Joseph Palmer made beards popular.

⑤ Joseph fought for the right to have beards.

[29~30] 다음 독서 기록장을 읽고 물음에 답하시오.

A Story About Joseph Palmer

I read the story about Joseph Palmer last week. I really enjoyed it. I learned from the story that we should not judge people by their appearance. Students who talk about other people's appearance must read the story. _____ⓐ_____, I have a question about it. Why did Joseph Palmer want to have a beard?

29 위 독서 기록장의 빈칸 ⓐ에 들어갈 알맞은 말을 고르시오.

① In addition   ② Therefore

③ However   ④ For example

⑤ Moreover

30 위 독서 기록장의 교훈으로 어울리는 속담을 고르시오.

① Too many cooks spoil the broth.

② Make hay while the sun shines.

③ Don't cry over spilt milk.

④ The grass is greener on the other side of the fence.

⑤ Don't judge a book by its cover.

01 출제율 90%

다음 짝지어진 단어의 관계가 같도록 빈칸에 알맞은 말을 쓰시오.

> guilty : innocent = friendly : _____

02 출제율 95%

〈보기〉에서 알맞은 단어를 선택하여 문장을 완성하시오.

┌─ 보기 ─┐
attack   attitude   avoid   whisper

- When a dog tried to (A)_____ me, my cat meowed loudly.
- I like your good (B)_____ : you always look on the bright side.

[03~04] 다음 대화를 읽고 물음에 답하시오.

M: What can I do for you?
G: I lost my younger brother.
M: Okay, ⓐcalm down. What's your brother's name?
G: His name is Wally Brown. He's five years old.
M: ⓑWhat does he look for?
G: He has brown hair and brown eyes.
M: What is he wearing?
G: ⓒHe is wearing a green shirt and black pants.
M: ⓓCan you tell me more?
G: Oh, he is carrying a red backpack.
M: All right. We'll go out and look for him. Also, we'll make an announcement about a missing child.
G: Thank you so much. ⓔI hope I'll find him soon.

03 출제율 85%

How does the girl feel and why? Complete the sentence.

➡ She is _____ because she _____ her younger brother.

04 출제율 95%

위 대화의 밑줄 친 어구의 쓰임이 적절하지 <u>않은</u> 것은?

① ⓐ   ② ⓑ   ③ ⓒ   ④ ⓓ   ⑤ ⓔ

05 출제율 100%

다음 중 짝지어진 대화가 <u>어색한</u> 것을 고르시오.

① A: I lost my puppy this afternoon.
　 B: I hope you'll find him soon.
② A: What does your sister look like?
　 B: She's a little fat and has long straight hair.
③ A: I plan to go fishing with my uncle on the weekend.
　 B: I hope you'll find it soon.
④ A: I'll enter the school dance contest next week. I hope I won't make mistakes.
　 B: Don't worry!
⑤ A: What does she look like?
　 B: She has an oval face and big black eyes.

[06~07] 다음 대화를 읽고 물음에 답하시오.

Somin: Look at the bulletin board. There are posters for the next school president.
Dain: Yeah, I've already made my choice. I'll vote for Jang Jimin.
Somin: You mean the boy with glasses? He looks smart, but I don't like his promises.
Dain: Then who will you choose?
Somin: Well, I am for number 3, Hong Jiho. She wants to make our school fun and exciting.
Dain: She always has short hair, right?
Somin: Yes, and she looks friendly.

06 위 대화와 포스터를 참고하여 Somin이가 지지하는 후보자에 관한 글을 완성하시오.

monthly talent shows
more club activity hours
Let's Make a Fun and
Exciting School
3
Hong Jiho

I will _____ _____ Hong Jiho. She has _____ _____. She looks _____. She thinks school should be _____ _____ _____. I agree with her. I like her _____ such as monthly talent shows. I hope Hong Jiho becomes the next school president.

07 위 대화의 내용과 일치하지 <u>않는</u> 것은?

① There will be an election for the next school president.
② Dain supports Jang Jimin.
③ Jimin wears glasses.
④ Somin doesn't like Jimin's promises.
⑤ Hong Jiho is Somin's friend.

[08~09] 다음 글을 읽고 물음에 답하시오.

Hi, I'm Gacha. I'm from Mongolia. When I first came to Songji Middle School two months ago, I was so (A)[happy / worried]. I was a little shy, and I wasn't good at Korean. (B)[However / Moreover], I'm a lucky girl. All my classmates are nice and friendly. I enjoy playing handball with them in P.E. class. I'm a (C)[good / bad] player. They call me "Golden Hand." There will be a sports day next week. I hope my class will win in the handball event.

08 위 글을 읽고 다음 질문의 답을 완성하시오.

What is Gacha's hope for the sports day?

➡ She _____ her _____ _____ _____ in the _____ event.

09 위 글의 괄호 (A)~(C)에서 알맞은 것을 고르시오.

	(A)	(B)	(C)
①	happy	However	bad
②	happy	Moreover	good
③	worried	Moreover	bad
④	worried	However	good
⑤	worried	However	bad

10 다음 대화의 빈칸 (A)와 (B)에 들어갈 말로 알맞은 것은?

A: What is your character's name?
B: Her name is Prettian.
C: _____ (A) _____
B: She's short and has a big head. She has an oval face and big black eyes.
D: _____ (B) _____
B: She's wearing a blue dress and big earrings.

① (A) What does she look like?
　 (B) What is she wearing?
② (A) How does she look like?
　 (B) What is she wearing?
③ (A) What does she look like?
　 (B) Is she wearing sunglasses?
④ (A) How does she look like?
　 (B) Can you tell me more?
⑤ (A) What is she looking at?
　 (B) Where is she?

11 다음 중 어법상 바르지 않은 것은? (2개)

출제율 95%

> I am sure ①that he ②will beg me ③ buy ④him a toy when we ⑤will arrive at the shop.

12 다음 중 어법상 어색한 문장의 개수는?

출제율 100%

> ⓐ Sora dropped by her aunt's before she went to school.
> ⓑ Would you like me bringing any food to the party?
> ⓒ Her parents expected her won the contest.
> ⓓ After he had a long trip, he was very tired.
> ⓔ She told him was on time.

① 1개　　② 2개　　③ 3개　　④ 4개　　⑤ 5개

13 주어진 어휘를 이용하여 다음 우리말을 영작하시오.

출제율 85%

(1) 선생님은 내게 문을 닫아달라고 부탁하셨다. (the teacher, ask, the door)

　➡ _____

(2) Dr. Smith는 그녀에게 일찍 잠자리에 들라고 충고했다. (advise, early, go to bed)

　➡ _____

(3) 축구 경기가 끝난 후에 선수들은 잔디 위에 누웠다. (the soccer match, the players, on the grass, lie, over)

　➡ _____
　_____

14 다음 문장에서 어법상 어색한 부분을 바르게 고쳐 다시 쓰시오.

출제율 90%

(1) Judy asked him made sandwiches.

　➡ _____

(2) Tom expected Jane be thin.

　➡ _____

(3) My advice caused him stop smoking.

　➡ _____

[15~16] 다음 글을 읽고 물음에 답하시오.

> In many ways, 42-year-old Joseph Palmer was an ordinary person. He had a job and cared for his family. But in 1830, after he moved to a small town in Massachusetts, he began to face difficulties. ⓐJoseph looked like different from other people: he had a long beard. People did not like it very much.
>
> The town's people avoided ⓑthe man with a beard. They did not want to sit next to him. They even whispered behind his back, "What is he trying to hide?"

15 위 글의 밑줄 친 ⓐ에서 어법상 틀린 부분을 고치시오.

출제율 95%

_____ ➡ _____

16 위 글의 밑줄 친 ⓑthe man with a beard가 가리키는 것을 본문에서 찾아 쓰시오.

출제율 90%

　➡ _____

[17~19] 다음 글을 읽고 물음에 답하시오.

> Some neighbors broke his windows. Others threw stones at him when he walked down the street. They told him to stop (A)[growing / to grow] a beard. Joseph did not ⓐmind. He just wanted the freedom (B)[having / to have] his beard.

One day, four men attacked Joseph and threw him on the ground. "We're going to cut off your beard!" they shouted. Joseph was a big man, and he was able to fight them off. But the men called the police and accused him of attacking them. Poor Joseph (C)[arrested / was arrested]. He said to the judge, "I'm the ____ⓑ____ here." Sadly, no one believed a man with a beard, and he went to prison for over a year.

출제율 95%

17 위 글의 괄호 (A)~(C)에서 어법상 알맞은 낱말을 골라 쓰시오.

➡ (A) _____ (B) _____ (C) _____

출제율 90%

18 위 글의 밑줄 친 ⓐmind와 같은 의미로 쓰인 것을 고르시오.

① Out of sight, out of mind.
② Never mind! She didn't mean what she said.
③ Keep your mind on your work!
④ I want to meet the greatest mind of the time.
⑤ A sound mind in a sound body.

출제율 95%

19 위 글의 빈칸 ⓑ에 들어갈 알맞은 말을 고르시오.

① attacker   ② lawyer   ③ prisoner
④ bully   ⑤ victim

[20~22] 다음 글을 읽고 물음에 답하시오.

Joseph's son, Thomas, wanted people to know the truth. He sent letters to newspapers across the country. People learned that Joseph was in prison just for protecting himself and his beard. Many people became angry about this, so the judge finally decided to set Joseph free.

After he was freed, Joseph traveled and told his story to lots of people. Slowly, people's attitudes toward beards changed. Before Joseph died, a man with a beard became the President of the United States. His name was Abraham Lincoln. He made beards popular, but Joseph Palmer fought for the right to have them.

출제율 85%

20 본문의 내용과 일치하도록 다음 빈칸 (A)와 (B)에 알맞은 단어를 쓰시오.

> (A)_____ _____ finally decided to set Joseph free because many people became angry about the truth that Joseph was in prison just for protecting himself and (B)_____ _____.

출제율 100%

21 위 글의 내용에 어울리는 속담을 고르시오.

① No news is good news.
② The grass is greener on the other side of the fence.
③ Where there is a will, there is a way.
④ Look before you leap.
⑤ Practice makes perfect.

출제율 95%

22 위 글을 읽고 답할 수 없는 것을 고르시오.

① Why did Joseph's son send letters to newspapers across the country?
② What did people learn through the letters?
③ After Joseph was freed, what did he do?
④ How many people changed their attitudes toward beards?
⑤ Who made beards popular?

01 다음 대화의 빈칸 (A)에 Gacha의 외모를 묻는 말을 쓰시오. (대명사를 이용할 것)

> B: Hi, Minsol. Is your class winning?
> G: Of course. We have a great handball player.
> B: You mean the girl from Mongolia?
> G: Yes, her name is Gacha.
> B: I've heard a lot about her. But __(A)__
> G: She's very tall and has a ponytail.
> B: Oh, is she the girl who scored the goal just now?
> G: Yes, that's her seventh goal.
> B: Wow, she's really great.

➡ _____

02 다음 글은 학생회장 후보를 지지하는 글이다. 글을 보고 아래의 대화를 완성하시오.

> "I will vote for Han Siwon. She looks confident and smart. She thinks school should be a safe place. I agree with her. I like her promises such as no more bullying. I hope Han Siwon becomes the next school president. I really want my school to be a safer place."

⬇

> G: Look at the bulletin board. There are posters for the next _____ _____.
> B: Yeah, I've already made my choice. I'll _____ for Han Siwon.
> G: She always has a ponytail, right?
> B: Yes. She looks _____ and smart. And she wants to make _____ _____ _____ _____.

03 다음 대화의 밑줄 친 우리말에 맞게 주어진 어휘를 이용하여 문장을 완성하시오.

> A: I have an important exam tomorrow!
> B: (A)나는 네가 시험을 잘 보길 바라. (hope, will, do well)
> A: (B)나도 그러길 바라. (hope, so) Thanks.

➡ (A) _____
　 (B) _____

04 다음 문장에서 어법상 어색한 부분을 바르게 고쳐 다시 쓰시오.

(1) My history teacher told us handed in the project by tomorrow.

➡ _____
_____

(2) The teacher warned the students be quiet in class.

➡ _____
_____

(3) Amy's best friend wants her listens to his songs.

➡ _____
_____

(4) Her manager always forces Melanie throwing away the trash.

➡ _____
_____

(5) The doctor encouraged Jack to not give up doing exercise.

➡ _____
_____

05 주어진 어휘를 이용하여 다음 우리말을 영작하시오.

(1) 엄마는 내게 그 개를 산책시키라고 말씀하셨다. (mom, walk the dog)

➡ _____

(2) Mark는 Maria가 복귀할 때까지 그녀의 고객들을 관리할 것이다. (control, customers, return)

➡ _____

06 다음 문장을 주어진 단어로 시작하는 문장으로 바꾸어 쓰시오.

> I set my alarm clock before I went to bed.

➡ After _____.

[07~09] 다음 글을 읽고 물음에 답하시오.

Some neighbors broke his windows. Others threw stones at him when he walked down the street. They told him to stop growing a beard. Joseph did not mind. He just wanted the ⓐ_____ to have his beard.

One day, four men attacked Joseph and threw him on the ground. "We're going to cut off your beard!" they shouted. ⓑJoseph은 덩치가 큰 사람이었고, 그는 그들을 싸워 물리칠 수 있었다. But the men called the police and accused him of attacking them. Poor Joseph was arrested. He said to the judge, "I'm the victim here." Sadly, no one believed a man with a beard, and he went to prison for over a year.

07 위 글의 빈칸 ⓐ에 free를 알맞은 형태로 쓰시오.

➡ _____

08 위 글의 밑줄 친 ⓑ의 우리말에 맞게 주어진 어휘를 이용하여 13 단어로 영작하시오.

> big, and, able, fight, off

➡ _____

_____

09 위 글의 내용과 일치하도록 다음 빈칸 (A)와 (B)에 알맞은 단어를 쓰시오.

> Though Joseph was a (A)_____ of bullying, he went to prison for over a year because no one believed a man with a (B)_____.

[10~11] 다음 글을 읽고 물음에 답하시오.

Joseph's son, Thomas, wanted people to know the truth. He sent letters to newspapers across the country. People learned that Joseph was in prison just for (A)[preventing / protecting] himself and his beard. Many people became (B)[angry / angrily] about this, so the judge finally decided to set Joseph (C)[free / freely].

10 위 글의 괄호 (A)~(C)에서 문맥이나 어법상 알맞은 낱말을 골라 쓰시오.

➡ (A) _____ (B) _____ (C) _____

11 다음 질문에 대한 알맞은 대답을 주어진 단어로 시작하여 쓰시오. (10 단어)

> Q: How did people learn that Joseph was in prison just for protecting himself and his beard?
>
> A: They learned it because _____
>
> _____
>
> _____.

01 (A)에 제시된 어구를 보고 사람의 외모를 묻는 질문과 그에 대한 대답을 쓰고, (B)는 주어진 상황에서 가질 수 있는 적절한 바람을 찾아 쓰시오.

(A) Minsu – short hair, wearing jeans / Sumi – tall, a ponytail, wearing glasses

(B) [상황] I lost my puppy this afternoon. / I have an important exam tomorrow!
          I'm going to my favorite singer's concert tonight.

     [바람] I hope you'll do well on the exam. / I hope you'll find it soon. /
          I hope you have a good time.

---

02 다음 〈보기〉의 동사와 to부정사를 이용하여 여러 가지 문장을 쓰시오.

보기

    want   ask   tell   allow   advise   force

---

(1) _____

(2) _____

(3) _____

(4) _____

(5) _____

(6) _____

03 다음 내용을 바탕으로 인물에 관한 책이나 이야기 중 감명 깊게 읽은 것을 정리하는 글을 쓰시오.

• 주인공: Steve Jobs   • 교훈: We should think differently.

• 추천 독자층: young people who study for the future

• 궁금한 점: How was his middle school life?   • 기억에 남는 문구: Stay hungry. Stay foolish.

A Story about Steve Jobs

I read a story about Steve Jobs. I really enjoyed (A)_____ his story. I learned from the story that we should think (B)_____. Young people (C)_____ study for the future must read the story. However, I have a question about the story. (D)_____ was his middle school life? I still remember his saying, "(E)_____ Stay foolish."

단원별 모의고사

01 다음 단어에 대한 영어 설명이 <u>어색한</u> 것은?

① victim: someone who has been hurt or killed
② choose: to decide which thing you want
③ attack: an action to try to frighten someone who is smaller or weaker
④ attitude: how you think or feel about something
⑤ arrest: to take the person away to ask them about a crime that they might have committed

02 다음 짝지어진 단어의 관계가 같도록 빈칸에 알맞은 말을 쓰시오.

> guilty : innocent = ease : _____

03 다음 영영풀이에 해당하는 단어를 고르시오.

> *v.* drop down to the floor
> *n.* the season between summer and winter

① fall   ② continue   ③ spring
④ autumn   ⑤ face

04 대화의 빈칸에 들어갈 말로 <u>어색한</u> 것은?

> A: What is your character's name?
> B: His name is Buster.
> A: What does he look like?
> B: _____
> A: Does he have big eyes?
> B: Yes, he does.

① He has no hair.
② He's tall and has curly hair.
③ He has brown hair and is wearing glasses.
④ He is very kind and attractive.
⑤ He has a round face and short straight hair.

05 대화의 빈칸에 들어갈 알맞은 말은?

> G: You look sad. What's wrong, Jongmin?
> B: My sister broke her arm this morning.
> G: What happened?
> B: She ____(A)____ her bike.
> G: That's too bad. I hope she'll ____(B)____ soon.

　　(A)　　　(B)
① broke – get better
② broke – fix it
③ felled – care for herself
④ got off – find him soon
⑤ fell off – get better

06 대화를 알맞은 순서로 배열한 것은?

> (A) She has curly hair and is wearing glasses.
> (B) I hear there is a new student in your class.
> (C) Which one? What does she look like?
> (D) Yes. She's from Jejudo. Oh, she's over there!

① (B) – (C) – (A) – (D)
② (B) – (D) – (C) – (A)
③ (C) – (A) – (B) – (D)
④ (C) – (B) – (D) – (A)
⑤ (D) – (C) – (B) – (A)

07 다음 대화의 빈칸에 들어갈 말로 가장 적절한 것은?

> A: I hope you'll do your best in the final game.
> B: Thanks. _____

① I'm a good player.
② I don't like your promises.
③ I wish you the same.
④ I don't like talent shows.
⑤ I hope you'll do well on the exam.

[08~10] 다음 대화를 읽고 물음에 답하시오.

> Man: What can I do for you?
> Girl: I lost my younger brother.
> Man: Okay, calm down. What's your brother's name? (①)
> Girl: His name is Wally Brown. He's five years old.
> Man: What does he look like? (②)
> Girl: He has brown hair and brown eyes.
> Man: What is he wearing? (③)
> Girl: He is wearing a green shirt and black pants.
> Man: _____(A)_____
> Girl: Oh, he is carrying a red backpack. (④)
> Man: All right. We'll go out and look for him. (⑤)
> Girl: Thank you so much. I hope I'll find him soon.

08 위 대화의 빈칸 (A)에 들어갈 말로 가장 자연스러운 것은?

① What does he like?
② Can you tell me more?
③ What does he look like?
④ Do you know where he is?
⑤ Is your brother wearing a blue cap?

09 위 대화의 (①)~(⑤) 중 주어진 문장이 들어갈 위치로 알맞은 것은?

> Also, we'll make an announcement about a missing child.

①   ②   ③   ④   ⑤

10 위 대화를 읽고 추론할 수 없거나 답을 할 수 없는 질문은?

① How does the girl feel?
② Where did the girl lose her brother?
③ Does the girl's brother have black hair?
④ What kind of color is her brother's backpack?
⑤ What will the man do after the dialog?

[11~12] 다음 대화를 읽고 물음에 답하시오.

> B: Hi, Minsol. Is your class winning?
> G: Of course. We have a great handball player.
> B: _____(A)_____
> G: Yes, her name is Gacha.
> B: I've heard a lot about her. But what does she look like?
> G: She's very tall and has a ponytail.
> B: Oh, (B)지금 막 골을 넣은 여자아이가 그녀니?
> G: Yes, that's her seventh goal.
> B: Wow, she's really great.

11 위 대화의 빈칸 (A)에 들어갈 말로 알맞은 것은?

① Who is she?
② What is her name?
③ Do you know where she is from?
④ What will you do for her?
⑤ You mean the girl from Mongolia?

12 위 대화의 밑줄 친 (B)의 우리말에 맞게 주어진 어구를 알맞게 배열하시오.

> she, is, who, the goal, the girl, scored, just now

➡ _____

13 다음 중 어법상 올바른 것은?

① Do you want me clean your house for you?

② He told Perry putting on a penguin shirt.

③ I would like you to explain the accident in more detail.

④ The doctor advised Kathy stopped smoking.

⑤ Ms. Green asked him carries the boxes.

14 다음 중 어법상 어색한 것은?

① I will go straight to the gym after I pass the school gate.

② I will wait for her until she will come back to me.

③ Before she passes the school gate, she ties her hair with a hairband.

④ After he did his homework, he watched TV.

⑤ She will buy a new coat as soon as she receives the money.

15 다음 빈칸에 들어갈 말로 알맞게 짝지어진 것은?

> • Do you expect me _____ up my dreams?
> • The students will ride bikes before they _____ lunch.

① to give – have   ② to give – will have

③ giving – have   ④ giving – will have

⑤ give – had

16 다음 상황에 알맞은 말을 어법에 맞게 빈칸에 쓰시오.

(1) The driver drove his car very fast. He said to the driver, "Don't drive so fast."

➡ He told the driver _____ _____ _____ _____ _____.

(2) Paul is good at playing the guitar. So Bella said to Paul, "Will you play the piano for me?"

➡ Bella asked Paul _____ _____ _____ _____ _____ _____.

17 그림을 참고하여 빈칸을 알맞게 채우시오.

18:00   20:00

➡ Bomi studied history _____.

➡ Bomi had dinner _____.

[18~19] 다음 글을 읽고 물음에 답하시오.

In many ways, 42-year-old Joseph Palmer was an ordinary person. He had a job and cared for his family. But in 1830, after he moved to a small town in Massachusetts, he began to face difficulties. Joseph looked different from other people: he had a long beard. People did not like it very much.

The town's people avoided the man with a beard. They did not want to sit next to him. They even whispered behind his _____ ⓐ _____, "What is he trying to hide?"

18 다음 질문에 대한 알맞은 대답을 주어진 단어로 시작하여 쓰시오. (5 단어)

> Q: Why did Joseph Palmer look different from other people?
> A: Because _____ .

➡ _____

19 위 글의 빈칸 ⓐ에 들어갈 알맞은 말을 고르시오.

① legs   ② head   ③ hands
④ back   ⑤ shoulders

[20~22] 다음 글을 읽고 물음에 답하시오.

Some neighbors broke his windows. Others threw stones ___ⓐ___ him when he walked down the street. They told him to stop growing a beard. Joseph did not mind. He just wanted the freedom to have his beard.

One day, four men attacked Joseph and threw him on the ground. "We're going to cut off your beard!" they shouted. Joseph was a big man, and he was able to fight ⓑthem off. But the men called the police and accused him ___ⓒ___ attacking them. Poor Joseph was arrested. He said to the ⓓjudge, "I'm the victim here." Sadly, no one believed a man with a beard, and he went to prison for over a year.

20 위 글의 빈칸 ⓐ와 ⓒ에 들어갈 전치사가 바르게 짝지어진 것은?

① at – of   ② in – of   ③ in – from
④ to – in   ⑤ at – by

21 위 글의 밑줄 친 ⓑthem이 가리키는 것을 본문에서 찾아 쓰시오.

➡ _____

22 위 글의 밑줄 친 ⓓjudge와 같은 의미로 쓰인 것을 고르시오.

① Did the court judge him guilty?
② The judge sentenced him to five years in prison.
③ God will judge all men.
④ He is a good judge of wine.
⑤ You must not judge a man by his income.

[23~24] 다음 글을 읽고 물음에 답하시오.

Joseph's son, Thomas, wanted people to know the truth. He sent letters to newspapers across the country. ⓐ사람들은 Joseph이 단지 자신과 자신의 턱수염을 지키려다 감옥에 갇혔다는 것을 알게 되었다. Many people became angry about this, so the judge finally decided to set Joseph free.

After he was freed, Joseph traveled and told his story to lots of people. Slowly, people's attitudes toward beards changed. Before Joseph died, a man with a beard became the President of the United States. His name was Abraham Lincoln. He made beards popular, but Joseph Palmer fought for the right to have them.

23 위 글의 밑줄 친 ⓐ의 우리말에 맞게 한 단어를 보충하여, 주어진 어휘를 알맞게 배열하시오.

> that / people / his beard / Joseph / learned / himself / in prison / and / protecting / just / was

➡ _____

_____

24 Who made beards popular? Answer in English. (three words)

➡ _____

INSIGHT
on the textbook

교과서 파헤치기

※ 다음 영어를 우리말로 쓰시오.

01 hard _____

02 appointment _____

03 attack _____

04 bacteria _____

05 cell _____

06 creature _____

07 different _____

08 digest _____

09 break _____

10 exercise _____

11 dangerous _____

12 antibody _____

13 defend _____

14 medicine _____

15 multiply _____

16 defense _____

17 impossible _____

18 invade _____

19 macrophage _____

20 balanced _____

21 stomachache _____

22 major _____

23 skin _____

24 regularly _____

25 scratch _____

26 healthy _____

27 fever _____

28 remember _____

29 germ _____

30 finally _____

31 success _____

32 terrible _____

33 luckily _____

34 necessary _____

35 be good for _____

36 plenty of _____

37 such as _____

38 at last _____

39 protect A from B _____

40 by the way _____

41 give up _____

42 in a few days _____

43 be famous for _____

※ 다음 우리말을 영어로 쓰시오.

01 위통. 복통 _____

02 공격하다; 공격 _____

03 박테리아, 세균 _____

04 실제로, 정말로 _____

05 몇의 _____

06 주사 _____

07 피부 _____

08 항체 _____

09 세포 _____

10 생물 _____

11 다른 _____

12 소화하다 _____

13 운동하다 _____

14 위험한 _____

15 방어하다 _____

16 마지막으로, 마침내 _____

17 약속 _____

18 세균, 미생물 _____

19 불가능한 _____

20 침입하다 _____

21 방어 _____

22 열 _____

23 다행히도 _____

24 대식 세포 _____

25 균형 잡힌, 안정된 _____

26 부러지다 _____

27 주요한, 중대한 _____

28 필요한 _____

29 규칙적으로 _____

30 약 _____

31 바이러스 _____

32 피해자, 희생자 _____

33 증식[번식]하다 _____

34 긁다, 할퀴다 _____

35 성공 _____

36 마침내, 드디어 _____

37 ~으로 유명하다 _____

38 ~할 준비가 되어 있다 _____

39 그런데 _____

40 포기하다 _____

41 많은 _____

42 나타나다 _____

43 조심하다 _____

※ 다음 영영풀이에 알맞은 단어를 <보기>에서 골라 쓴 후, 우리말 뜻을 쓰시오.

1 _____ : the fact of getting or achieving wealth, respect, or fame: _____

2 _____ : to fight in order to keep someone or something safe: _____

3 _____ : an agreement to meet with someone at a particular time: _____

4 _____ : very important: _____

5 _____ : any one of a group of very small living things that often cause disease: _____

6 _____ : any one of the very small parts that together form all living things: _____

7 _____ : to increase in number by reproducing: _____

8 _____ : an act of putting something such as medicine or vaccine into the body with a needle: _____

9 _____ : a very small living thing that causes disease: _____

10 _____ : to enter or be in a place where you are not wanted: _____

11 _____ : having good or equal amounts of all the necessary parts of something: _____

12 _____ : used to say that something good or lucky has happened: _____

13 _____ : to rub your skin with your fingernails because it feels uncomfortable: _____

14 _____ : an infectious disease like a very bad cold, which causes fever, pains, and weakness: _____

15 _____ : a person who has been attacked, injured, robbed, or killed by someone else: _____

16 _____ : to change food that you have eaten by a biological process into simpler forms that can be used by the body: _____

보기			
digest	luckily	major	balanced
invade	bacteria	defend	shot
flu	appointment	victim	cell
multiply	success	germ	scratch

※ 다음 우리말과 일치하도록 빈칸에 알맞은 말을 쓰시오.

Communicate: Listen - Listen and Answer Dialog 1

B: _____ I go home _____, Ms. Song? I _____ _____ so good.

W: What _____ _____ be the _____?

B: I have a _____ _____. It really _____.

W: _____ _____ _____ get some medicine at the _____ _____?

B: I _____ did. But it _____ _____.

W: Okay. You _____ go. _____ _____ a doctor, okay?

B: _____. Thanks.

Communicate: Listen - Listen and Answer Dialog 2

(The phone rings.)

B: Hello, Sora.

G: Hi, Jongha. I _____ you were _____. Are you _____ now?

B: Yes, I _____ _____ the doctor, and I _____ _____ now.

G: _____ _____ hear that. _____ _____, I called you _____ _____ about our science project.

B: Yeah, we _____ _____. Can you _____ _____ tomorrow?

G: Okay. _____ _____ at Simpson's Donuts _____ nine.

B: At nine? That's too _____. I _____ _____ on the weekend.

G: _____ _____ 10 then?

B: That _____ fine.

Communicate: Listen - Listen More

M: Hi, Minsol. What's _____ _____ your dog?

G: She _____ _____ herself. Actually, she _____ some hair.

M: When did she first _____ _____ _____?

G: _____ three days _____.

M: _____ me _____. (pause) She _____ _____ _____ on her skin. I'll give _____ _____ _____.

G: Thank you.

M: I _____ _____ check your dog again. _____ you _____ next Monday?

G: That's _____ _____ me.

M: Okay. _____ _____.

B: 송 선생님, 집에 일찍 가도 될까요? 몸이 너무 안 좋아요.
W: 무슨 문제가 있니?
B: 배가 너무 아파요. 정말 아파요.
W: 양호실에서 약을 좀 먹는 게 어떠니?
B: 벌써 먹었어요. 하지만 도움이 되지 않았어요.
W: 알겠다. 가도 돼. 병원에 가봐, 알았지?
B: 물론이죠. 고맙습니다.

(전화벨이 울린다.)
B: 여보세요, 소라야.
G: 안녕, 종하야. 아프다고 들었어. 이제 좀 괜찮니?
B: 응, 병원에 갔었는데, 이제 좀 나아졌어.
G: 다행이구나. 그런데, 우리 과학 프로젝트에 대해 얘기하려고 전화했어.
B: 그래, 우리 만나야겠다. 내일 만날 수 있니?
G: 좋아. 9시에 Simpson's Donuts에서 만나자.
B: 9시? 너무 일러. 난 주말에 늦잠을 자.
G: 그럼 10시는 어때?
B: 괜찮아.

M: 안녕, 민솔. 너의 개에게 무슨 문제가 있니?
G: 계속 자기 몸을 긁어요. 사실, 털이 좀 빠졌어요.
M: 너의 개는 언제 처음으로 문제가 생겼니?
G: 약 3일 전에요.
M: 어디 보자. (잠시 멈춘다) 피부에 바이러스가 있어. 약을 좀 줄게.
G: 감사합니다.
M: 네 개를 다시 확인할 필요가 있어. 다음 주 월요일에 올 수 있니?
G: 좋아요.
M: 알겠다. 나중에 보자.

Communicate: Listen - All Ears

M: 1. Can you _____ _____ next Friday?

    2. What's _____ _____ your cat?

M: 1. 다음 주 금요일에 만날까?
2. 너의 고양이에게 무슨 문제가 있니?

Communicate: Speak 2 - Talk in pairs

A: _____ wrong _____ you?

B: I _____ a _____ _____.

A: That's _____ _____. You _____ _____ some water.

B: Okay, _____ _____.

A: 무슨 일 있니?
B: 목이 아파.
A: 그것 참 안됐구나. 너는 물을 좀 마셔야 해.
B: 알았어, 그럴게.

Communicate: Speak 2 - Talk in groups

A: _____ _____ basketball this Saturday.

B: Sure, _____ _____?

A: Can you _____ _____ _____ ten?

B: That's _____ _____ me. Where _____ we _____?

A: _____ _____ at the school gym.

B: Okay. _____ you _____.

A: 이번 토요일에 농구하자.
B: 물론, 좋고말고.
A: 10시에 만날 수 있니?
B: 난 괜찮아. 우리 어디서 만날까?
A: 학교 체육관에서 만나자.
B: 알았어, 거기서 보자.

Wrap Up - Listening ❺

B: Mom, I _____ _____ well.

W: What _____ _____ _____ the problem?

B: I think I _____ _____ _____.

W: Really? _____ _____ _____. Umm, you do _____ _____ _____. I'll _____ you some _____.

B: _____ _____, Mom.

B: 엄마, 몸이 안 좋아요.
W: 뭐가 문제인 것 같니?
B: 열이 있는 것 같아요.
W: 정말? 어디 보자. 음, 정말 열이 있네. 약을 좀 갖다 줄게.
B: 고마워요, 엄마.

Wrap Up - Listening ❻

G: I'm _____ _____ _____ to the Comics Museum tomorrow. Will you _____ _____ me?

B: I really _____ _____ _____.

G: _____ you _____ it at 11?

B: That's _____ _____ me.

G: Okay. _____ _____ _____ the subway station.

G: 내일 만화 박물관에 갈 생각이야. 나하고 같이 갈래?
B: 정말 가고 싶어.
G: 11시에 만날 수 있니?
B: 난 괜찮아.
G: 좋아. 지하철역에서 만나자.

※ 다음 우리말에 맞도록 대화를 영어로 쓰시오.

Communicate: Listen - Listen and Answer Dialog 1

B: _____

W: _____

B: _____

W: _____

B: _____

W: _____

B: _____

Communicate: Listen - Listen and Answer Dialog 2

(The phone rings.)

B: _____

G: _____

B: _____

G: _____

B: _____

G: _____

B: _____

G: _____

B: _____

Communicate: Listen - Listen More

M: _____

G: _____

M: _____

G: _____

M: _____

G: _____

M: _____

G: _____

M: _____

해석

B: 송 선생님, 집에 일찍 가도 될까요? 몸이 너무 안 좋아요.
W: 무슨 문제가 있니?
B: 배가 너무 아파요. 정말 아파요.
W: 양호실에서 약을 좀 먹는 게 어떠니?
B: 벌써 먹었어요. 하지만 도움이 되지 않았어요.
W: 알겠다. 가도 돼. 병원에 가봐, 알았지?
B: 물론이죠. 고맙습니다.

(전화벨이 울린다.)
B: 여보세요, 소라야.
G: 안녕, 종하야. 아프다고 들었어. 이제 좀 괜찮니?
B: 응, 병원에 갔었는데, 이제 좀 나아졌어.
G: 다행이구나. 그런데, 우리 과학 프로젝트에 대해 얘기하려고 전화했어.
B: 그래, 우리 만나야겠다. 내일 만날 수 있니?
G: 좋아, 9시에 Simpson's Donuts에서 만나자.
B: 9시? 너무 일러. 난 주말에 늦잠을 자.
G: 그럼 10시는 어때?
B: 괜찮아.

M: 안녕, 민솔. 너의 개에게 무슨 문제가 있니?
G: 계속 자기 몸을 긁어요. 사실, 털이 좀 빠졌어요.
M: 너의 개는 언제 처음으로 문제가 생겼니?
G: 약 3일 전에요.
M: 어디 보자. (잠시 멈춘다) 피부에 바이러스가 있어. 약을 좀 줄게.
G: 감사합니다.
M: 네 개를 다시 확인할 필요가 있어. 다음 주 월요일에 올 수 있니?
G: 좋아요.
M: 알겠다. 나중에 보자.

Communicate: Listen - All Ears

M: 1. _____

    2. _____

Communicate: Speak 2 - Talk in pairs

A: _____

B: _____

A: _____

B: _____

Communicate: Speak 2 - Talk in groups

A: _____

B: _____

A: _____

B: _____

A: _____

B: _____

Wrap Up - Listening ❺

B: _____

W: _____

B: _____

W: _____

B: _____

Wrap Up - Listening ❻

G: _____

B: _____

G: _____

B: _____

G: _____

M: 1. 다음 주 금요일에 만날까?
    2. 너의 고양이에게 무슨 문제가 있니?

A: 무슨 일 있니?
B: 목이 아파.
A: 그것 참 안됐구나. 너는 물을 좀 마셔야 해.
B: 알았어, 그럴게.

A: 이번 토요일에 농구하자.
B: 물론, 좋고말고.
A: 10시에 만날 수 있니
B: 난 괜찮아. 우리 어디서 만날까?
A: 학교 체육관에서 만나자.
B: 알았어, 거기서 보자.

B: 엄마, 몸이 안 좋아요.
W: 뭐가 문제인 것 같니?
B: 열이 있는 것 같아요.
W: 정말? 어디 보자. 음, 정말 열이 있네. 약을 좀 갖다 줄게.
B: 고마워요, 엄마.

G: 내일 만화 박물관에 갈 생각이야. 나하고 같이 갈래?
B: 정말 가고 싶어.
G: 11시에 만날 수 있니?
B: 난 괜찮아.
G: 좋아. 지하철역에서 만나자.

※ 다음 우리말과 일치하도록 빈칸에 알맞은 것을 골라 쓰시오.

1 Germs are _____, but _____ is impossible to see them _____ your eyes.
    A. with   B. it   C. everywhere

2 There _____ two major _____ of germs: _____ and viruses.
    A. are   B. bacteria   C. kinds

3 _____ are very small _____.
    A. creatures   B. bacteria

4 _____ are _____.
    A. good   B. some

5 They _____ help you _____ the food _____ you eat.
    A. that   B. digest   C. can

6 _____ are bad and can _____ you sick.
    A. make   B. others

7 Viruses are germs _____ can only live _____ the cells of other _____ bodies.
    A. inside   B. living   C. that

8 They _____ diseases _____ as the flu.
    A. such   B. cause

9 "Bad" germs can _____ your body _____ your _____, mouth, nose, and eyes.
    A. skin   B. through   C. enter

10 What _____ when they _____?
    A. invade   B. happens

11 The germs _____ in the _____.
    A. body   B. multiply

12 Your body _____ a war _____.
    A. zone   B. becomes

13 You start to _____ tired and _____.
    A. weak   B. feel

14 Luckily, your _____ has an army of _____.
    A. defense   B. body

15 The T cells _____ the _____!
    A. alarm   B. sound

16 The B cells _____ to fight the _____ _____ antibodies.
    A. with   B. germs   C. arrive

17 The _____ cells show _____ and _____ the germs.
    A. eat   B. up   C. macrophage

18 _____, this army is _____ the white blood _____.
    A. cells   B. together   C. called

19 If all _____ well, they win the _____.
    A. fight   B. goes

20 _____ a _____ days, you start to _____ better.
    A. few   B. feel   C. in

1 세균은 어디에나 있지만 눈으로 세균을 보는 것은 불가능하다.

2 세균에는 두 가지 주요한 종류가 있다: 박테리아와 바이러스이다.

3 박테리아는 매우 작은 생물이다.

4 어떤 것들은 좋다.

5 그것들은 당신이 먹는 음식을 소화하는 데 도움을 줄 수 있다.

6 다른 것들은 나쁘고 당신을 아프게 할 수 있다.

7 바이러스는 다른 살아 있는 몸의 세포 안에서만 살 수 있는 세균이다.

8 그들은 독감과 같은 질병을 일으킨다.

9 '나쁜' 세균은 피부, 입, 코, 눈을 통해 몸에 들어갈 수 있다.

10 그들이 침입하면 어떻게 되는가?

11 세균은 몸속에서 증식한다.

12 당신의 몸은 전쟁 지역이 된다.

13 당신은 피곤하고 약해지기 시작한다.

14 다행히도, 당신의 몸은 방어 부대를 가지고 있다.

15 T세포가 경보를 발한다!

16 B세포는 항체로 세균과 싸우기 위해 도착한다.

17 대식 세포가 나타나서 세균을 먹는다.

18 이 군대는 함께 백혈구라고 부른다.

19 모든 것이 잘되면 싸움에서 이긴다.

20 며칠 후면 당신은 회복되기 시작한다.

21 The body remembers the _____, so it cannot make _____ of _____ again.
A. copies   B. invader   C. itself

22 But the germs are _____, _____.
A. too   B. smart

23 They can _____ form and _____ the body.
A. change   B. trick

24 There are _____ ways to _____ yourself _____ germs.
A. protect   B. from   C. several

25 First, _____ your hands _____ soap and _____ water.
A. with   B. warm   C. wash

26 A balanced _____ will _____ your body strong and _____.
A. healthy   B. keep   C. diet

27 _____ is also important to _____ regularly and get _____ of sleep.
A. exercise   B. plenty   C. it

28 _____, get the necessary _____.
A. shots   B. finally

29 They are the best _____ against _____.
A. germs   B. defense

30 If you _____ these _____, you will not be a _____ of "bad" germs.
A. victim   B. steps   C. follow

31 _____ more _____ of me.
A. copies   B. make

32 It's _____ job to _____ the body.
A. defend   B. my

33 That _____ a nice _____!
A. meal   B. was

34 Are _____ any more germs to _____?
A. eat   B. there

35 _____ year, I'll _____ in my cousin.
A. send   B. next

36 He'll _____ you then for _____ fight!
A. another   B. see

37 _____ _____ I do now?
A. can   B. what

38 I'm _____ to fight _____ germs.
A. any   B. ready

39 We _____ _____.
A. up   B. give

40 We can't _____ you _____.
A. sick   B. make

---

21 몸은 침입자를 기억하므로 침입자는 다시 복제할 수 없다.

22 하지만 세균들도 영리하다.

23 그들은 형태를 바꿀 수 있고 몸을 속일 수 있다.

24 세균으로부터 당신 자신을 보호하는 몇 가지 방법이 있다.

25 먼저 비누와 따뜻한 물로 손을 씻어라.

26 균형 잡힌 식단은 당신의 몸을 튼튼하고 건강하게 해줄 것이다.

27 규칙적으로 운동하고 충분한 잠을 자는 것도 중요하다.

28 마지막으로 필요한 주사를 맞아라.

29 그것들은 세균을 막는 최고의 방어 수단이다.

30 만약 당신이 이 단계를 따른다면, 당신은 "나쁜" 세균의 희생자가 되지 않을 것이다.

31 나를 더 복제해 줘.

32 몸을 지키는 게 내 일이야.

33 정말 맛있는 식사였어!

34 먹을 세균이 더 있니?

35 내년에는 내 사촌을 보낼게.

36 그때 그가 또 싸우려고 널 만나게 될 거야!

37 지금 내가 무엇을 할 수 있을까?

38 나는 어떤 세균과도 싸울 준비가 되어 있어.

39 우리는 포기한다.

40 우리는 널 아프게 할 수 없어.

※ 다음 우리말과 일치하도록 빈칸에 알맞은 말을 쓰시오.

1　Germs are _____, but it is _____ _____ _____ them with your eyes.

2　There are two _____ _____ of germs: _____ and _____.

3　Bacteria _____ very small _____.

4　_____ are _____.

5　They can _____ _____ _____ the food that you eat.

6　_____ are bad and can _____ you _____.

7　Viruses are _____ that can only live _____ the cells of _____ _____ _____.

8　They _____ diseases _____ _____ the flu.

9　"Bad" germs _____ _____ your body _____ your _____, _____, nose, and eyes.

10　What _____ when they _____?

11　The germs _____ in the _____.

12　Your body _____ a war _____.

13　You start to _____ _____ and _____.

14　_____, your body has an _____ _____ _____.

15　The T cells _____ the _____!

16　The B cells arrive _____ _____ the _____ with _____.

17　The _____ cells _____ _____ and eat the germs.

18　Together, this army is called the _____ _____ _____.

19　If all _____ _____, they _____ the fight.

20　In a _____, you start to _____ _____.

1　세균은 어디에나 있지만 눈으로 세균을 보는 것은 불가능하다.

2　세균에는 두 가지 주요한 종류가 있다: 박테리아와 바이러스이다.

3　박테리아는 매우 작은 생물이다.

4　어떤 것들은 좋다.

5　그것들은 당신이 먹는 음식을 소화하는 데 도움을 줄 수 있다.

6　다른 것들은 나쁘고 당신을 아프게 할 수 있다.

7　바이러스는 다른 살아 있는 몸의 세포 안에서만 살 수 있는 세균이다.

8　그들은 독감과 같은 질병을 일으킨다.

9　'나쁜' 세균은 피부, 입, 코, 눈을 통해 몸에 들어갈 수 있다.

10　그들이 침입하면 어떻게 되는가?

11　세균은 몸속에서 증식한다.

12　당신의 몸은 전쟁 지역이 된다.

13　당신은 피곤하고 약해지기 시작한다.

14　다행히도, 당신의 몸은 방어 부대를 가지고 있다.

15　T세포가 경보를 발한다!

16　B세포는 항체로 세균과 싸우기 위해 도착한다.

17　대식 세포가 나타나서 세균을 먹는다.

18　이 군대는 함께 백혈구라고 부른다.

19　모든 것이 잘되면 싸움에서 이긴다.

20　며칠 후면 당신은 회복되기 시작한다.

21 The body remembers the _____, so it _____ _____ _____ of itself again.

22 _____ the germs are _____, _____.

23 They can _____ _____ and trick the body.

24 There are _____ _____ _____ _____ yourself from germs.

25 First, _____ your hands _____ _____ and warm water.

26 A balanced diet will _____ your body _____ and _____.

27 It is also _____ _____ _____ regularly and get _____ _____ sleep.

28 _____, get the _____ _____.

29 They are the best _____ _____ germs.

30 If you follow these _____, you will not _____ _____ _____ of "bad" germs.

31 _____ more _____ _____ me.

32 It's my _____ _____ _____ the body.

33 That was a _____ _____!

34 Are there any _____ _____ _____ _____?

35 Next year, I'll _____ _____ my cousin.

36 He'll see you then _____ _____ _____!

37 _____ can I _____ now?

38 _____ _____ _____ fight any germs.

39 We _____ _____.

40 We can't _____ _____ _____.

21	몸은 침입자를 기억하므로 침입자는 다시 복제할 수 없다.
22	하지만 세균들도 영리하다.
23	그들은 형태를 바꿀 수 있고 몸을 속일 수 있다.
24	세균으로부터 당신 자신을 보호하는 몇 가지 방법이 있다.
25	먼저 비누와 따뜻한 물로 손을 씻어라.
26	균형 잡힌 식단은 당신의 몸을 튼튼하고 건강하게 해줄 것이다.
27	규칙적으로 운동하고 충분한 잠을 자는 것도 중요하다.
28	마지막으로 필요한 주사를 맞아라.
29	그것들은 세균을 막는 최고의 방어 수단이다.
30	만약 당신이 이 단계를 따른다면, 당신은 "나쁜" 세균의 희생자가 되지 않을 것이다.
31	나를 더 복제해 줘.
32	몸을 지키는 게 내 일이야.
33	정말 맛있는 식사였어!
34	먹을 세균이 더 있니?
35	내년에는 내 사촌을 보낼게.
36	그때 그가 또 싸우려고 널 만나게 될 거야!
37	지금 내가 무엇을 할 수 있을까?
38	나는 어떤 세균과도 싸울 준비가 되어 있어.
39	우리는 포기한다.
40	우리는 널 아프게 할 수 없어.

※ 다음 문장을 우리말로 쓰시오.

1 Germs are everywhere, but it is impossible to see them with your eyes.

➡ _____

2 There are two major kinds of germs: bacteria and viruses.

➡ _____

3 Bacteria are very small creatures.

➡ _____

4 Some are good.

➡ _____

5 They can help you digest the food that you eat.

➡ _____

6 Others are bad and can make you sick.

➡ _____

7 Viruses are germs that can only live inside the cells of other living bodies.

➡ _____

8 They cause diseases such as the flu.

➡ _____

9 "Bad" germs can enter your body through your skin, mouth, nose, and eyes.

➡ _____

10 What happens when they invade?

➡ _____

11 The germs multiply in the body.

➡ _____

12 Your body becomes a war zone.

➡ _____

13 You start to feel tired and weak.

➡ _____

14 Luckily, your body has an army of defense.

➡ _____

15 The T eslls sound the alarm!

➡ _____

16 The B cells arrive to fight the germs with antibodies.

➡ _____

17 The macrophage cells show up and eat the germs.
➡ _____

18 Together, this army is called the white blood cells.
➡ _____

19 If all goes well, they win the fight.
➡ _____

20 In a few days, you start to feel better.
➡ _____

21 The body remembers the invader, so it cannot make copies of itself again.
➡ _____

22 But the germs are smart, too.
➡ _____

23 They can change form and trick the body.
➡ _____

24 There are several ways to protect yourself from germs.
➡ _____

25 First, wash your hands with soap and warm water.
➡ _____

26 A balanced diet will keep your body strong and healthy.
➡ _____

27 It is also important to exercise regularly and get plenty of sleep.
➡ _____

28 Finally, get the necessary shots.
➡ _____

29 They are the best defense against germs.
➡ _____

30 If you follow these steps, you will not be a victim of "bad" germs.
➡ _____

31 Make more copies of me.
➡ _____

32 It's my job to defend the body.
➡ _____

33 That was a nice meal!
➡ _____

34 Are there any more germs to eat?
➡ _____

35 Next year, I'll send in my cousin.
➡ _____

36 He'll see you then for another fight!
➡ _____

37 I'm ready to fight any germs.
➡ _____

38 We can't make you sick.
➡ _____

※ 다음 괄호 안의 단어들을 우리말에 맞도록 바르게 배열하시오.

1 (everywhere, / are / germs / but / is / it / impossible / see / to / your / eyes. / with / them)
➡ _____

2 (are / major / there / kinds / two / germs: / of / viruses. / and / bacteria)
➡ _____

3 (very / creatures. / small / bacteria / are)
➡ _____

4 (good. / some / are)
➡ _____

5 (help / they / digest / can / you / the / eat. / you / that / food)
➡ _____

6 (bad / others / and / are / you / can / sick. / make)
➡ _____

7 (germs / that / are / viruses / live / can / inside / only / other / of / living / the / bodies. / cells)
➡ _____

8 (diseases / they / cause / the / such / flu. / as)
➡ _____

9 (your / germs / enter / "bad" / body / can / your / through / mouth, / and / skin, / eyes. / nose,)
➡ _____

10 (happens / they / what / invade? / when)
➡ _____

11 (the / multiply / body. / the / germs / in)
➡ _____

12 (body / a / your / zone / war / becomes)
➡ _____

13 (start / tired / you / feel / to / weak. / and)
➡ _____

14 (luckily, / body / has / army / your / defense. / an / of)
➡ _____

15 (the / cells / T / alarm! / the / sound)
➡ _____

16 (the / cells / to / B / fight / arrive / the / antibodies. / with / germs)
➡ _____

17 (cells / the / macrophage / up / eat / and / show / germs. / the)
➡ _____

18 (together, / is / army / this / called / the / blood / cells. / white)
➡ _____

19 (all / well, / if / goes / win / they / fight. / the)
➡ _____

20 (a / days, / few / in / you / feel / to / better. / start)
➡ _____

1 세균은 어디에나 있지만 눈으로 세균을 보는 것은 불가능하다.
2 세균에는 두 가지 주요한 종류가 있다: 박테리아와 바이러스이다.
3 박테리아는 매우 작은 생물이다.
4 어떤 것들은 좋다.
5 그것들은 당신이 먹는 음식을 소화하는 데 도움을 줄 수 있다.
6 다른 것들은 나쁘고 당신을 아프게 할 수 있다.
7 바이러스는 다른 살아 있는 몸의 세포 안에서만 살 수 있는 세균이다.
8 그들은 독감과 같은 질병을 일으킨다.
9 '나쁜' 세균은 피부, 입, 코, 눈을 통해 몸에 들어갈 수 있다.
10 그들이 침입하면 어떻게 되는가?
11 세균은 몸속에서 증식한다.
12 당신의 몸은 전쟁 지역이 된다.
13 당신은 피곤하고 약해지기 시작한다.
14 다행히도, 당신의 몸은 방어 부대를 가지고 있다.
15 T세포가 경보를 발한다!
16 B세포는 항체로 세균과 싸우기 위해 도착한다.
17 대식 세포가 나타나서 세균을 먹는다.
18 이 군대는 함께 백혈구라고 부른다.
19 모든 것이 잘되면 싸움에서 이긴다.
20 며칠 후면 당신은 회복되기 시작한다.

21 (body / the / remembers / invader, / the / so / cannot / it / copies / itself / of / again. / make)
➡ _____

22 (the / but / germs / too. / smart, / are)
➡ _____

23 (can / change / they / and / form / the / body. / trick)
➡ _____

24 (are / there / ways / to / several / protect / germs. / yourself / from)
➡ _____

25 (first, / hands / with / wash / your / soap / water. / and / warm)
➡ _____

26 (diet / balanced / will / a / body / keep / healthy. / your / and / strong)
➡ _____

27 (it / also / important / is / exercise / to / and / plenty / regularly / of / sleep. / get)
➡ _____

28 (finally, / the / shots. / necessary / get)
➡ _____

29 (are / best / they / the / defense / germs. / against)
➡ _____

30 (you / these / follow / steps, / if / you / be / not / will / germs. / a / "bad" / of / victim)
➡ _____

31 (copies / make / me. / of / more)
➡ _____

32 (it's / to / job / my / body. / the / defend)
➡ _____

33 (was / meal! / that / nice / a)
➡ _____

34 (there / more / are / any / eat? / to / germs)
➡ _____

35 (year, / next / send / cousin. / I'll / in / my)
➡ _____

36 (see / then / he'll / for / fight! / another / you)
➡ _____

37 (can / now? / what / do / I)
➡ _____

38 (fight / ready / to / I'm / germs. / any)
➡ _____

39 (give / up. / we)
➡ _____

40 (can't / sick. / we / make / you)
➡ _____

21 몸은 침입자를 기억하므로 침입자는 다시 복제할 수 없다.

22 하지만 세균들도 영리하다.

23 그들은 형태를 바꿀 수 있고 몸을 속일 수 있다.

24 세균으로부터 당신 자신을 보호하는 몇 가지 방법이 있다.

25 먼저 비누와 따뜻한 물로 손을 씻어라.

26 균형 잡힌 식단은 당신의 몸을 튼튼하고 건강하게 해줄 것이다.

27 규칙적으로 운동하고 충분한 잠을 자는 것도 중요하다.

28 마지막으로 필요한 주사를 맞아라.

29 그것들은 세균을 막는 최고의 방어 수단이다.

30 만약 당신이 이 단계를 따른다면, 당신은 "나쁜" 세균의 희생자가 되지 않을 것이다.

31 나를 더 복제해 줘.

32 몸을 지키는 게 내 일이야.

33 정말 맛있는 식사였어!

34 먹을 세균이 더 있니?

35 내년에는 내 사촌을 보낼게.

36 그때 그가 또 싸우려고 널 만나게 될 거야!

37 지금 내가 무엇을 할 수 있을까?

38 나는 어떤 세균과도 싸울 준비가 되어 있어.

39 우리는 포기한다.

40 우리는 널 아프게 할 수 없어.

※ 다음 우리말을 영어로 쓰시오.

1 세균은 어디에나 있지만 눈으로 세균을 보는 것은 불가능하다.
➡ _____

2 세균에는 두 가지 주요한 종류가 있다: 박테리아와 바이러스이다.
➡ _____

3 박테리아는 매우 작은 생물이다.
➡ _____

4 어떤 것들은 좋다.
➡ _____

5 그것들은 당신이 먹는 음식을 소화하는 데 도움을 줄 수 있다.
➡ _____

6 다른 것들은 나쁘고 당신을 아프게 할 수 있다.
➡ _____

7 바이러스는 다른 살아 있는 몸의 세포 안에서만 살 수 있는 세균이다.
➡ _____

8 그들은 독감과 같은 질병을 일으킨다.
➡ _____

9 '나쁜' 세균은 피부, 입, 코, 눈을 통해 몸에 들어갈 수 있다.
➡ _____

10 그들이 침입하면 어떻게 되는가?
➡ _____

11 세균은 몸속에서 증식한다.
➡ _____

12 당신의 몸은 전쟁 지역이 된다.
➡ _____

13 당신은 피곤하고 약해지는 것을 느끼기 시작한다.
➡ _____

14 다행히도, 당신의 몸은 방어 군대를 가지고 있다.
➡ _____

15 T세포가 경보를 발한다!
➡ _____

16 B세포는 항체로 세균과 싸우기 위해 도착한다.
➡ _____

17 대식 세포가 나타나서 세균을 먹는다.
➡ _____

18 이 군대는 함께 백혈구라고 부른다.
➡ _____

19 모든 것이 잘되면 싸움에서 이긴다.
➡ _____

20 며칠 후면 당신은 회복되기 시작한다.
➡ _____

21 몸은 침입자를 기억하므로 다시 복제할 수 없다.
➡ _____

22 하지만 세균들도 영리하다.
➡ _____

23 그들은 형태를 바꿀 수 있고 몸을 속일 수 있다.
➡ _____

24 세균으로부터 여러분 자신을 보호하는 몇 가지 방법이 있다.
➡ _____

25 먼저 비누와 따뜻한 물로 손을 씻어라.
➡ _____

26 균형 잡힌 식단은 당신의 몸을 튼튼하고 건강하게 해줄 것이다.
➡ _____

27 규칙적으로 운동하고 충분한 잠을 자는 것도 중요하다.
➡ _____

28 마지막으로 필요한 주사를 맞아라.
➡ _____

29 그것들은 세균을 막는 최고의 방어이다.
➡ _____

30 만약 당신이 이 단계를 따른다면, 당신은 "나쁜" 세균의 희생자가 되지 않을 것이다.
➡ _____

31 나를 더 복제해 주세요.
➡ _____

32 몸을 지키는 게 내 일이야.
➡ _____

33 정말 맛있는 식사였어!
➡ _____

34 먹을 세균이 더 있니?
➡ _____

35 내년에는 내 사촌을 보낼게.
➡ _____

36 그때 그가 또 싸우려고 널 보게 될 거야!
➡ _____

37 지금 내가 무엇을 할 수 있을까?
➡ _____

38 나는 어떤 세균과도 싸울 준비가 되어 있어.
➡ _____

39 우리는 포기한다.
➡ _____

40 우리는 널 아프게 할 수 없어.
➡ _____

※ 다음 우리말과 일치하도록 빈칸에 알맞은 말을 쓰시오.

My Writing Portfolio - Step 1

1. Sit _____, Move _____

2. It is _____ to _____ online games too much.

3. It is time _____ go _____ and exercise.

4. Stay _____

5. _____ too many snacks is not _____ for your health.

6. It is _____ to eat _____ fruit and vegetables.

1. 덜 앉고, 더 움직여라
2. 온라인 게임을 너무 많이 하는 것은 위험하다.
3. 이제 외출해서 운동할 시간이다.
4. 건강을 유지해라
5. 과자를 너무 많이 먹는 것은 건강에 좋지 않다.
6. 과일과 채소를 충분히 먹는 것이 중요하다.

Words in Action - B

1. Frida Kahlo was a _____ _____ [artist].

2. She is _____ for her _____ paintings.

3. Charles Schulz was a _____ who created the famous _____ Charlie Brown.

4. Park Gyeongri was a _____ Korean _____.

5. She _____ 25 years _____ *Toji*.

6. James Cameron is the _____ of the movie, *Avatar*.

7. Jang Yeongsil was a(n) _____ [scientist] who _____ water clocks.

1. Frida Kahlo는 멕시코 화가[예술가]였다.
2. 그녀는 독특한 그림으로 유명하다.
3. Charles Schulz는 유명한 캐릭터인 Charlie Brown을 만든 만화가였다.
4. 박경리는 위대한 한국 작가였다.
5. 그녀는 토지를 쓰는 데 25년이 걸렸다.
6. James Cameron은 영화 '아바타'의 감독이다.
7. 장영실은 물시계를 만든 발명가[과학자]였다.

Wrap Up - Reading

1. Every day you _____ your hands _____ _____ different things.

2. You _____ your phone and computer.

3. You open and _____ doors _____ your hands, _____.

4. There _____ germs on everything _____ you touch.

5. If you eat snacks _____ your hands, the germs on your hands can _____ _____ your body.

6. Then _____ _____ you do?

7 _____ your hands _____ soap!

1. 여러분은 매일 다른 것들을 만지기 위해 손을 사용한다.
2. 여러분은 여러분의 전화기와 컴퓨터를 만진다.
3. 여러분은 또한 손으로 문을 열고 닫는다.
4. 여러분이 만지는 모든 것에는 세균이 있다.
5. 만약 여러분이 손으로 과자를 먹는다면, 여러분의 손에 있는 세균은 여러분의 몸으로 들어갈 수 있다.
6. 그럼 어떻게 해야 할까?
7. 비누로 손을 씻어라!

※ 다음 우리말을 영어로 쓰시오.

My Writing Portfolio - Step 1

1. 덜 앉고, 더 움직여라
➡ _____

2. 온라인 게임을 너무 많이 하는 것은 위험하다.
➡ _____

3. 이제 외출해서 운동할 시간이다.
➡ _____

4. 건강을 유지해라
➡ _____

5. 과자를 너무 많이 먹는 것은 건강에 좋지 않다.
➡ _____

6. 과일과 채소를 충분히 먹는 것이 중요하다.
➡ _____

Words in Action - B

1. Frida Kahlo는 멕시코 화가[예술가]였다.
➡ _____

2. 그녀는 독특한 그림으로 유명하다.
➡ _____

3. Charles Schulz는 유명한 캐릭터인 Charlie Brown을 만든 만화가였다.
➡ _____

4. 박경리는 위대한 한국 작가였다.
➡ _____

5. 그녀는 토지를 쓰는 데 25년이 걸렸다.
➡ _____

6. James Cameron은 영화 '아바타'의 감독이다.
➡ _____

7. 장영실은 물시계를 만든 발명가[과학자]였다.
➡ _____

Wrap Up - Reading

1. 여러분은 매일 다른 것들을 만지기 위해 손을 사용한다.
➡ _____

2. 여러분은 여러분의 전화기와 컴퓨터를 만진다.
➡ _____

3. 여러분은 또한 손으로 문을 열고 닫는다.
➡ _____

4. 여러분이 만지는 모든 것에는 세균이 있다.
➡ _____

5. 만약 여러분이 손으로 과자를 먹는다면, 여러분의 손에 있는 세균은 여러분의 몸으로 들어갈 수 있다.
➡ _____

6. 그럼 어떻게 해야 할까?
➡ _____

7. 비누로 손을 씻어라!
➡ _____

※ 다음 영어를 우리말로 쓰시오.

01	wildlife
02	wrong
03	leftover
04	pollution
05	artificial
06	bright
07	careful
08	create
09	volume
10	pick
11	disturb
12	effect
13	enough
14	allow
15	rhythm
16	almost
17	environment
18	carefully
19	especially
20	famous
21	clearly

22	follow
23	threaten
24	human
25	lastly
26	migrate
27	solve
28	natural
29	protect
30	rule
31	serious
32	starry
33	trash
34	volunteer
35	feed
36	according to
37	be familiar with
38	take care of
39	care about
40	have an effect
41	in danger
42	in fact
43	throw away

※ 다음 우리말을 영어로 쓰시오.

01 위협하다	22 특히, 특별히
02 인간, 사람	23 유명한
03 마지막으로	24 규칙
04 (알을) 낳다	25 심각한
05 모든 곳에서	26 별이 총총한
06 이동하다, 이주하다	27 칫솔
07 해결하다	28 쓰레기
08 보호하다	29 자원봉사로 일하다; 자원봉사자
09 최근의	30 먹이를 주다
10 남은 음식	31 음량, 볼륨
11 오염	32 (꽃을) 꺾다
12 인공의, 인위적인	33 방해하다
13 밝은	34 잘못된, 틀린
14 주의 깊은	35 리듬
15 야생 동물	36 ~에 관심을 가지다
16 창조[창작]하다	37 ~에 따르면
17 영향, 결과	38 조치를 취하다
18 거의	39 (볼륨을) 줄이다
19 환경	40 위험에 처한
20 주의 깊게	41 ~로 고통 받다
21 자연의	42 ~에 익숙하다, ~을 잘 알다
	43 수백만의

※ 다음 영영풀이에 알맞은 단어를 <보기>에서 골라 쓴 후, 우리말 뜻을 쓰시오.

1 _____ : full of stars: _____

2 _____ : not natural or real: _____

3 _____ : to make or produce something: _____

4 _____ : to produce an egg outside of the body: _____

5 _____ : the process of making air, water, soil, etc. dirty: _____

6 _____ : to give food to someone or something: _____

7 _____ : a regular, repeated pattern of events, changes, activities, etc.: _____

8 _____ : to stop someone from working, sleeping, etc.: _____

9 _____ : animals living in nature: _____

10 _____ : a change that results when something is done or happens: _____

11 _____ : the natural world in which people, animals, and plants live: _____

12 _____ : to move from one area to another at different times of the year: _____

13 _____ : to keep someone or something from being harmed, lost, etc.: _____

14 _____ : things that are no longer useful or wanted and that have been thrown away: _____

15 _____ : food that has not been finished at a meal and that is often served at another meal: _____

16 _____ : the amount of sound that is produced by a television, radio, stereo, etc.: _____

leftover	trash	protect	starry
feed	migrate	environment	wildlife
volume	rhythm	effect	disturb
create	artificial	lay	pollution

※ 다음 우리말과 일치하도록 빈칸에 알맞은 말을 쓰시오.

Communicate: Listen - Listen and Answer Dialog 1

G: Is it _____ _____ _____ a poster on the _____ _____,
Mr. Cha?

M: A poster?

G: Here. It's a poster _____ World _____ _____.

M: _____ me _____. It's a great poster. _____ you _____ it?

G: My club _____ made it _____. I think people _____ _____
_____ _____ our oceans.

M: I _____. Well, we don't have space _____ _____.

G: Then _____ I _____ it _____ the door?

M: Sure. _____ _____.

G: 게시판에 포스터를 붙여도 될까요, 차 선생님?
M: 포스터?
G: 이거요. 이것은 세계 해양의 날에 대한 포스터예요.
M: 어디 보자. 포스터가 멋지네. 네가 만들었니?
G: 저희 동아리 회원들이 함께 그것을 만들었어요. 저는 사람들이 우리의 바다에 대해 더 관심을 가져야 한다고 생각해요.
M: 나도 그렇게 생각해. 음, 지금은 공간이 없어.
G: 그럼 문에 붙여도 될까요?
M: 물론. 어서 해.

Communicate: Listen - Listen and Answer Dialog 2

G: What _____ you _____, Minsu?

B: I'm _____ _____ _____ _____.

G: Well, you're _____ _____ _____ do that.

B: Why _____?

G: It _____ _____ the water. It can _____ _____ people and
animals _____ _____.

B: I _____. Then _____ _____ I _____?

G: You _____ _____ it to a drugstore. They'll take _____ of it.

B: Oh, I _____ know that. I'll _____ _____ _____.

G: 뭐 하고 있니, 민수야?
B: 사용하지 않는 약을 버리고 있어.
G: 음, 그렇게 해서는 안 돼.
B: 왜 안 돼?
G: 그것은 물을 오염시킬 수 있어. 또한 사람과 동물을 위험에 빠뜨릴 수 있어.
B: 알겠어. 그럼 내가 어떻게 해야 하지?
G: 약국에 가져가야 해. 그들이 그것을 처리할 거야.
B: 오, 난 몰랐어. 더 주의할게.

Communicate: Listen - Listen More

G: Wow! I _____ this _____, Dad.

M: Oh, I _____ something. I _____ _____ our toothbrushes.

G: I _____ a store _____ _____ _____ here.

M: Okay. I'll _____ _____ some _____.

G: Sure. It's _____ _____. You _____ _____ _____.

M: _____ _____.

G: Dad, is _____ _____ _____ _____ some *ramyeon*?

M: Of _____. But you're _____ _____ _____ _____
_____ any leftovers.

G: I know that. I really _____ _____ the _____.

G: 와우! 이곳이 정말 좋아요, 아빠.
M: 오, 깜빡 잊은 게 있어. 칫솔을 가져오지 않았어.
G: 여기 오는 길에 가게를 봤어요.
M: 좋아, 내가 가서 칫솔 좀 사 올게.
G: 그래요. 어두워지고 있어요. 운전 조심하세요.
M: 걱정하지 마.
G: 아빠, 라면을 좀 요리해도 돼요?
M: 물론이지. 하지만 남은 음식은 버리면 안 돼.
G: 알아요. 저는 환경에 정말 관심이 많아요.

Communicate: Listen - All Ears

M: 1. You're _____ _____ _____ do that.

2. People _____ _____ _____ _____ our oceans.

M: 1. 너는 그렇게 해서는 안 돼.
2. 사람들은 우리의 바다에 대해 더 관심을 가져야 해.

Communicate: Speak - Talk in groups

A: _____ _____ _____ _____ study _____ breaks.

B: What's _____ _____ that?

A: It's a new _____ _____. You _____ do that.

B: Okay. I'll _____ _____ _____.

A: 쉬는 시간에 공부하면 안 돼.
B: 그게 뭐가 문젠데?
A: 새로운 학급 규칙이야. 그렇게 해선 안 돼.
B: 알았어. 규칙을 기억할게.

My Writing Portfolio - Step 1

M: _____ _____ K-Zoo. Please _____ carefully and _____ the rules. First, you're not _____ _____ _____ the animals. It can _____ them _____. And you're _____ _____ _____ _____ the animals. It can be very _____. _____, _____ _____ stones or trash _____ them. _____ your time _____ K-Zoo. Thank you.

M: K-Zoo에 오신 것을 환영합니다. 주의 깊게 듣고 규칙을 따르세요. 첫 번째, 동물들에게 먹이를 주면 안 돼요. 그것은 동물들을 아프게 할 수 있습니다. 그리고 동물들을 만지면 안 돼요. 그것은 매우 위험할 수 있습니다. 마지막으로, 동물들에게 돌이나 쓰레기를 던지지 마세요. K-Zoo에서 즐거운 시간을 보내세요. 감사합니다.

Wrap Up - Listening ❺

G: Dad, _____ _____ _____ _____ _____ _____ with my friends this Saturday?

M: _____ are your _____?

G: Well, my _____ singer _____ _____ _____ _____ _____ _____ at Olympic Park.

M: Okay, but _____ _____ _____ 9 o'clock.

G: No _____. The concert will _____ _____ by about 8:00.

G: 아빠, 이번 토요일에 친구들과 외출해도 될까요?
M: 너희들의 계획이 뭐니?
G: 음, 제가 가장 좋아하는 가수가 올림픽 공원에서 콘서트를 할 예정이에요.
M: 좋아, 하지만 9시까지는 집에 오거라.
G: 그럼요. 콘서트는 8시쯤에 끝날 거예요.

Wrap Up - Listening ❻

W: Hey, _____ _____ the sign!

B: _____ sign?

W: The one _____ _____. You're _____ _____ _____ _____ flowers here.

B: Oh, I'm _____. I _____ _____ _____ that.

W: 이봐요, 표지판을 보세요!
B: 무슨 표지판이요?
W: 저쪽에 있는 거요. 여기서 꽃을 따면 안 돼요.
B: 아, 미안해요. 전 몰랐어요.

※ 다음 우리말에 맞도록 대화를 영어로 쓰시오.

Communicate: Listen - Listen and Answer Dialog 1

G: _____

M: _____

G: _____

M: _____

G: _____

_____

M: _____

G: _____

M: _____

G: 게시판에 포스터를 붙여도 될까요, 차 선생님?

M: 포스터?

G: 이거요. 이것은 세계 해양의 날에 대한 포스터예요.

M: 어디 보자. 포스터가 멋지네. 네가 만 들었니?

G: 저희 동아리 회원들이 함께 그것을 만들었어요. 저는 사람들이 우리의 바다에 대해 더 관심을 가져야 한다 고 생각해요.

M: 나도 그렇게 생각해. 음, 지금은 공간 이 없어.

G: 그럼 문에 붙여도 될까요?

M: 물론. 어서 해.

Communicate: Listen - Listen and Answer Dialog 2

G: _____

B: _____

G: _____

B: _____

G: _____

B: _____

G: _____

B: _____

G: 뭐 하고 있니, 민수야?

B: 사용하지 않는 약을 버리고 있어.

G: 음, 그렇게 해서는 안 돼.

B: 왜 안 돼?

G: 그것은 물을 오염시킬 수 있어. 또한 사람과 동물을 위험에 빠뜨릴 수 있 어.

B: 알겠어. 그럼 내가 어떻게 해야 하지?

G: 약국에 가져가야 해. 그들이 그것을 처리할 거야.

B: 오, 난 몰랐어. 더 주의할게.

Communicate: Listen - Listen More

G: _____

M: _____

G: _____

M: _____

G: _____

M: _____

G: _____

M: _____

G: _____

G: 와우! 이곳이 정말 좋아요, 아빠.

M: 오, 깜빡 잊은 게 있어. 칫솔을 가져 오지 않았어.

G: 여기 오는 길에 가게를 봤어요.

M: 좋아, 내가 가서 칫솔 좀 사 올게.

G: 그래요. 어두워지고 있어요. 운전 조 심하세요.

M: 걱정하지 마.

G: 아빠, 라면을 좀 요리해도 돼요?

M: 물론이지. 하지만 남은 음식은 버리 면 안 돼.

G: 알아요. 저는 환경에 정말 관심이 많 아요.

Communicate: Listen - All Ears

M: 1. _____

    2. _____

Communicate: Speak - Talk in groups

A: _____

B: _____

A: _____

B: _____

My Writing Portfolio - Step 1

M: _____

    _____

    _____

    _____

Wrap Up - Listening ❺

G: _____

M: _____

G: _____

M: _____

G: _____

Wrap Up - Listening ❻

W: _____

B: _____

W: _____

B: _____

M: 1. 너는 그렇게 해서는 안 돼.
   2. 사람들은 우리의 바다에 대해 더 관심을 가져야 해.

A: 쉬는 시간에 공부하면 안 돼.
B: 그게 뭐가 문젠데?
A: 새로운 학급 규칙이야. 그렇게 해선 안 돼.
B: 알았어. 규칙을 기억할게.

M: K-Zoo에 오신 것을 환영합니다. 주의 깊게 듣고 규칙을 따르세요. 첫 번째, 동물들에게 먹이를 주면 안 돼요. 그것은 동물들을 아프게 할 수 있습니다. 그리고 동물들을 만지면 안 돼요. 그것은 매우 위험할 수 있습니다. 마지막으로, 동물들에게 돌이나 쓰레기를 던지지 마세요. K-Zoo에서 즐거운 시간을 보내세요. 감사합니다.

G: 아빠, 이번 토요일에 친구들과 외출해도 될까요?
M: 너희들의 계획이 뭐니?
G: 음, 제가 가장 좋아하는 가수가 올림픽 공원에서 콘서트를 할 예정이에요.
M: 좋아, 하지만 9시까지는 집에 오거라.
G: 그럼요. 콘서트는 8시쯤에 끝날 거예요.

W: 이봐요, 표지판을 보세요!
B: 무슨 표지판이요?
W: 저쪽에 있는 거요. 여기서 꽃을 따면 안 돼요.
B: 아, 미안해요. 전 몰랐어요.

※ 다음 우리말과 일치하도록 빈칸에 알맞은 것을 골라 쓰시오.

1 _____ at this beautiful _____ .

    A. painting   B. look

2 It was _____ by the famous Dutch _____ Vincent van Gogh _____ 1889.

    A. in   B. created   C. artist

3 In Van Gogh's _____ , almost everyone could _____ up and see a wonderful _____ night sky.

    A. look   B. starry   C. time

4 Now, how _____ of us _____ as lucky _____ Van Gogh?

    A. as   B. are   C. many

5 In _____ , many people in today's _____ cannot enjoy a starry night _____ .

    A. world   B. sky   C. fact

6 This is so _____ of light _____ .

    A. pollution   B. because

7 _____ of us are _____ with air, water, and _____ pollution.

    A. land   B. familiar   C. most

8 We know _____ they are serious _____ , and we are taking _____ to solve them.

    A. problems   B. action   C. that

9 But did you _____ that _____ can also _____ pollution?

    A. light   B. cause   C. know

10 _____ pollution—too much light in the _____ place at the wrong time—is almost _____ around the world.

    A. wrong   B. light   C. everywhere

11 It can have serious _____ _____ humans and _____ .

    A. wildlife   B. on   C. effects

---

1 이 아름다운 그림을 보세요.

2 그것은 1889년에 유명한 네덜란드 미술가 빈센트 반 고흐에 의해 만들어졌습니다.

3 반 고흐의 시대에는 거의 모든 사람들이 위를 쳐다보고 멋진 별이 빛나는 밤하늘을 볼 수 있었습니다.

4 이제, 우리들 중 얼마나 많은 사람이 반 고흐만큼 운이 있을까요?

5 사실, 오늘날 세계의 많은 사람들은 별이 빛나는 밤하늘을 즐길 수 없습니다.

6 이것은 빛의 오염 때문에 그렇습니다.

7 우리들 중 대부분은 공기, 물, 토양 오염에 익숙합니다.

8 우리는 그것들이 심각한 문제라는 것을 알고 있으며, 그것들을 해결하기 위해 조치를 취하고 있습니다.

9 하지만 여러분은 빛이 오염도 일으킬 수 있다는 것을 알고 있었나요?

10 빛의 오염—잘못된 시간에 잘못된 장소에서의 너무 많은 빛—은 전 세계의 거의 모든 곳에 있습니다.

11 그것은 인간과 야생동물에게 심각한 영향을 미칠 수 있습니다.

12 According to a recent _____, about 89% of the world's _____ lives under skies that are not dark _____ at night.

A. report   B. population   C. enough

13 _____ in big cities, people _____ cannot _____ a starry night.

A. see   B. especially   C. often

14 They can also _____ from sleep problems _____ the natural rhythm of day and night is _____ by artificial light.

A. because   B. disturbed   C. suffer

15 Wildlife is _____ by light pollution, _____.

A. too   B. threatened

16 Birds that _____ or hunt at night find their way by _____ light, but light in big cities can _____ them to wander off course.

A. natural   B. cause   C. migrate

17 Every year _____ of birds die after _____ buildings _____ have bright lights.

A. that   B. hitting   C. millions

18 Sea turtles cannot _____ find a place to lay eggs _____ beaches are too _____ at night.

A. since   B. easily   C. bright

19 Also, many baby sea turtles _____ because artificial light _____ them away from the _____.

A. ocean   B. draws   C. die

20 _____, light pollution is as _____ as other _____ of pollution.

A. forms   B. serious   C. clearly

21 We _____ to _____ ways to _____ the problem.

A. solve   B. find   C. have

22 _____ we do not, we _____ see stars _____ in our dreams or paintings.

A. may   B. only   C. if

---

12 최근 보고서에 따르면, 세계 인구의 약 89%가 밤에 충분히 어둡지 않은 하늘 아래서 살고 있습니다.

13 특히 대도시에서는 별이 빛나는 밤을 종종 볼 수 없습니다.

14 그들은 또한 인공적인 빛에 의해 낮과 밤의 자연적인 리듬이 방해를 받기 때문에 수면 문제로 고통을 겪을 수도 있습니다.

15 야생동물도 빛의 오염으로 위협받고 있습니다.

16 밤에 이동하거나 사냥하는 새들은 자연광을 통해 길을 찾지만, 대도시의 빛은 길을 벗어나도록 할 수 있습니다.

17 매년 수백만 마리의 새들이 밝은 불빛이 있는 건물에 부딪치고서 죽습니다.

18 바다거북들은 밤에 해변이 너무 밝기 때문에 알을 낳을 장소를 쉽게 찾을 수 없습니다.

19 또한, 많은 아기 바다거북들은 인공 빛이 그들을 바다에서 멀어지게 하기 때문에 죽습니다.

20 분명히, 빛 오염은 다른 형태의 오염만큼이나 심각합니다.

21 우리는 그 문제를 해결할 방법을 찾아야 합니다.

22 만약 우리가 하지 않으면, 우리는 우리의 꿈이나 그림에서만 별을 볼 수 있을지 모릅니다.

※ 다음 우리말과 일치하도록 빈칸에 알맞은 말을 쓰시오.

1 _____ _____ this beautiful _____.

2 It _____ _____ _____ the famous Dutch _____ Vincent van Gogh in 1889.

3 In Van Gogh's _____, almost everyone could _____ _____ and see a _____ _____ _____ _____.

4 Now, how _____ of us are _____ _____ _____ Van Gogh?

5 In _____, many people in today's _____ cannot enjoy a starry night _____.

6 This is so _____ of _____ _____.

7 Most of us _____ _____ _____ air, water, and _____ _____.

8 We know _____ they are serious _____, and we _____ _____ _____ _____ _____ them.

9 But did you _____ that light can also _____ _____?

10 _____ pollution—too much light in the _____ _____ at the _____ _____ almost _____ around the world.

11 It can have _____ _____ _____ humans and _____.

1	이 아름다운 그림을 보세요.
2	그것은 1889년에 유명한 네덜란드 미술가 빈센트 반 고흐에 의해 만들어졌습니다.
3	반 고흐의 시대에는 거의 모든 사람들이 위를 쳐다보고 멋진 별이 빛나는 밤하늘을 볼 수 있었습니다.
4	이제, 우리들 중 얼마나 많은 사람이 반 고흐만큼 운이 있을까요?
5	사실, 오늘날 세계의 많은 사람들은 별이 빛나는 밤하늘을 즐길 수 없습니다.
6	이것은 빛의 오염 때문에 그렇습니다.
7	우리들 중 대부분은 공기, 물, 토양 오염에 익숙합니다.
8	우리는 그것들이 심각한 문제라는 것을 알고 있으며, 그것들을 해결하기 위해 조치를 취하고 있습니다.
9	하지만 여러분은 빛이 오염도 일으킬 수 있다는 것을 알고 있었나요?
10	빛의 오염—잘못된 시간에 잘못된 장소에서의 너무 많은 빛—은 전 세계의 거의 모든 곳에 있습니다.
11	그것은 인간과 야생동물에게 심각한 영향을 미칠 수 있습니다.

12 _____ _____ a recent _____, about 89% of the world's _____ lives under skies that are not _____ _____ at night.

13 _____ in big cities, people _____ _____ _____ a starry night.

14 They can also _____ _____ sleep problems _____ the natural rhythm of day and night _____ _____ _____ _____ _____.

15 Wildlife _____ _____ _____ light pollution, _____.

16 Birds that _____ or hunt at night find their way _____ _____ _____, but light in big cities can _____ them to _____ _____ _____.

17 Every year _____ _____ _____ die _____ _____ buildings that have bright lights.

18 Sea turtles cannot _____ find a _____ _____ _____ eggs _____ beaches are too _____ at night.

19 Also, many baby sea turtles _____ because artificial light _____ them _____ _____ the _____.

20 _____, light pollution is as _____ as _____ _____ of pollution.

21 We _____ _____ _____ ways to _____ the problem.

22 _____ we _____ _____, we _____ _____ stars _____ in our dreams or paintings.

12 최근 보고서에 따르면, 세계 인구의 약 89%가 밤에 충분히 어둡지 않은 하늘 아래서 살고 있습니다.

13 특히 대도시에서는 별이 빛나는 밤을 종종 볼 수 없습니다.

14 그들은 또한 인공적인 빛에 의해 낮과 밤의 자연적인 리듬이 방해를 받기 때문에 수면 문제로 고통을 겪을 수도 있습니다.

15 야생동물도 빛의 오염으로 위협받고 있습니다.

16 밤에 이동하거나 사냥하는 새들은 자연광을 통해 길을 찾지만, 대도시의 빛은 길을 벗어나도록 할 수 있습니다.

17 매년 수백만 마리의 새들이 밝은 불빛이 있는 건물에 부딪치고서 죽습니다.

18 바다거북들은 밤에 해변이 너무 밝기 때문에 알을 낳을 장소를 쉽게 찾을 수 없습니다.

19 또한, 많은 아기 바다거북들은 인공 빛이 그들을 바다에서 멀어지게 하기 때문에 죽습니다.

20 분명히, 빛 오염은 다른 형태의 오염만큼이나 심각합니다.

21 우리는 그 문제를 해결할 방법을 찾아야 합니다.

22 만약 우리가 하지 않으면, 우리는 우리의 꿈이나 그림에서만 별을 볼 수 있을지 모릅니다.

※ 다음 문장을 우리말로 쓰시오.

1 ▶ Look at this beautiful painting.

➡ _____

2 ▶ It was created by the famous Dutch artist Vincent van Gogh in 1889.

➡ _____

3 ▶ In Van Gogh's time, almost everyone could look up and see a wonderful starry night sky.

➡ _____

4 ▶ Now, how many of us are as lucky as Van Gogh?

➡ _____

5 ▶ In fact, many people in today's world cannot enjoy a starry night sky.

➡ _____

6 ▶ This is so because of light pollution.

➡ _____

7 ▶ Most of us are familiar with air, water, and land pollution.

➡ _____

8 ▶ We know that they are serious problems, and we are taking action to solve them.

➡ _____

9 ▶ But did you know that light can also cause pollution?

➡ _____

10 ▶ Light pollution—too much light in the wrong place at the wrong time—is almost everywhere around the world.

➡ _____

11 ▶ It can have serious effects on humans and wildlife.

➡ _____

12 According to a recent report, about 89% of the world's population lives under skies that are not dark enough at night.

➡ _____

13 Especially in big cities, people often cannot see a starry night.

➡ _____

14 They can also suffer from sleep problems because the natural rhythm of day and night is disturbed by artificial light.

➡ _____

15 Wildlife is threatened by light pollution, too.

➡ _____

16 Birds that migrate or hunt at night find their way by natural light, but light in big cities can cause them to wander off course.

➡ _____

17 Every year millions of birds die after hitting buildings that have bright lights.

➡ _____

18 Sea turtles cannot easily find a place to lay eggs since beaches are too bright at night.

➡ _____

19 Also, many baby sea turtles die because artificial light draws them away from the ocean.

➡ _____

20 Clearly, light pollution is as serious as other forms of pollution.

➡ _____

21 We have to find ways to solve the problem.

➡ _____

22 If we do not, we may see stars only in our dreams or paintings.

➡ _____

※ 다음 괄호 안의 단어들을 우리말에 맞도록 바르게 배열하시오.

1 (painting. / look / this / at / beautiful)

➡ _____

2 (by / was / Dutch / it / created / famous / the / Vincent / artist / 1889. / Gogh / in / van)

➡ _____

3 (time, / in / Van / Gogh's / everyone / could / almost / up / look / and / wonderful / sky. / a / see / night / starry)

➡ _____
_____

4 (now, / of / how / many / us / as / are / Van / Gogh? / as / lucky)

➡ _____

5 (fact, / in / people / world / many / in / today's / a / cannot / sky. / night / enjoy / starry)

➡ _____

6 (is / because / pollution. / this / light / so / of)

➡ _____

7 (of / most / us / with / are / familiar / air, / pollution. / land / and / water,)

➡ _____

8 (know / they / we / that / are / problems, / serious / and / taking / to / we / action / them. / are / solve)

➡ _____
_____

9 (but / you / know / did / can / light / that / pollution? / also / cause)

➡ _____

10 (pollution / light / — / much / too / place / light / the / in / wrong / at / time / wrong / the / — / around / everywhere / is / the / almost / world.)

➡ _____
_____

11 (it / serious / have / can / effects / humans / on / wildlife. / and)

➡ _____

1 이 아름다운 그림을 보세요.

2 그것은 1889년에 유명한 네덜란드 미술가 빈센트 반 고흐에 의해 만들어졌습니다.

3 반 고흐의 시대에는 거의 모든 사람들이 위를 쳐다보고 멋진 별이 빛나는 밤하늘을 볼 수 있었습니다.

4 이제, 우리들 중 얼마나 많은 사람이 반 고흐만큼 운이 있을까요?

5 사실, 오늘날 세계의 많은 사람들은 별이 빛나는 밤하늘을 즐길 수 없습니다.

6 이것은 빛의 오염 때문에 그렇습니다.

7 우리들 중 대부분은 공기, 물, 토양 오염에 익숙합니다.

8 우리는 그것들이 심각한 문제라는 것을 알고 있으며, 그것들을 해결하기 위해 조치를 취하고 있습니다.

9 하지만 여러분은 빛이 오염도 일으킬 수 있다는 것을 알고 있었나요?

10 빛의 오염—잘못된 시간에 잘못된 장소에서의 너무 많은 빛—은 전 세계의 거의 모든 곳에 있습니다.

11 그것은 인간과 야생동물에게 심각한 영향을 미칠 수 있습니다.

2>2>22>22>22>22>22>22>22>22>22>22>22>22>22>22>22>22

12 (a / report, / to / according / recent / of / world's / the / 89% / about / under / population / skies / lives / that / at / dark / night. / not / are / enough)

➡ _____

13 (in / cities, / especially / big / people / cannot / a / often / night. / starry / see)

➡ _____

14 (they / also / from / can / suffer / problems / sleep / because / rhythm / the / of / natural / day / is / night / and / light. / by / artificial / disturbed)

➡ _____

15 (is / wildlife / light / threatened / too. / pollution, / by)

➡ _____

16 (that / birds / hunt / or / migrate / night / at / their / find / way / light, / natural / by / but / in / light / can / cities / big / wander / cause / to / them / course. / off)

➡ _____

17 (year / birds / every / of / die / millions / hitting / after / have / buildings / lights. / that / bright)

➡ _____

18 (cannot / turtles / sea / find / easily / a / lay / place / eggs / to / since / are / beaches / too / night. / bright / at)

➡ _____

19 (many / also, / baby / die / turtles / sea / artificial / because / draws / light / away / from / them / ocean. / the)

➡ _____

20 (pollution / clearly, / is / light / as / other / serious / of / as / pollution. / forms)

➡ _____

21 (we / find / have / to / ways / problem. / the / solve / to)

➡ _____

22 (do / if / not, / we / may / stars / see / only / we / our / in / paintings. / or / dreams)

➡ _____

12 최근 보고서에 따르면, 세계 인구의 약 89%가 밤에 충분히 어둡지 않은 하늘 아래서 살고 있습니다.

13 특히 대도시에서는 별이 빛나는 밤을 종종 볼 수 없습니다.

14 그들은 또한 인공적인 빛에 의해 낮과 밤의 자연적인 리듬이 방해를 받기 때문에 수면 문제로 고통을 겪을 수도 있습니다.

15 야생동물도 빛의 오염으로 위협받고 있습니다.

16 밤에 이동하거나 사냥하는 새들은 자연광을 통해 길을 찾지만, 대도시의 빛은 길을 벗어나도록 할 수 있습니다.

17 매년 수백만 마리의 새들이 밝은 불빛이 있는 건물에 부딪치고서 죽습니다.

18 바다거북들은 밤에 해변이 너무 밝기 때문에 알을 낳을 장소를 쉽게 찾을 수 없습니다.

19 또한, 많은 아기 바다거북들은 인공 빛이 그들을 바다에서 멀어지게 하기 때문에 죽습니다.

20 분명히, 빛 오염은 다른 형태의 오염만큼이나 심각합니다.

21 우리는 그 문제를 해결할 방법을 찾아야 합니다.

22 만약 우리가 하지 않으면, 우리는 우리의 꿈이나 그림에서만 별을 볼 수 있을지 모릅니다.

본문 Test **35**

※ 다음 우리말을 영어로 쓰시오.

1 이 아름다운 그림을 보세요.

➡ _____

2 그것은 1889년에 유명한 네덜란드 미술가 빈센트 반 고흐에 의해 만들어졌습니다.

➡ _____

3 반 고흐의 시대에는 거의 모든 사람들이 위를 쳐다보고 멋진 별이 빛나는 밤하늘을 볼 수 있었습니다.

➡ _____

4 이제, 우리들 중 얼마나 많은 사람이 반 고흐만큼 운이 있을까요?

➡ _____

5 사실, 오늘날 세계의 많은 사람들은 별이 빛나는 밤하늘을 즐길 수 없습니다.

➡ _____

6 이것은 빛의 오염 때문에 그렇습니다.

➡ _____

7 우리 대부분은 공기, 물, 토양 오염에 익숙합니다.

➡ _____

8 우리는 그것들이 심각한 문제라는 것을 알고 있으며, 그것들을 해결하기 위해 조치를 취하고 있습니다.

➡ _____

9 하지만 여러분은 빛이 오염도 일으킬 수 있다는 것을 알고 있었나요?

➡ _____

10 빛의 오염—잘못된 시간에 잘못된 장소에서의 너무 많은 빛—은 전 세계의 거의 모든 곳에 있습니다.

➡ _____

_____

11 그것은 인간과 야생동물에게 심각한 영향을 미칠 수 있습니다.

➡ _____

12 최근 보고서에 따르면, 세계 인구의 약 89%가 밤에 충분히 어둡지 않은 하늘 아래서 살고 있습니다.

➡ _____

_____

13 특히 대도시에서는 별이 빛나는 밤을 종종 볼 수 없습니다.

➡ _____

14 그들은 또한 인공적인 빛에 의해 낮과 밤의 자연적인 리듬이 방해를 받기 때문에 수면 문제로

고통을 겪을 수도 있습니다.

➡ _____

_____

15 야생동물도 빛의 오염으로 위협받고 있습니다.

➡ _____

16 밤에 이동하거나 사냥하는 새들은 자연광을 통해 길을 찾지만, 대도시의 빛은 길을 벗어나도록 할 수 있습니다.

➡ _____

_____

17 매년 수백만 마리의 새들이 밝은 불빛이 있는 건물에 부딪치고서 죽습니다.

➡ _____

18 바다거북들은 밤에 해변이 너무 밝기 때문에 알을 낳을 장소를 쉽게 찾을 수 없습니다.

➡ _____

19 또한, 많은 아기 바다거북들은 인공 빛이 그들을 바다에서 멀어지게 하기 때문에 죽습니다.

➡ _____

20 분명히, 빛 오염은 다른 형태의 오염만큼이나 심각합니다.

➡ _____

21 우리는 그 문제를 해결할 방법을 찾아야 합니다.

➡ _____

22 만약 우리가 하지 않으면, 우리는 우리의 꿈이나 그림에서만 별을 볼 수 있을지 모릅니다.

➡ _____

※ 다음 우리말과 일치하도록 빈칸에 알맞은 말을 쓰시오.

My Writing Portfolio - Step 1

1. _____ penguin

2. _____: _____ Africa

3. Food: _____

4. _____: grows _____ _____ _____ 60-70 cm

5. _____ _____: 10-30 years

6. Why are they _____ _____?

7. Sometimes they _____ _____ _____ _____.

8. Also, people _____ too many _____, and African penguins _____ _____ _____ food.

1. 아프리카 펭귄
2. 서식지: 남아프리카
3. 먹이: 생선
4. 크기: 60~70센티미터까지 자란다
5. 수명: 10~30년
6. 왜 그들은 위험에 처해 있는가?
7. 때때로 그들은 해양 오염으로 고통을 받는다.
8. 또한, 사람들이 너무 많은 물고기를 잡아서 아프리카 펭귄들은 충분한 먹이가 없다.

Have Fun Together

1. Excuse me. You're _____ _____ _____ make a fire and cook here.

2. In this park, you _____ _____ wild animals.

3. They can _____ _____, you know.

4. Please _____ _____ the sign.

5. It says you're _____ _____ _____ _____ the birds.

6. Will you please _____ your _____ _____?

7. You _____ _____ it in the mountains.

8. That's the _____ here.

9. Excuse me. You're not _____ _____ _____ flowers _____ fruits.

10. I understand _____ hot, _____ swimming _____ _____ _____ this national park.

11. Will you _____ _____ the volume please?

12. You're not _____ _____ _____ music _____.

13. Excuse me. You're _____ _____ _____ _____ here.

1. 실례합니다. 여기서 불을 피우고 요리하면 안 돼요.
2. 이 공원에서는 야생 동물들에게 먹이를 주면 안 돼요.
3. 여러분도 알다시피, 그들은 아플 수 있어요.
4. 표지판을 보세요.
5. 새들을 만지면 안 된다고 쓰여 있어요.
6. 쓰레기 좀 집에 가져가 줄래요?
7. 산에 버려두면 안 돼요.
8. 그게 바로 여기 규칙이에요.
9. 실례합니다. 꽃이나 과일을 따면 안 돼요.
10. 더운 건 알지만, 이 국립공원에서는 수영이 허용되지 않아요.
11. 소리 좀 줄여주시겠어요?
12 음악을 크게 틀면 안 돼요.
13 실례합니다. 여기서 낚시하면 안 돼요.

※ 다음 우리말을 영어로 쓰시오.

My Writing Portfolio - Step 1

1. 아프리카 펭귄
 ➡ _____

2. 서식지: 남아프리카
 ➡ _____

3. 먹이: 생선
 ➡ _____

4. 크기: 60∼70센티미터까지 자란다
 ➡ _____

5. 수명: 10∼30년
 ➡ _____

6. 왜 그들은 위험에 처해 있는가?
 ➡ _____

7. 때때로 그들은 해양 오염으로 고통을 받는다.
 ➡ _____

8. 또한, 사람들이 너무 많은 물고기를 잡아서 아프리카 펭귄들은 충분한 먹이가 없다.
 ➡ _____

Have Fun Together

1. 실례합니다. 여기서 불을 피우고 요리하면 안 돼요.
 ➡ _____

2. 이 공원에서는 야생 동물들에게 먹이를 주면 안 돼요.
 ➡ _____

3. 여러분도 알다시피, 그들은 아플 수 있어요.
 ➡ _____

4. 표지판을 보세요.
 ➡ _____

5. 새들을 만지면 안 된다고 쓰여 있어요.
 ➡ _____

6. 쓰레기 좀 집에 가져가 줄래요?
 ➡ _____

7. 산에 버려두면 안 돼요.
 ➡ _____

8. 그게 바로 여기 규칙이에요.
 ➡ _____

9. 실례합니다. 꽃이나 과일을 따면 안 돼요.
 ➡ _____

10. 더운 건 알지만, 이 국립공원에서는 수영이 허용되지 않아요.
 ➡ _____

11. 소리 좀 줄여주시겠어요?
 ➡ _____

12. 음악을 크게 틀면 안 돼요.
 ➡ _____

13. 실례합니다. 여기서 낚시하면 안 돼요.
 ➡ _____

※ 다음 영어를 우리말로 쓰시오.

01	professor	22	hit
02	buy	23	university
03	call	24	invite
04	continue	25	jump rope
05	allow	26	crazy
06	because	27	decide
07	surprised	28	suddenly
08	cost	29	loud
09	different	30	special
10	proudly	31	shout
11	dish	32	metal
12	early	33	owner
13	clock	34	reply
14	comic book	35	respond
15	everything	36	a piece of cake
16	plan	37	be late for
17	excuse	38	be proud of
18	explain	39	on the other side of
19	wall	40	come back
20	flat	41	get up late
21	global warming	42	take a test
		43	laugh out loud

※ 다음 우리말을 영어로 쓰시오.

01	사다	22	점수
02	~라고 부르다	23	소리, 소음
03	놀란	24	미친, 정신이상인
04	교수	25	결정하다
05	값비싼	26	갑자기
06	대답(응답)하다	27	설명하다
07	초대하다	28	주인
08	줄넘기하다	29	시끄러운
09	벽	30	외치다, 소리치다
10	자랑스럽게	31	구석, 모퉁이
11	인찌	32	변명, 핑계 거리
12	다른	33	치다, 때리다
13	계속하다	34	(값·비용이) ~이다[들다]
14	허락하다	35	큰 소리로 웃다
15	바람이 빠진, 펑크 난	36	자다, 취침하다
16	대답하다	37	~을 자랑으로 여기다
17	특별한	38	~의 반대편에(는)
18	지구 온난화	39	돌아오다
19	금속	40	늦잠을 자다
20	모든 것	41	토요일에
21	대학	42	~에 늦다
		43	시험을 보다

※ 다음 영영풀이에 알맞은 단어를 <보기>에서 골라 쓴 후, 우리말 뜻을 쓰시오.

1 _____ : not having enough air: _____

2 _____ : costing a lot of money: _____

3 _____ : a loud or unpleasant sound: _____

4 _____ : to say something very loudly: _____

5 _____ : unable to think in a clear or sensible way: _____

6 _____ : a person or group that owns something: _____

7 _____ : to do something without stopping: _____

8 _____ : a shallow container that you cook or serve food in: _____

9 _____ : very quickly in usually an unexpected way: _____

10 _____ : to have an amount of money as a price: _____

11 _____ : to make something clear or easy to understand: _____

12 _____ : to ask someone to come to a party, wedding, meal, etc.: _____

13 _____ : a teacher especially of the highest rank at a college or university: _____

14 _____ : a reason that you give to explain a mistake, bad behavior, etc.: _____

15 _____ : to say or write something as an answer to a question or request: _____

16 _____ : an institution at the highest level of education where you can study for a degree or do research: _____

보기			
explain	cost	excuse	professor
invite	crazy	respond	flat
expensive	dish	continue	owner
noise	suddenly	shout	university

※ 다음 우리말과 일치하도록 빈칸에 알맞은 것을 골라 쓰시오.

1 A _____ That _____
　A. Talks　　　　B. Clock

2 Dean _____ his friends _____ his room _____ evening.
　A. to　　　　B. one　　　　C. invited

3 He was _____ of everything _____ his room: a nice bed, many _____ books, and a new computer.
　A. comic　　　　B. proud　　　　C. in

4 _____ the corner, he also _____ a very big metal _____ .
　A. dish　　　　B. in　　　　C. had

5 A friend _____ , " _____ that big dish?"
　A. what's　　　　B. asked

6 "Oh, that's my _____ clock. It _____ ." Dean replied _____ .
　A. talks　　　　B. proudly　　　　C. special

7 " _____ you _____ the dish, you'll know the _____ ."
　A. hit　　　　B. time　　　　C. if

8 Then he _____ the dish _____ his hand.
　A. with　　　　B. hit

9 It _____ a really _____ noise.
　A. loud　　　　B. made

10 Suddenly, his sister who was _____ the other side of the wall _____ , "Are you _____ ?"
　A. crazy　　　　B. on　　　　C. shouted

11 _____ eleven o'clock _____ night. Time to go to _____ !"
　A. bed　　　　B. it's　　　　C. at

12 A _____ _____
　A. Tire　　　　B. Flat

13 Jessie and Nicole are _____ _____ .
　A. friends　　　　B. university

14 They visited Jessie's grandma _____ Florida _____ Saturday.
　A. on　　　　B. in

15 They planned to come _____ early on Monday _____ they _____ a big test that afternoon.
　A. had　　　　B. because　　　　C. back

16 But they _____ up _____ and could not _____ it to the test.
　A. make　　　　B. late　　　　C. got

17 They needed a good excuse for _____ late, so they _____ to tell the professor that their car _____ a flat tire.
　A. decided　　　　B. got　　　　C. being

1 말하는 시계

2 어느 날 저녁 Dean은 친구들을 자기 방으로 초대했다.

3 그는 방에 있는 모든 것 즉, 멋진 침대, 많은 만화책들, 그리고 새 컴퓨터를 자랑스러워했다.

4 구석에 그는 커다란 금속 접시도 가지고 있었다.

5 한 친구가 "저 큰 접시는 뭐니?"라고 물었다.

6 "아, 저건 내 특별한 시계야. 그건 말을 해." Dean이 자랑스럽게 대답했다.

7 "접시를 치면, 시간을 알게 될 거야."

8 그러고 나서 그는 손으로 접시를 쳤다.

9 그것은 정말 큰 소리를 냈다.

10 갑자기 벽 반대편에 있던 그의 누나가 소리쳤다. "너 미쳤니?"

11 밤 11시야. 잘 시간이야!"

12 펑크 난 타이어

13 Jessie와 Nicole은 대학 친구이다.

14 그들은 토요일에 플로리다에 계시는 Jessie의 할머니를 방문했다.

15 그들은 월요일 오후에 큰 시험이 있기 때문에 그날 일찍 돌아올 계획이었다.

16 하지만 그들은 늦게 일어나서 시험에 맞춰 올 수 없었다.

17 그들은 지각한 것에 대한 좋은 핑계 거리가 필요해서 교수에게 차의 타이어에 펑크가 났다고 말하기로 결정했다.

18 The professor agreed _____ it was just bad luck and _____
them _____ take the test on Wednesday.
A. allowed   B. to   C. that

19 _____ they came to _____ the test on Wednesday morning,
the professor _____ Jessie and Nicole in different rooms.
A. put   B. when   C. take

20 _____ they sat _____, they read the _____ question.
A. down   B. as   C. first

21 For 5 points, explain _____ _____.
A. warming   B. global

22 It was a _____ of _____ to them. Then, the test _____.
A. continued   B. cake   C. piece

23 For 95 _____, _____ the question:
A. answer   B. points

24 _____ _____?
A. tire   B. which

25 A _____ _____
A. parrot   B. special

26 _____ day Abril went to a pet shop _____ _____ a
parrot.
A. to   B. buy   C. one

27 "_____ _____ is this blue _____?" she asked.
A. much   B. one   C. how

28 "It _____ $2,000," said the _____ _____ owner.
A. shop   B. costs   C. pet

29 "_____ is it so _____?" asked Abril.
A. expensive   B. why

30 "This parrot is a very _____ _____. It can _____ the
piano!"
A. one   B. play   C. special

31 "What _____ the green _____?" she asked.
A. one   B. about

32 "It _____ $5,000 _____ it can play the piano, paint pictures,
and _____ rope."
A. because   B. jump   C. costs

33 "Then what _____ the red _____?" Abril _____.
A. asked   B. one   C. about

34 The owner _____ that it _____ $10,000.
A. costs   B. responded

35 She was _____ and _____, "What does it do?"
A. asked   B. surprised

36 "I don't know," _____ the owner, "but the _____ two birds
_____ it 'teacher.'"
A. call   B. other   C. said

Step1

18 교수는 그것이 단지 불운이라는 것에 동의했고 수요일에 그들이 시험을 볼 수 있도록 허락했다.

19 수요일 아침에 그들이 시험을 보러 왔을 때, 교수는 Jessie와 Nicole을 다른 방에 들어가게 했다.

20 그들은 앉아서 첫 번째 문제를 읽었다.

21 5점짜리, 지구 온난화를 설명하시오.

22 그것은 그들에게 식은 죽 먹기였다. 그러고 나서, 시험은 계속되었다.

23 95점짜리, 질문에 답하시오.

24 어느 타이어였는가?

25 특별한 앵무새

26 어느 날 Abril은 앵무새를 사러 애완동물 가게에 갔다.

27 "이 파란 앵무새는 얼마죠?" 그녀가 물었다.

28 "이것은 2,000달러예요," 애완동물 가게 주인이 말했다.

29 "왜 그렇게 비싸죠?" Abril이 물었다.

30 "이것은 아주 특별한 앵무새입니다. 피아노를 칠 수 있어요!"

31 "초록색 앵무새는요?" 그녀가 물었다.

32 "이것은 피아노를 치고, 그림을 그리고, 줄넘기를 할 수 있기 때문에 5,000달러입니다."

33 "그럼 빨간 앵무새는요?" Abril이 물었다.

34 주인은 10,000달러라고 대답했다.

35 그녀는 놀라서 물었다. "그것은 뭘 할 수 있죠?"

36 "모르겠어요, 하지만 다른 두 새들이 그것을 '선생님'이라고 불러요."라고 주인이 말했다.

※ 다음 우리말과 일치하도록 빈칸에 알맞은 말을 쓰시오.

1 A _____ That _____

2 Dean _____ his friends _____ his room _____ _____.

3 He _____ _____ _____ everything _____ his room: a nice bed, many _____ _____, and a _____ _____.

4 _____ the corner, he also _____ a very big _____ _____.

5 A friend _____, "_____ that _____ _____?"

6 "Oh, that's my _____ clock. It _____." Dean replied _____.

7 "_____ you _____ the dish, you'll know _____ _____."

8 Then he _____ the dish _____ _____ _____.

9 It _____ a really _____ _____.

10 _____, his sister who was _____ _____ _____ the wall _____, "_____ you _____?"

11 _____ eleven o'clock _____ night. _____ _____ _____ _____ _____!"

12 A _____ _____

13 Jessie and Nicole _____ _____ _____.

14 They _____ Jessie's grandma _____ Florida _____ _____.

15 They planned to _____ _____ _____ on Monday _____ they had a _____ _____ that afternoon.

16 But they _____ _____ _____ and could not _____ _____ _____ the test.

17 They needed a good excuse _____ _____ _____, so they _____ _____ the professor that their car _____ a _____ _____.

1 말하는 시계

2 어느 날 저녁 Dean은 친구들을 자기 방으로 초대했다.

3 그는 방에 있는 모든 것 즉, 멋진 침대. 많은 만화책들, 그리고 새 컴퓨터를 자랑스러워했다.

4 구석에 그는 커다란 금속 접시도 가지고 있었다.

5 한 친구가 "저 큰 접시는 뭐니?"라고 물었다.

6 "아, 저건 내 특별한 시계야. 그건 말을 해." Dean이 자랑스럽게 대답했다.

7 "접시를 치면, 시간을 알게 될 거야."

8 그러고 나서 그는 손으로 접시를 쳤다.

9 그것은 정말 큰 소리를 냈다.

10 갑자기 벽 반대편에 있던 그의 누나가 소리쳤다. "너 미쳤니?"

11 밤 11시야. 잘 시간이야!"

12 펑크 난 타이어

13 Jessie와 Nicole은 대학 친구이다.

14 그들은 토요일에 플로리다에 계시는 Jessie의 할머니를 방문했다.

15 그들은 월요일 오후에 큰 시험이 있기 때문에 그날 일찍 돌아올 계획이었다.

16 하지만 그들은 늦게 일어나서 시험에 맞춰 올 수 없었다.

17 그들은 지각한 것에 대한 좋은 핑계 거리가 필요해서 교수에게 차의 타이어에 펑크가 났다고 말하기로 결정했다.

18 The professor _____ _____ it was just _____ _____ and _____ them _____ _____ the test on Wednesday.

19 _____ they _____ _____ _____ the test _____ Wednesday morning, the professor _____ Jessie and Nicole in _____ _____ .

20 _____ they _____ _____ , they read the first question.

21 For 5 points, _____ _____ _____ .

22 It was _____ _____ _____ _____ to them. Then, the test _____ .

23 For 95 points, _____ the question:

24 _____ tire?

25 A _____ Parrot

26 _____ _____ Abril _____ _____ a pet shop _____ _____ a parrot.

27 " _____ _____ is this blue _____ ?" she _____ .

28 "It _____ $2,000," said the _____ _____ _____ .

29 " _____ is it _____ _____ ?" asked Abril.

30 "This parrot is a very _____ _____ . It can _____ _____ _____ !"

31 " _____ _____ the green one?" she asked.

32 "It costs $5,000 _____ it _____ _____ the piano, _____ pictures, and _____ _____ ."

33 "Then _____ _____ the red one?" Abril asked.

34 The owner _____ that it _____ $10,000.

35 She was _____ and asked, "What _____ it _____ ?"

36 "I don't know," _____ the owner, "but the _____ _____ _____ _____ it 'teacher.'"

---

18 교수는 그것이 단지 불운이라는 것에 동의했고 수요일에 그들이 시험을 볼 수 있도록 허락했다.

19 수요일 아침에 그들이 시험을 보러 왔을 때, 교수는 Jessie와 Nicole을 다른 방에 들어가게 했다.

20 그들은 앉아서 첫 번째 문제를 읽었다.

21 5점짜리, 지구 온난화를 설명하시오.

22 그것은 그들에게 식은 죽 먹기였다. 그러고 나서, 시험은 계속되었다.

23 95점짜리, 질문에 답하시오.

24 어느 타이어였는가?

25 특별한 앵무새

26 어느 날 Abril은 앵무새를 사러 애완동물 가게에 갔다.

27 "이 파란 앵무새는 얼마죠?" 그녀가 물었다.

28 "이것은 2,000달러예요," 애완동물 가게 주인이 말했다.

29 "왜 그렇게 비싸죠?" Abril이 물었다.

30 "이것은 아주 특별한 앵무새입니다. 피아노를 칠 수 있어요!"

31 "초록색 앵무새는요?" 그녀가 물었다.

32 "이것은 피아노를 치고, 그림을 그리고, 줄넘기를 할 수 있기 때문에 5,000달러입니다."

33 "그럼 빨간 앵무새는요?" Abril이 물었다.

34 주인은 10,000달러라고 대답했다.

35 그녀는 놀라서 물었다. "그것은 뭘 할 수 있죠?"

36 "모르겠어요, 하지만 다른 두 새들이 그것을 '선생님'이라고 불러요."라고 주인이 말했다.

※ 다음 문장을 우리말로 쓰시오.

1 ▸ A Clock That Talks

➡ _____

2 ▸ Dean invited his friends to his room one evening.

➡ _____

3 ▸ He was proud of everything in his room: a nice bed, many comic books, and a new computer.

➡ _____

4 ▸ In the corner, he also had a very big metal dish.

➡ _____

5 ▸ A friend asked, "What's that big dish?"

➡ _____

6 ▸ "Oh, that's my special clock. It talks," Dean replied proudly.

➡ _____

7 ▸ "If you hit the dish, you'll know the time."

➡ _____

8 ▸ Then he hit the dish with his hand.

➡ _____

9 ▸ It made a really loud noise.

➡ _____

10 ▸ Suddenly, his sister who was on the other side of the wall shouted, "Are you crazy?

➡ _____

11 ▸ It's eleven o'clock at night. Time to go to bed!"

➡ _____

12 ▸ A Flat Tire

➡ _____

13 ▸ Jessie and Nicole are university friends.

➡ _____

14 ▸ They visited Jessie's grandma in Florida on Saturday.

➡ _____

15 ▸ They planned to come back early on Monday because they had a big test that afternoon.

➡ _____

16 ▸ But they got up late and could not make it to the test.

➡ _____

17 ▸ They needed a good excuse for being late, so they decided to tell the professor that their car got a flat tire.

➡ _____

18 The professor agreed that it was just bad luck and allowed them to take the test on Wednesday.
➡ _____

19 When they came to take the test on Wednesday morning, the professor put Jessie and Nicole in different rooms.
➡ _____

20 As they sat down, they read the first question.
➡ _____

21 For 5 points, explain global warming.
➡ _____

22 It was a piece of cake to them. Then, the test continued.
➡ _____

23 For 95 points, answer the question.
➡ _____

24 Which tire?
➡ _____

25 A Special Parrot
➡ _____

26 One day Abril went to a pet shop to buy a parrot.
➡ _____

27 "How much is this blue one?" she asked.
➡ _____

28 "It costs $2,000," said the pet shop owner.
➡ _____

29 "Why is it so expensive?" asked Abril.
➡ _____

30 "This parrot is a very special one. It can play the piano!"
➡ _____

31 "What about the green one?" she asked.
➡ _____

32 "It costs $5,000 because it can play the piano, paint pictures, and jump rope."
➡ _____

33 "Then what about the red one?" Abril asked.
➡ _____

34 The owner responded that it costs $10,000.
➡ _____

35 She was surprised and asked, "What does it do?"
➡ _____

36 "I don't know," said the owner, "but the other two birds call it 'teacher.'"
➡ _____

※ 다음 괄호 안의 단어들을 우리말에 맞도록 바르게 배열하시오.

1 (That / A / Talks / Clock)
➡ _____

2 (Dean / his / invited / friends / room / his / to / evening. / one)
➡ _____

3 (was / everything / of / he / in / proud / room: / his / bed, / nice / a / books, / many / comic / and / computer. / new / a)
➡ _____

4 (the / corner, / in / also / he / a / had / metal / big / dish. / very)
➡ _____

5 (asked, / friend / a / "what's / dish?" / big / that)
➡ _____

6 ("oh, / my / clock. / that's / special // talks, / it / proudly. / replied / Dean)
➡ _____

7 ("if / hit / dish, / you / the / you'll / time." / the / know)
➡ _____

8 (he / the / then / dish / hit / hand. / his / with)
➡ _____

9 (a / noise. / made / it / loud / really)
➡ _____

10 (suddenly, / who / sister / on / was / his / other / the / side / of / shouted, / wall / the / crazy? / you / "are)
➡ _____

11 (eleven / at / it's / night. / o'clock // go / bed!" / to / to / time)
➡ _____

12 (Tire / Flat / a)
➡ _____

13 (and / Nicole / university / Jessie / friends. / are)
➡ _____

14 (Jessie's / visited / grandma / Florida / in / they / Saturday. / on)
➡ _____

15 (they / come / to / planned / early / back / Monday / on / they / because / big / a / had / afternoon. / that / test)
➡ _____

16 (but / up / they / got / late / and / could / it / make / not / test. / the / to)
➡ _____

17 (needed / excuse / they / good / a / late, / being / for / so / they / tell / decided / to / professor / the / their / tire. / a / car / flat / got)
➡ _____

1 말하는 시계

2 어느 날 저녁 Dean은 친구들을 자기 방으로 초대했다.

3 그는 방에 있는 모든 것 즉, 멋진 침대, 많은 만화책들, 그리고 새 컴퓨터를 자랑스러워했다.

4 구석에 그는 커다란 금속 접시도 가지고 있었다.

5 한 친구가 "저 큰 접시는 뭐니?"라고 물었다.

6 "아, 저건 내 특별한 시계야. 그건 말을 해." Dean이 자랑스럽게 대답했다.

7 "접시를 치면, 시간을 알게 될 거야."

8 그러고 나서 그는 손으로 접시를 쳤다.

9 그것은 정말 큰 소리를 냈다.

10 갑자기 벽 반대편에 있던 그의 누나가 소리쳤다. "너 미쳤니?"

11 밤 11시야. 잘 시간이야!"

12 펑크 난 타이어

13 Jessie와 Nicole은 대학 친구이다.

14 그들은 토요일에 플로리다에 계시는 Jessie의 할머니를 방문했다.

15 그들은 월요일 오후에 큰 시험이 있기 때문에 그날 일찍 돌아올 계획이었다.

16 하지만 그들은 늦게 일어나서 시험에 맞춰 올 수 없었다.

17 그들은 지각한 것에 대한 좋은 핑계 거리가 필요해서 교수에게 차의 타이어에 펑크가 났다고 말하기로 결정했다.

Step4

18 (professor / that / the / agreed / was / it / luck / just / bad / and / them / to / allowed / the / take / test / Wednesday. / on)
➡ _____

19 (they / when / take / to / came / test / the / Wednesday / on / morning, / professor / the / and / put / Nicole / in / Jessie / rooms. / different)
➡ _____

20 (they / sat / as / down, / read / they / the / question. / first)
➡ _____

21 (points / 5 / for / warming. / global / explain)
➡ _____

22 (was / it / cake / of / a / piece / them. / to // the / continued. / then, / test)
➡ _____

23 (for / points, / 95 / question. / the / answer)
➡ _____

24 (tire? / which)
➡ _____

25 (Parrot / a / Special)
➡ _____

26 (Abril / day / went / one / a / to / shop / pet / to / parrot. / a / buy)
➡ _____

27 (much / "how / blue / is / this / one?" / asked. / she)
➡ _____

28 ($2,000," / costs / "it / the / owner. / shop / said / pet)
➡ _____

29 (expensive?" / it / is / so "why / Abril. / asked)
➡ _____

30 (is / parrot / "this / very / a / one. / special // the / can / piano!" / it / play)
➡ _____

31 (the / one?" / about / "what / green / asked. / she)
➡ _____

32 (costs / $5,000 / "it / because / can / it / the / play / piano, / and / jump / paint / rope." / pictures,)
➡ _____

33 ("then / about / the / what / one?" / red / asked. / Abril)
➡ _____

34 (owner / the / responded / it / that / $10,000. / costs)
➡ _____

35 (was / she / asked, / and / surprised / does / "what / do?" / it)
➡ _____

36 (don't / I / know," / owner, / said / the / "but / the / two / other / call / birds / 'teacher.'" / it)
➡ _____

18 교수는 그것이 단지 불운이라는 것에 동의했고 수요일에 그들이 시험을 볼 수 있도록 허락했다.
19 수요일 아침에 그들이 시험을 보러 왔을 때, 교수는 Jessie와 Nicole을 다른 방에 들어가게 했다.
20 그들은 앉아서 첫 번째 문제를 읽었다.
21 5점짜리, 지구 온난화를 설명하시오.
22 그것은 그들에게 식은 죽 먹기였다. 그러고 나서, 시험은 계속되었다.
23 95점짜리, 질문에 답하시오.
24 어느 타이어였는가?
25 특별한 앵무새
26 어느 날 Abril은 앵무새를 사러 애완동물 가게에 갔다.
27 "이 파란 앵무새는 얼마죠?" 그녀가 물었다.
28 "이것은 2,000달러예요," 애완동물 가게 주인이 말했다.
29 "왜 그렇게 비싸죠?" Abril이 물었다.
30 "이것은 아주 특별한 앵무새입니다. 피아노를 칠 수 있어요!"
31 "초록색 앵무새는요?" 그녀가 물었다.
32 "이것은 피아노를 치고, 그림을 그리고, 줄넘기를 할 수 있기 때문에 5,000달러입니다."
33 "그럼 빨간 앵무새는요?" Abril이 물었다.
34 주인은 10,000달러라고 대답했다.
35 그녀는 놀라서 물었다. "그것은 뭘 할 수 있죠?"
36 "모르겠어요, 하지만 다른 두 새들이 그것을 '선생님'이라고 불러요."라고 주인이 말했다.

50 Special Lesson. Laugh Out Loud

※ **다음 우리말을 영어로 쓰시오.**

1 말하는 시계

➡ _____

2 어느 날 저녁 Dean은 친구들을 자기 방으로 초대했다.

➡ _____

3 그는 방에 있는 모든 것 즉, 멋진 침대, 많은 만화책들, 그리고 새 컴퓨터를 자랑스러워했다.

➡ _____

4 구석에 그는 커다란 금속 접시도 가지고 있었다.

➡ _____

5 한 친구가 "저 큰 접시는 뭐니?"라고 물었다.

➡ _____

6 "아, 저건 내 특별한 시계야. 그건 말을 해." Dean이 자랑스럽게 대답했다.

➡ _____

7 "접시를 치면, 시간을 알게 될 거야."

➡ _____

8 그러고 나서 그는 손으로 접시를 쳤다.

➡ _____

9 그것은 정말 큰 소리를 냈다

➡ _____

10 갑자기 벽 반대편에 있던 그의 누나가 소리쳤다. "너 미쳤니?"

➡ _____

11 밤 11시야. 잘 시간이야!"

➡ _____

12 펑크 난 타이어

➡ _____

13 Jessie와 Nicole은 대학 친구이다.

➡ _____

14 그들은 토요일에 플로리다에 계시는 Jessie의 할머니를 방문했다.

➡ _____

15 그들은 월요일 오후에 큰 시험이 있기 때문에 그날 일찍 돌아올 계획이었다.

➡ _____

16 하지만 그들은 늦게 일어나서 시험에 맞춰 올 수 없었다.

➡ _____

17 그들은 지각한 것에 대한 좋은 핑계 거리가 필요해서 교수에게 차의 타이어에 펑크가 났다고 말하기로 결정했다.

➡ _____

18 교수는 그것이 단지 불운이라는 것에 동의했고 수요일에 그들이 시험을 볼 수 있도록 허락했다.
➡ _____

19 수요일 아침에 그들이 시험을 보러 왔을 때, 교수는 Jessie와 Nicole을 다른 방에 들어가게 했다.
➡ _____

20 그들은 앉아서 첫 번째 문제를 읽었다.
➡ _____

21 5점짜리, 지구 온난화를 설명하시오.
➡ _____

22 그것은 그들에게 식은 죽 먹기였다. 그러고 나서, 시험은 계속되었다.
➡ _____

23 95점짜리, 질문에 답하시오.
➡ _____

24 어느 타이어였는가?
➡ _____

25 특별한 앵무새
➡ _____

26 어느 날 Abril은 앵무새를 사러 애완동물 가게에 갔다.
➡ _____

27 "이 파란 앵무새는 얼마죠?" 그녀가 물었다.
➡ _____

28 "이것은 2,000달러예요," 애완동물 가게 주인이 말했다.
➡ _____

29 "왜 그렇게 비싸죠?" Abril이 물었다.
➡ _____

30 "이것은 아주 특별한 앵무새입니다. 피아노를 칠 수 있어요!"
➡ _____

31 "초록색 앵무새는요?" 그녀가 물었다.
➡ _____

32 "이것은 피아노를 치고, 그림을 그리고, 줄넘기를 할 수 있기 때문에 5,000달러입니다."
➡ _____

33 "그럼 빨간 앵무새는요?" Abril이 물었다.
➡ _____

34 주인은 10,000달러라고 대답했다.
➡ _____

35 그녀는 놀라서 물었다. "그것은 뭘 할 수 있죠?"
➡ _____

36 "모르겠어요, 하지만 다른 두 새들이 그것을 '선생님'이라고 불러요."라고 주인이 말했다.
➡ _____

※ 다음 영어를 우리말로 쓰시오.

01	attitude	22	freedom
02	accuse	23	confident
03	throw	24	president
04	behind	25	receive
05	promise	26	right
06	protect	27	allowance
07	avoid	28	truth
08	bullying	29	arrest
09	difficulty	30	victim
10	free	31	ordinary
11	appearance	32	friendly
12	character	33	whisper
13	guilty	34	popular
14	worried	35	care for ~
15	judge	36	be afraid of ~
16	shy	37	calm down
17	prison	38	set+목적어+free
18	beard	39	accuse A of B
19	missing	40	thanks to ~
20	attack	41	be for ~
21	neighbor	42	fight off ~
		43	vote for ~

※ 다음 우리말을 영어로 쓰시오.

01 등

02 통과하다, 지나가다

03 활동

04 휴대하다, 지니다

05 소리치다, 외치다

06 희생자

07 투표하다

08 선택

09 들어가다, 참개[출전]하다

10 숨기다

11 속삭이다

12 다정한, 친절한

13 외모

14 체포하다

15 운이 좋은

16 직면하다, (힘든 상황에) 처하다

17 신경 쓰다, 꺼리다

18 유죄의

19 선택하다, 고르다

20 곱슬곱슬한

21 평범한

22 인기 있는, 대중적인

23 언제든지, 언제나

24 공약, 약속

25 매월의, 한 달에 한 번의

26 득점하다

27 자유

28 보호하다

29 자신감 있는

30 용돈

31 이웃

32 고발하다, 비난하다

33 실종된, 행방불명된

34 감옥

35 지금까지

36 ~을 두려워하다

37 B 때문에 A를 고발하다

38 ~을 자르다

39 ~을 잘하다

40 ~ 덕분에

41 ~을 뽑다, ~에게 투표하다

42 ~에게 동의하다

43 ~을 돌보다

※ 다음 영영풀이에 알맞은 단어를 <보기>에서 골라 쓴 후, 우리말 뜻을 쓰시오.

1 _____ : to make something happen: _____

2 _____ : someone who lives near you: _____

3 _____ : to stay away from a person or place: _____

4 _____ : to get points, goals, runs, etc., in a game or contest: _____

5 _____ : how you think or feel about something: _____

6 _____ : the belief that you are able to do things well or be successful: _____

7 _____ : a person who appears in a story, book, play, movie, or television show:
_____

8 _____ : to speak very quietly so that other people cannot hear: _____

9 _____ : to use violence to hurt or damage someone: _____

10 _____ : an action to try to frighten someone who is smaller or weaker: _____

11 _____ : to decide which thing you want. _____

12 _____ : to keep someone or something safe from something dangerous or bad:
_____

13 _____ : the money you get back when you pay more money than something
costs: _____

14 _____ : someone who has been hurt or killed: _____

15 _____ : an amount of money that parents give to a child each week: _____

16 _____ : to take the person away to ask them about a crime that they might have
committed: _____

attack	allowance	cause	score
neighbor	victim	bullying	attitude
choose	avoid	protect	confidence
whisper	change	character	arrest

※ 다음 우리말과 일치하도록 빈칸에 알맞은 말을 쓰시오.

 해석

Communicate: Listen - Listen and Answer. Talk

G: Hi, I'm Gacha. I'm _____ Mongolia. When I first came to Songji Middle School two months _____, I was so _____. I was a little _____, and I wasn't _____ at Korean. However, I'm a _____ girl. All my classmates are nice and _____. I enjoy _____ handball with them in P.E. class. I'm a good player. They _____ me "Golden Hand." There _____ _____ a sports day next week. _____ _____ my class _____ _____ in the handball event.

여: 안녕, 나는 Gacha라고 해. 나는 몽골에서 왔어. 두 달 전에 내가 처음 송지 중학교에 왔을 때, 나는 무척 걱정이 되었어. 나는 좀 수줍음을 탔고 한국어를 잘 못했어. 하지만 난 운이 좋은 아이야. 내 학급 친구들은 모두 멋지고 다정해. 나는 체육 시간에 친구들과 핸드볼 하는 것을 즐겨. 난 실력이 좋은 선수야. 친구들은 나를 '황금손'이라고 불러. 다음 주에 운동회가 있을 거야. 난 우리 반이 핸드볼 대회에서 이기길 바라.

Communicate: Listen - Listen and Answer. Dialog

B: Hi, Minsol. _____ your class _____?
G: Of _____. We have a _____ _____ _____.
B: You _____ _____ _____ _____ Mongolia?
G: Yes, _____ _____ is Gacha.
B: I've heard a lot about her. But _____ does she _____ _____?
G: She's _____ _____ and _____ a _____.
B: Oh, is she the girl _____ _____ the goal _____ _____?
G: Yes, that's _____ _____ _____.
B: Wow, she's _____ _____.

남: 안녕, 민솔아. 너희 반이 이기고 있니?
여: 물론이지. 우리는 훌륭한 핸드볼 선수가 있거든.
남: 몽골에서 온 여자아이 말하니?
여: 응, 그녀의 이름은 Gacha야.
남: 그녀에 대해 많이 들었어. 그런데 그녀는 어떻게 생겼어?
여: 그녀는 키가 크고 말총머리를 하고 있어.
남: 아, 지금 막 골을 넣은 여자아이가 그녀니?
여: 맞아, 저건 그녀의 일곱 번째 골이야.
남: 와, 그녀는 정말 잘하는구나.

Communicate: Listen - Listen More

M: _____ _____ _____ _____ _____ for you?
G: I _____ my _____ _____.
M: Okay, _____ _____. What's your _____ name?
G: His name is Wally Brown. He's _____ _____ _____.
M: _____ does he _____ _____?
G: He _____ brown hair and brown eyes.
M: What _____ he _____?
G: He is _____ a _____ _____ and black pants.
M: Can you _____ _____ _____?
G: Oh, he is _____ _____ _____ _____ _____.
M: All right. We'll go out and _____ _____ him. Also, we'll _____ _____ _____ about a _____ child.
G: Thank you so much. _____ _____ I'll _____ him soon.

남: 무엇을 도와드릴까요?
여: 남동생을 잃어버렸어요.
남: 알겠어요, 진정하세요. 남동생 이름이 뭐죠?
여: 그의 이름은 Wally Brown이에요. 다섯 살이고요.
남: 어떻게 생겼나요?
여: 그는 갈색 머리이고 갈색 눈을 지녔어요.
남: 그는 무엇을 입고 있나요?
여: 그는 초록색 셔츠와 검은 바지를 입고 있어요.
남: 더 말해 줄 수 있나요?
여: 아, 그는 빨간 배낭을 메고 있어요.
남: 알겠어요. 우리가 나가서 그를 찾아볼게요. 또, 우리가 미아 방송을 할 겁니다.
여: 정말 감사합니다. 동생을 빨리 찾길 바라요.

Communicate: Speak 2 - Talk in pairs

A: I _____ _____ _____ _____ tomorrow!
B: _____ you'll _____ _____ _____ the exam.
A: I _____ _____, _____. Thanks.

A: 나는 내일 중요한 시험이 있어!
B: 네가 시험을 잘 보길 바라.
A: 나도 그러길 바라. 고마워.

Communicate: Speak 2 - Talk in groups

A: _____ is _____ ?

B: _____ _____ is Buster.

A: _____ _____ he _____ ?

B: He _____ _____ _____ .

A: Does he _____ _____ _____ ?

B: Yes, he _____ .

Communicate: Speak - Rap Time

(1) **A:** I _____ my puppy _____ _____ .

   B: _____ _____ you'll _____ him soon.

(2) **A:** I hope you'll _____ _____ _____ in the final game.

   B: Thanks. _____ _____ you _____ _____ .

(3) **A:** _____ _____ your sister _____ _____ , Claire?

   B: She's tall and _____ _____ _____ _____ _____ .

(4) **A:** _____ your father _____ a blue cap?

   B: Yeah. Now, he's _____ _____ _____ .

My Speaking Portfolio

G: _____ _____ the _____ _____ . There _____ posters
for the next _____ _____ .

B: Yeah, I've _____ _____ my _____ . I'll _____ _____
Jang Jimin.

G: You _____ the boy _____ _____ ? He _____ _____ ,
but I don't like his _____ .

B: Then _____ _____ you _____ ?

G: Well, I am for number 1, Han Siwon. She _____ _____
_____ our school _____ _____ _____ .

B: She _____ _____ a ponytail, _____ ?

G: Yes, and Hong Jiho _____ _____ .

B: She _____ _____ , but I don't like _____ _____ _____ .

Wrap Up

1. **B:** I hear _____ _____ a new student in your class.

   G: Yes. She's _____ Jejudo. Oh, she's _____ _____ !

   B: _____ one? _____ _____ _____ she _____ like?

   G: She has _____ hair and is _____ _____ .

2. **G:** You _____ _____ . What's _____ , Jongmin?

   B: My sister _____ _____ _____ _____ this morning.

   G: What _____ ?

   B: She _____ _____ her bike.

   G: _____ _____ _____ . _____ _____ _____ she'll _____
_____ soon.

A: 네 캐릭터의 이름은 뭐니?
B: 그의 이름은 Buster야.
A: 그는 어떻게 생겼니?
B: 그는 머리카락이 없어.
A: 그는 눈이 크니?
B: 응, 맞아.

(1) A: 나는 오늘 오후에 내 강아지를 잃어버렸어.
   B: 네가 그를 곧 찾기를 바랄게.
(2) A: 나는 네가 결선에서 최선을 다하길 바라.
   B: 고마워. 나도 네가 그러길 바라.
(3) A: 네 언니는 어떻게 생겼니, Claire?
   B: 그녀는 키가 크고 긴 생머리야.
(4) A: 네 아버지는 파란 모자를 쓰고 계시니?
   B: 응. 지금 지도를 보고 계셔.

여: 이 게시판을 봐. 다음 학생회장의 포스터가 있어.
남: 응, 나는 이미 결정을 내렸어. 나는 장지민에게 투표할 거야.
여: 안경을 쓴 남자아이 얘기하는 거야? 그는 똑똑해 보이지만 나는 그의 공약이 마음에 들지 않아.
남: 그럼 넌 누굴 선택할 거야?
여: 음, 나는 1번 한시원을 지지해. 그녀는 우리 학교를 안전한 장소로 만들고 싶어 해.
남: 그녀는 항상 말총머리를 해, 그렇지?
여: 맞아, 그리고 홍지호도 괜찮아 보여.
남: 그녀는 친절해 보이지만, 나는 장기자랑이 싫어.

1. 남: 너희 반에 새로 온 학생이 있다고 들었어.
   여: 응. 그녀는 제주도에서 왔어. 어, 그녀가 저기에 있어!
   남: 어느 아이? 어떻게 생겼어?
   여: 그녀는 곱슬머리이고 안경을 끼고 있어.
2. 여: 너 슬퍼 보여. 무슨 일이니, 종민아?
   남: 여동생이 오늘 아침에 팔이 부러졌어.
   여: 무슨 일이 있었는데?
   남: 자전거에서 떨어졌어.
   여: 안됐구나. 그녀가 곧 회복되기를 바라.

대화문 Test

※ 다음 우리말에 맞도록 대화를 영어로 쓰시오.

Communicate: Listen - Listen and Answer. Talk

G: _____
_____
_____
_____
_____
_____

Communicate: Listen - Listen and Answer. Dialog

B: _____
G: _____
B: _____
G: _____
B: _____
G: _____
B: _____
G: _____
B: _____

Communicate: Listen - Listen More

M: _____
G: _____
M: _____
G: _____
M: _____
G: _____
M: _____
G: _____
M: _____
G: _____
M: _____
G: _____

Communicate: Speak 2 - Talk in pairs

A: _____
B: _____
A: _____

해석

여: 안녕, 나는 Gacha라고 해. 나는 몽골에서 왔어. 두 달 전에 내가 처음 송지 중학교에 왔을 때, 나는 무척 걱정이 되었어. 나는 좀 수줍음을 탔고 한국어를 잘 못했어. 하지만 난 운이 좋은 아이야. 내 학급 친구들은 모두 멋지고 다정해. 나는 체육 시간에 친구들과 핸드볼 하는 것을 즐겨. 난 실력이 좋은 선수야. 친구들은 나를 '황금손'이라고 불러. 다음 주에 운동회가 있을 거야. 난 우리 반이 핸드볼 대회에서 이기길 바라.

남: 안녕, 민솔아. 너희 반이 이기고 있니?
여: 물론이지. 우리는 훌륭한 핸드볼 선수가 있거든.
남: 몽골에서 온 여자아이 말하니?
여: 응, 그녀의 이름은 Gacha야.
남: 그녀에 대해 많이 들었어. 그런데 그녀는 어떻게 생겼어?
여: 그녀는 키가 크고 말총머리를 하고 있어.
남: 아, 지금 막 골을 넣은 여자아이가 그녀니?
여: 맞아, 저건 그녀의 일곱 번째 골이야.
남: 와, 그녀는 정말 잘하는구나.

남: 무엇을 도와드릴까요?
여: 남동생을 잃어버렸어요.
남: 알겠어요, 진정하세요. 남동생 이름이 뭐죠?
여: 그의 이름은 Wally Brown이에요. 다섯 살이고요.
남: 어떻게 생겼나요?
여: 그는 갈색 머리이고 갈색 눈을 지녔어요.
남: 그는 무엇을 입고 있나요?
여: 그는 초록색 셔츠와 검은 바지를 입고 있어요.
남: 더 말해 줄 수 있나요?
여: 아, 그는 빨간 배낭을 메고 있어요.
남: 알겠어요. 우리가 나가서 그를 찾아볼게요. 또, 우리가 미아 방송을 할 겁니다.
여: 정말 감사합니다. 동생을 빨리 찾길 바라요.

A: 나는 내일 중요한 시험이 있어!
B: 네가 시험을 잘 보길 바라.
A: 나도 그러길 바라. 고마워.

58 Lesson 5. Understanding Others

Communicate: Speak 2 - Talk in groups

A: _____

B: _____

A: _____

B: _____

A: _____

B: _____

Communicate: Speak - Rap Time

(1) A: _____

    B: _____

(2) A: _____

    B: _____

(3) A: _____

    B: _____

(4) A: _____

    B: _____

My Speaking Portfolio

G: _____

B: _____

G: _____

B: _____

G: _____

B: _____

G: _____

B: _____

Wrap Up

1. B: _____

  G: _____

  B: _____

  G: _____

2. G: _____

  B: _____

  G: _____

  B: _____

  G: _____

A: 네 캐릭터의 이름은 뭐니?
B: 그의 이름은 Buster야.
A: 그는 어떻게 생겼니?
B: 그는 머리카락이 없어.
A: 그는 눈이 크니?
B: 응, 맞아.

(1) A: 나는 오늘 오후에 내 강아지를 잃어버렸어.
   B: 네가 그를 곧 찾기를 바랄게.
(2) A: 나는 네가 결선에서 최선을 다하길 바라.
   B: 고마워. 나도 네가 그러길 바라.
(3) A: 네 언니는 어떻게 생겼니, Claire?
   B: 그녀는 키가 크고 긴 생머리야.
(4) A: 네 아버지는 파란 모자를 쓰고 계시니?
   B: 응. 지금 지도를 보고 계셔.

여: 이 게시판을 봐. 다음 학생회장의 포스터가 있어.
남: 응, 나는 이미 결정을 내렸어. 나는 장지민에게 투표할 거야.
여: 안경을 쓴 남자아이 얘기하는 거야? 그는 똑똑해 보이지만 나는 그의 공약이 마음에 들지 않아.
남: 그럼 넌 누굴 선택할 거야?
여: 음, 나는 1번 한시원을 지지해. 그녀는 우리 학교를 안전한 장소로 만들고 싶어 해.
남: 그녀는 항상 말총머리를 해, 그렇지?
여: 맞아, 그리고 홍지호도 괜찮아 보여.
남: 그녀는 친절해 보이지만, 나는 장기 자랑이 싫어.

1. 남: 너희 반에 새로 온 학생이 있다고 들었어.
  여: 응. 그녀는 제주도에서 왔어. 어, 그녀가 저기에 있어!
  남: 어느 아이? 어떻게 생겼어?
  여: 그녀는 곱슬머리이고 안경을 끼고 있어.
2. 여: 너 슬퍼 보여. 무슨 일이니, 종민아?
  남: 여동생이 오늘 아침에 팔이 부러졌어.
  여: 무슨 일이 있었는데?
  남: 자전거에서 떨어졌어.
  여: 안됐구나. 그녀가 곧 회복되기를 바라.

※ 다음 우리말과 일치하도록 빈칸에 알맞은 것을 골라 쓰시오.

1 The _____ To Be _____

A. Different   B. Right

2 In many _____, 42-year-old Joseph Palmer was an _____
_____.

A. ordinary   B. ways   C. person

3 He _____ a job and _____ _____ his family.

A. for   B. cared   C. had

4 But in 1830, _____ he _____ to a small town in
Massachusetts, he began to _____ _____.

A. face   B. moved   C. difficulties   D. after

5 Joseph _____ _____ from _____ people: he had a long
beard.

A. different   B. other   C. looked

6 People _____ not _____ it very much.

A. like   B. did

7 The town's people _____ the man _____ a _____.

A. with   B. avoided   C. beard

8 They _____ not want to _____ next _____ him.

A. to   B. did   C. sit

9 They even _____ _____ his back, "What is he _____ to
hide?"

A. behind   B. trying   C. whispered

10 _____ neighbors _____ his windows.

A. broke   B. some

11 Others _____ stones _____ him when he walked _____
the street.

A. threw   B. down   C. at

12 They _____ him to _____ _____ a beard.

A. stop   B. told   C. growing

13 Joseph _____ not _____.

A. mind   B. did

14 He _____ wanted the freedom _____ _____ his beard.

A. have   B. just   C. to

15 _____ day, four men _____ Joseph and _____ him on
the ground.

A. attacked   B. one   C. threw

---

1 다를 권리

2 여러 면에서 42살의 Joseph Palmer는 평범한 사람이었다.

3 그는 직업이 있었고 가족을 돌보았다.

4 하지만 1830년에 매사추세츠에 있는 작은 도시로 이사를 한 후에 그는 어려움에 직면하기 시작했다.

5 Joseph은 다른 사람들과 달라 보였다. 그는 기다란 턱수염을 기르고 있었다.

6 사람들은 그것을 별로 좋아하지 않았다.

7 마을 사람들은 턱수염을 가진 그 남자를 피했다.

8 그들은 그의 곁에 앉고 싶어 하지 않았다.

9 그들은 심지어 그의 등 뒤에서 "그가 무엇을 숨기려는 거지?"라고 속삭였다.

10 어떤 이웃들은 그의 창문을 깼다.

11 다른 사람들은 그가 길을 걸어 내려갈 때 그에게 돌을 던졌다.

12 그들은 그에게 턱수염을 그만 기르라고 말했다.

13 Joseph은 신경 쓰지 않았다.

14 그는 그저 자신의 턱수염을 기를 자유를 원했다.

15 어느 날, 네 명의 남자가 Joseph을 공격했고 그를 바닥에 던졌다.

16 "We're going to _____ _____ your beard!" they _____.

A. cut   B. shouted   C. off

17 Joseph was a big man, and he was _____ to _____ them _____.

A. fight   B. able   C. off

18 But the men _____ the police and _____ him _____ attacking them.

A. accused   B. called   C. of

19 Poor Joseph _____ _____.

A. arrested   B. was

20 He said to the _____, "I'm the _____ here."

A. victim   B. judge

21 Sadly, no one _____ a man _____ a beard, and he went to _____ for _____ a year.

A. with   B. over   C. believed   D. prison

22 Joseph's son, Thomas, _____ people to _____ the _____.

A. know   B. wanted   C. truth

23 He _____ letters _____ newspapers _____ the country.

A. sent   B. across   C. to

24 People learned that Joseph was _____ _____ just for _____ _____ and his beard.

A. prison   B. himself   C. protecting   D. in

25 Many people _____ _____ about this, so the judge finally decided to _____ Joseph _____.

A. angry   B. free   C. set   D. became

26 After he was _____, Joseph _____ and told his story to _____ of people.

A. freed   B. lots   C. traveled

27 Slowly, people's _____ _____ beards _____.

A. toward   B. changed   C. attitudes

28 _____ Joseph _____, a man with a _____ became the President of the United States.

A. died   B. before   C. beard

29 _____ _____ was Abraham Lincoln.

A. name   B. his

30 He _____ beards _____, but Joseph Palmer _____ for the _____ to have them.

A. fought   B. right   C. popular   D. made

---

16 "우리가 당신의 턱수염을 잘라 버리겠어!"라고 그들은 소리쳤다.

17 Joseph은 덩치가 큰 사람이었고, 그는 그들을 싸워 물리칠 수 있었다.

18 하지만 그 남자들은 경찰을 불렀고, 자신들을 공격한 것으로 그를 고발했다.

19 불쌍한 Joseph은 체포되었다.

20 그는 "저는 여기서 희생자입니다."라고 판사에게 말했다.

21 슬프게도, 아무도 턱수염을 가진 남자를 믿지 않았고, 그는 일 년이 넘는 기간 동안 감옥에 갔다.

22 Joseph의 아들인 Thomas는 사람들이 진실을 알기를 원했다.

23 그는 전국에 있는 신문사에 편지를 보냈다.

24 사람들은 Joseph이 단지 자신과 자신의 턱수염을 지키려다 감옥에 갇혔다는 것을 알게 되었다.

25 많은 사람들은 이에 대해 분개했고, 그래서 판사는 결국 Joseph을 석방하기로 결정했다.

26 Joseph은 석방된 뒤에 순회를 하며 많은 사람들에게 자신의 이야기를 전했다.

27 사람들의 턱수염에 대한 태도는 서서히 변해갔다.

28 Joseph이 죽기 전에, 턱수염을 가진 남자가 미국의 대통령이 되었다.

29 그의 이름은 Abraham Lincoln (에이브러햄 링컨)이었다.

30 그는 턱수염을 대중적으로 만들었지만, Joseph Palmer는 그것을 기를 권리를 위하여 싸웠다.

※ 다음 우리말과 일치하도록 빈칸에 알맞은 말을 쓰시오.

1 The _____ _____ _____ _____

2 _____ _____ _____, 42-year-old Joseph Palmer was _____ _____ _____.

3 He _____ _____ _____ and _____ _____ his family.

4 But in 1830, _____ he _____ _____ a small town in Massachusetts, he began _____ _____ _____.

5 Joseph _____ _____ _____ other people: he had a long beard.

6 People _____ _____ _____ _____ _____ very much.

7 The town's people _____ _____ _____ _____ _____ _____.

8 They did not want _____ _____ _____ _____ _____.

9 They even whispered _____ _____ _____, "What is he _____ _____ _____?"

10 _____ neighbors _____ _____ _____.

11 _____ _____ _____ _____ him when he _____ _____ the street.

12 They _____ him _____ _____ _____ a beard.

13 Joseph _____ _____ _____.

14 He just wanted the _____ _____ _____ his beard.

15 One day, four men _____ Joseph and _____ _____ _____ _____ _____.

1 다를 권리

2 여러 면에서 42살의 Joseph Palmer는 평범한 사람이었다.

3 그는 직업이 있었고 가족을 돌보았다.

4 하지만 1830년에 매사추세츠에 있는 작은 도시로 이사를 한 후에 그는 어려움에 직면하기 시작했다.

5 Joseph은 다른 사람들과 달라 보였다. 그는 기다란 턱수염을 기르고 있었다.

6 사람들은 그것을 별로 좋아하지 않았다.

7 마을 사람들은 턱수염을 가진 그 남자를 피했다.

8 그들은 그의 곁에 앉고 싶어 하지 않았다.

9 그들은 심지어 그의 등 뒤에서 "그가 무엇을 숨기려는 거지?"라고 속삭였다.

10 어떤 이웃들은 그의 창문을 깼다.

11 다른 사람들은 그가 길을 걸어 내려갈 때 그에게 돌을 던졌다.

12 그들은 그에게 턱수염을 그만 기르라고 말했다.

13 Joseph은 신경 쓰지 않았다.

14 그는 그저 자신의 턱수염을 기를 자유를 원했다.

15 어느 날, 네 명의 남자가 Joseph을 공격했고 그를 바닥에 던졌다.

16 "We're going to _____ _____ your beard!" they _____.

17 Joseph was a big man, and he _____ _____

_____ _____ _____.

18 But the men called the police and _____ _____ _____

_____ them.

19 Poor Joseph _____ _____.

20 He said to _____ _____, "I'm _____ _____ here."

21 Sadly, no one believed _____ _____ _____ _____

_____, and he _____ _____ _____ for over a year.

22 Joseph's son, Thomas, _____ people _____ _____ the

truth.

23 He _____ letters _____ newspapers _____ _____

_____

24 People learned that Joseph _____ _____ _____ just for

_____ _____ and his beard.

25 Many people _____ _____ about this, so the judge finally

_____ _____ _____ Joseph _____.

26 After he _____ _____, Joseph traveled and told his story to

_____ _____ people.

27 Slowly, people's _____ _____ _____ _____.

28 _____ Joseph _____, a man _____ _____ _____

became the President of the United States.

29 _____ _____ was Abraham Lincoln.

30 He _____ _____ _____, but Joseph Palmer _____

_____ the _____ _____ _____ them.

16 "우리가 당신의 턱수염을 잘라 버리겠어!"라고 그들은 소리쳤다.

17 Joseph은 덩치가 큰 사람이었고, 그는 그들을 싸워 물리칠 수 있었다.

18 하지만 그 남자들은 경찰을 불렀고, 자신들을 공격한 것으로 그를 고발했다.

19 불쌍한 Joseph은 체포되었다.

20 그는 "저는 여기서 희생자입니다."라고 판사에게 말했다.

21 슬프게도, 아무도 턱수염을 가진 남자를 믿지 않았고, 그는 일 년이 넘는 기간 동안 감옥에 갔다.

22 Joseph의 아들인 Thomas는 사람들이 진실을 알기를 원했다.

23 그는 전국에 있는 신문사에 편지를 보냈다.

24 사람들은 Joseph이 단지 자신과 자신의 턱수염을 지키려다 감옥에 갇혔다는 것을 알게 되었다.

25 많은 사람들은 이에 대해 분개했고, 그래서 판사는 결국 Joseph을 석방하기로 결정했다.

26 Joseph은 석방된 뒤에 순회를 하며 많은 사람들에게 자신의 이야기를 전했다.

27 사람들의 턱수염에 대한 태도는 서서히 변해갔다.

28 Joseph이 죽기 전에, 턱수염을 가진 남자가 미국의 대통령이 되었다.

29 그의 이름은 Abraham Lincoln (에이브러햄 링컨)이었다.

30 그는 턱수염을 대중적으로 만들었지만, Joseph Palmer는 그것을 기를 권리를 위하여 싸웠다.

※ 다음 문장을 우리말로 쓰시오.

1 The Right To Be Different

➡ _____

2 In many ways, 42-year-old Joseph Palmer was an ordinary person.

➡ _____

3 He had a job and cared for his family.

➡ _____

4 But in 1830, after he moved to a small town in Massachusetts, he began to face difficulties.

➡ _____

5 Joseph looked different from other people: he had a long beard.

➡ _____

6 People did not like it very much.

➡ _____

7 The town's people avoided the man with a beard.

➡ _____

8 They did not want to sit next to him.

➡ _____

9 They even whispered behind his back, "What is he trying to hide?"

➡ _____

10 Some neighbors broke his windows.

➡ _____

11 Others threw stones at him when he walked down the street.

➡ _____

12 They told him to stop growing a beard.

➡ _____

13 Joseph did not mind.

➡ _____

14 He just wanted the freedom to have his beard.

➡ _____

15 One day, four men attacked Joseph and threw him on the ground.

➡ _____

16 "We're going to cut off your beard!" they shouted.

➡ _____

17 Joseph was a big man, and he was able to fight them off.

➡ _____

18 But the men called the police and accused him of attacking them.

➡ _____

19 Poor Joseph was arrested.

➡ _____

20 He said to the judge, "I'm the victim here."

➡ _____

21 Sadly, no one believed a man with a beard, and he went to prison for over a year.

➡ _____

22 Joseph's son, Thomas, wanted people to know the truth.

➡ _____

23 He sent letters to newspapers across the country.

➡ _____

24 People learned that Joseph was in prison just for protecting himself and his beard.

➡ _____

25 Many people became angry about this, so the judge finally decided to set Joseph free.

➡ _____

26 After he was freed, Joseph traveled and told his story to lots of people.

➡ _____

27 Slowly, people's attitudes toward beards changed.

➡ _____

28 Before Joseph died, a man with a beard became the President of the United States.

➡ _____

29 His name was Abraham Lincoln.

➡ _____

30 He made beards popular, but Joseph Palmer fought for the right to have them.

➡ _____

※ 다음 괄호 안의 단어들을 우리말에 맞도록 바르게 배열하시오.

1 (Right / The / Different / Be / To)
➡ _____

2 (many / in / ways, / Joseph / 42-year-old / Palmer / an / was / person. / ordinary)
➡ _____

3 (had / he / job / a / and / for / cared / family. / his)
➡ _____

4 (in / but / 1830, / he / after / to / moved / small / a / town / Massachusetts, / in / began / he / difficulties. / face / to)
➡ _____
➡ _____

5 (looked / Joseph / from / different / people: / other / had / he / beard. / long / a)
➡ _____

6 (did / people / like / not / much. / it / very)
➡ _____

7 (town's / the / people / avoided / man / the / beard. / a / with)
➡ _____

8 (did / they / want / not / sit / to / him. / to / next)
➡ _____

9 (even / they / behind / whispered / back, / his / "what / he / is / hide?" / to / trying)
➡ _____

10 (neighbors / some / windows. / his / broke)
➡ _____

11 (threw / others / at / stones / him / when / walked / he / street. / the / down)
➡ _____

12 (told / they / to / him / growing / stop / beard. / a)
➡ _____

13 (did / Joseph / mind. / not)
➡ _____

14 (just / he / wanted / freedom / the / have / to / beard. / his)
➡ _____

15 (day, / one / men / four / Joseph / attacked / and / him / threw / ground. / the / on)
➡ _____

1 다를 권리

2 여러 면에서 42살의 Joseph Palmer는 평범한 사람이었다.

3 그는 직업이 있었고 가족을 돌보았다.

4 하지만 1830년에 매사추세츠에 있는 작은 도시로 이사를 한 후에 그는 어려움에 직면하기 시작했다.

5 Joseph은 다른 사람들과 달라 보였다. 그는 기다란 턱수염을 기르고 있었다.

6 사람들은 그것을 별로 좋아하지 않았다.

7 마을 사람들은 턱수염을 가진 그 남자를 피했다.

8 그들은 그의 곁에 앉고 싶어 하지 않았다.

9 그들은 심지어 그의 등 뒤에서 "그가 무엇을 숨기려는 거지?"라고 속삭였다.

10 어떤 이웃들은 그의 창문을 깼다.

11 다른 사람들은 그가 길을 걸어 내려갈 때 그에게 돌을 던졌다.

12 그들은 그에게 턱수염을 그만 기르라고 말했다.

13 Joseph은 신경 쓰지 않았다.

14 그는 그저 자신의 턱수염을 기를 자유를 원했다.

15 어느 날, 네 명의 남자가 Joseph을 공격했고 그를 바닥에 던졌다.

16 (going / "we're / cut / to / your / off / beard!" / shouted. / they)
➡ _____

17 (was / Joseph / big / a / man, / and / was / he / to / able / off. / them / fight)
➡ _____

18 (the / but / called / men / police / the / and / him / accused / of / them / attacking)
➡ _____

19 (Joseph / poor / arrested. / was)
➡ _____

20 (said / he / the / to / judge, / "I'm / the / here." / victim)
➡ _____

21 (no / sadly, / one / a / believed / man / with / beard, / a / and / went / he / prison / to / for / year. / a / over)
➡ _____

22 (son, / Joseph's / Thomas, / people / wanted / know / to / truth. / the)
➡ _____

23 (sent / he / letters / newspapers / to / country. / the / across)
➡ _____

24 (learned / people / Joseph / that / in / was / prison / just / protecting / for / himself / beard. / his / and)
➡ _____

25 (people / many / angry / became / this, / about / so / judge / the / decided / finally / set / to / free. / Joseph)
➡ _____
_____

26 (he / after / freed, / was / Joseph / and / traveled / told / story / his / people. / of / lots / to)
➡ _____

27 (people's / slowly, / attitudes / beards / changed. / toward)
➡ _____

28 (Joseph / before / died, / man / a / with / beard / a / became / President / the / of / States. / United / the)
➡ _____

29 (name / his / Lincoln. / Abraham)
➡ _____

30 (made / he / popular, / beards / but / Palmer / Joseph / for / fought / right / the / them. / have / to)
➡ _____
_____

16 "우리가 당신의 턱수염을 잘라 버리겠어!"라고 그들은 소리쳤다.

17 Joseph은 덩치가 큰 사람이었고, 그는 그들을 싸워 물리칠 수 있었다.

18 하지만 그 남자들은 경찰을 불렀고, 자신들을 공격한 것으로 그를 고발했다.

19 불쌍한 Joseph은 체포되었다.

20 그는 "저는 여기서 희생자입니다."라고 판사에게 말했다.

21 슬프게도, 아무도 턱수염을 가진 남자를 믿지 않았고, 그는 일 년이 넘는 기간 동안 감옥에 갔다.

22 Joseph의 아들인 Thomas는 사람들이 진실을 알기를 원했다.

23 그는 전국에 있는 신문사에 편지를 보냈다.

24 사람들은 Joseph이 단지 자신과 자신의 턱수염을 지키려다 감옥에 갇혔다는 것을 알게 되었다.

25 많은 사람들은 이에 대해 분개했고, 그래서 판사는 결국 Joseph을 석방하기로 결정했다.

26 Joseph은 석방된 뒤에 순회를 하며 많은 사람들에게 자신의 이야기를 전했다.

27 사람들의 턱수염에 대한 태도는 서서히 변해갔다.

28 Joseph이 죽기 전에, 턱수염을 가진 남자가 미국의 대통령이 되었다.

29 그의 이름은 Abraham Lincoln (에이브러햄 링컨)이었다.

30 그는 턱수염을 대중적으로 만들었지만, Joseph Palmer는 그것을 기를 권리를 위하여 싸웠다.

※ 다음 우리말을 영어로 쓰시오.

1 다를 권리

➡ _____

2 여러 면에서 42살의 Joseph Palmer는 평범한 사람이었다.

➡ _____

3 그는 직업이 있었고 가족을 돌보았다.

➡ _____

4 하지만 1830년에 매사추세츠에 있는 작은 도시로 이사를 한 후에 그는 어려움에 직면하기 시작했다.

➡ _____

5 Joseph은 다른 사람들과 달라 보였다. 그는 기다란 턱수염을 기르고 있었다.

➡ _____

6 사람들은 그것을 별로 좋아하지 않았다.

➡ _____

7 마을 사람들은 턱수염을 가진 그 남자를 피했다.

➡ _____

8 그들은 그의 곁에 앉고 싶어 하지 않았다.

➡ _____

9 그들은 심지어 그의 등 뒤에서 "그가 무엇을 숨기려는 거지?"라고 속삭였다.

➡ _____

10 어떤 이웃들은 그의 창문을 깼다.

➡ _____

11 다른 사람들은 그가 길을 걸어 내려갈 때 그에게 돌을 던졌다.

➡ _____

12 그들은 그에게 턱수염을 그만 기르라고 말했다.

➡ _____

13 Joseph은 신경 쓰지 않았다.

➡ _____

14 그는 그저 자신의 턱수염을 기를 자유를 원했다.

➡ _____

15 어느 날, 네 명의 남자가 Joseph을 공격했고 그를 바닥에 던졌다.

➡ _____

16 "우리가 당신의 턱수염을 잘라 버리겠어!"라고 그들은 소리쳤다.

➡ _____

17 Joseph은 덩치가 큰 사람이었고, 그는 그들을 싸워 물리칠 수 있었다.

➡ _____

18 하지만 그 남자들은 경찰을 불렀고, 자신들을 공격한 것으로 그를 고발했다.

➡ _____

19 불쌍한 Joseph은 체포되었다.

➡ _____

20 그는 "저는 여기서 희생자입니다."라고 판사에게 말했다.

➡ _____

21 슬프게도, 아무도 턱수염을 가진 남자를 믿지 않았고, 그는 일 년이 넘는 기간 동안 감옥에 갔다.

➡ _____

22 Joseph의 아들인 Thomas는 사람들이 진실을 알기를 원했다.

➡ _____

23 그는 전국에 있는 신문사에 편지를 보냈다.

➡ _____

24 사람들은 Joseph이 단지 자신과 자신의 턱수염을 지키려다 감옥에 갇혔다는 것을 알게 되었다.

➡ _____

25 많은 사람들은 이에 대해 분개했고, 그래서 판사는 결국 Joseph을 석방하기로 결정했다.

➡ _____

26 Joseph은 석방된 뒤에 순회를 하며 많은 사람들에게 자신의 이야기를 전했다.

➡ _____

27 사람들의 턱수염에 대한 태도는 서서히 변해갔다.

➡ _____

28 Joseph이 죽기 전에, 턱수염을 가진 남자가 미국의 대통령이 되었다.

➡ _____

29 그의 이름은 Abraham Lincoln(에이브러햄 링컨)이었다.

➡ _____

30 그는 턱수염을 대중적으로 만들었지만, Joseph Palmer는 그것을 기를 권리를 위하여 싸웠다.

➡ _____

※ 다음 우리말과 일치하도록 빈칸에 알맞은 말을 쓰시오.

My Speaking Portfolio

1. I _____ _____ for Han Siwon.

2. She _____ _____ and _____.

3. She _____ school _____ _____ a safe place.

4. I _____ _____ her.

5. I like her promises _____ _____ no more _____.

6. I _____ Han Siwon _____ the next school president.

7. I really want my school _____ _____ _____ _____ _____.

My Writing Portfolio: My Book Report

1. The _____ _____ _____ Different

2. A Story _____ Joseph Palmer

3. I read the story _____ Joseph Palmer _____ _____.

4. I _____ _____ it.

5. I _____ _____ the story _____ we should not judge people by their _____.

6. Students _____ _____ about other people's appearance _____ read the story.

7. _____, I _____ _____ _____ about it.

8. _____ did Joseph Palmer want _____ _____ _____ _____?

Words in Action

1. _____ _____ the travel fair. _____ is _____.

2. What countries do you _____ _____ _____?

3. _____ you want _____ _____ South America, you can _____ the booths on the left.

4. If you _____ _____, you can have drinks and _____ _____ _____.

---

1. 나는 한시원을 뽑을 겁니다.
2. 그녀는 자신감 있고 똑똑해 보입니다.
3. 그녀는 학교가 안전한 장소가 되어야 한다고 생각합니다.
4. 저는 그녀에게 동의합니다.
5. 나는 집단 괴롭힘 없애기 같은 공약들이 좋습니다.
6. 나는 한시원이 다음 학생회장이 되길 바랍니다.
7. 나는 우리 학교가 더 안전한 장소가 되길 정말 바랍니다.

1. 다를 권리
2. Joseph Palmer에 관한 이야기
3. 나는 지난주에 Joseph Palmer에 관한 이야기를 읽었다.
4. 나는 그게 정말 재미있었다.
5. 나는 그 이야기로부터 우리는 사람들을 외모로 판단해서는 안 된다는 것을 배웠다.
6. 다른 사람들의 외모에 관해 이야기하는 학생들은 이 이야기를 꼭 읽어야 한다.
7. 하지만, 나는 그것에 관한 질문이 하나 있다.
8. Joseph Palmer는 왜 턱수염을 기르고 싶었을까?

1. 여행 박람회에 오신 것을 환영합니다. 입장료는 무료입니다.
2. 여러분은 어떤 나라들을 마음에 두고 있나요?
3. 여러분이 남아메리카를 방문하고 싶다면, 왼쪽에 있는 부스들을 살펴볼 수 있습니다.
4. 배가 고파진다면, 음료와 간단한 간식을 드실 수 있습니다.

※ 다음 우리말을 영어로 쓰시오.

My Speaking Portfolio

1. 나는 한시원을 뽑을 겁니다.
➡ _____

2. 그녀는 자신감 있고 똑똑해 보입니다.
➡ _____

3. 그녀는 학교가 안전한 장소가 되어야 한다고 생각합니다.
➡ _____

4. 저는 그녀에게 동의합니다.
➡ _____

5. 나는 집단 괴롭힘 없애기 같은 공약들이 좋습니다.
➡ _____

6. 나는 한시원이 다음 학생회장이 되길 바랍니다.
➡ _____

7. 나는 우리 학교가 더 안전한 장소가 되길 정말 바랍니다.
➡ _____

My Writing Portfolio: My Book Report

1. 다를 권리
➡ _____

2. Joseph Palmer에 관한 이야기
➡ _____

3. 나는 지난주에 Joseph Palmer에 관한 이야기를 읽었다.
➡ _____

4. 나는 그게 정말 재미있었다.
➡ _____

5. 나는 그 이야기로부터 우리는 사람들을 외모로 판단해서는 안 된다는 것을 배웠다.
➡ _____

6. 다른 사람들의 외모에 관해 이야기하는 학생들은 이 이야기를 꼭 읽어야 한다.
➡ _____

7. 하지만, 나는 그것에 관한 질문이 하나 있다.
➡ _____

8. Joseph Palmer는 왜 턱수염을 기르고 싶었을까?
➡ _____

Words in Action

1. 여행 박람회에 오신 것을 환영합니다. 입장료는 무료입니다.
➡ _____

2. 여러분은 어떤 나라들을 마음에 두고 있나요?
➡ _____

3. 여러분이 남아메리카를 방문하고 싶다면, 왼쪽에 있는 부스들을 살펴볼 수 있습니다.
➡ _____
_____

4. 배가 고파진다면, 음료와 간단한 간식을 드실 수 있습니다.
➡ _____

MEMO

적중100

1학기

정답 및 해설

천재 | 이재영

중 2

적중100

영어 기출 문제집

적중 100

1학기

정답 및 해설

천재 | 이재영

중 2

Lesson 3

Healthy Life, Happy Life

시험대비 실력평가   p.08

01 ②	02 ②	03 ④	04 attack
05 ⑤	06 cell	07 By the way	08 ②

01 나머지는 모두 동사의 행위자를 나타내는 말이고, ②는 '위 험'을 뜻하는 단어이다.

02 show up: 나타나다 / be good for: ~에 좋다

03 번식해서 수가 증가하다: 증식하다(multiply)

04 반의어 관계이다. 어려운 : 쉬운 = 방어하다 : 공격하다

05 make it: (모임 등에) 가다, 참석하다

06 모든 생물을 구성하는 아주 작은 부분들의 어느 하나: cell(세포)

07 by the way: 그런데(화제를 바꿀 때 쓰는 표현)

08 plenty of: 많은 / think of: ~을 생각하다

서술형 시험대비   p.09

01 (1) actor   (2) cartoonist   (3) inventor
02 (1) such as   (2) is famous for   (3) few days
03 (1) germs   (2) digest   (3) multiply   (4) balanced
04 (1) healthy   (2) Luckily   (3) dangerous
05 (1) show up   (2) good for
   (3) plenty of   (4) catch a cold
06 (1) (s)cratch   (2) (v)ictim   (3) (b)acteria

01 (1), (3)은 '동사 : 행위자' 관계이고, (2)는 '명사 - 행위자' 관 계이다.

02 (1) such as: ~과 같은 (2) be famous for: ~으로 유명 하다 (3) in a few days: 며칠 후에

03 (1) germ: 세균 (2) digest: 소화시키다 (3) multiply: 증식 [번식]하다 (4) balanced: 균형 잡힌

04 (1) healthy: 건강한 (2) luckily: 다행히도 (3) dangerous: 위험한

05 (1) show up: 나타나다 (2) be good for: ~에 좋다 (3) plenty of: 많은 (4) catch a cold: 감기에 걸리다

06 (1) scratch: 긁다 (2) victim: 피해자, 희생자 (3) bacteria: 박테리아

교과서 Conversation

핵심 Check   p.10~11

1 (1) wrong / stomachache   (2) matter / runny nose
  (3) What, problem / have a toothache
2 (1) make it / Sure, then   (2) How about going / problem   (3) Let's play / Sorry, I can't

교과서 대화문 익히기

Check(√) True or False   p.12

1 T   2 F   3 T   4 F

교과서 확인학습   p.14~15

Communicate: Listen - Listen and Answer Dialog 1

Can, early, don't feel / seems to / have stomachache, hurts / Why don't, medicine / already, didn't help / can, Go see / Sure

Communicate: Listen - Listen and Answer Dialog 2

heard, okay / the doctor, feel better / to hear, By the way, to talk / should meet, make it / Let's meet, at / early, late / How about / sounds

Communicate: Listen - Listen More

wrong with / scratching, lost, hair / have the problem / About, ago / Let, see, have a virus / neet to check, Can make / fine with / See

Communicate: Listen - All Ears

make / wrong

Communicate: Speak 2 - Talk in pairs

What's wrong / have sore throat / bad, should drink / will

Communicate: Speak 2 - Talk in group

Let's / why not / Can you make / with, should, meet / Let's, at / See you

Wrap Up - Listening ❺

don't feel / What, problem / have a fever / Let me see, do / get you some medicine / Thank

Wrap Up - Listening ❻

thinking of, come with / to go / make it at / fine with / Let's, at

시험대비 기본평가   p.16

01 ③   02 ④   03 ④   04 ②

01 Can you make it at ~?은 약속 시간을 정할 때 쓰는 표현이다.

02 What's wrong?은 What's the problem?과 바꾸어 쓸 수 있다.

03 B가 동의하고 5시에 만나자고 말했으므로 약속 시간을 정하는 표현인 ④가 알맞다.

04 이어지는 대답으로 보아 상태를 묻는 질문이 알맞다.

시험대비 실력평가   p.17~18

01 ⑤   02 How[What] about getting   03 ④

04 stomachache   05 ②   06 ④

07 meet   08 ②   09 They will meet at the school gym at ten.   10 ③   11 By the way   12 ④   13 ②   14 late

15 ⑤

01 What seems to be the problem?과 What's the matter with you?는 '어디가 안 좋으니?'라는 의미이다.

02 Why don't you + 동사원형 ～?은 How[What] about ing ～?로 바꿔 쓸 수 있다.

03 ⓒ와 ④는 '허가', ①, ②, ⑤는 '가능, 능력', ③은 '추측'을 나타낸다.

04 위의 또는 위 부근의 통증: 위통, 복통(stomachache)

05 ② 소년은 배가 몹시 아프다고 했다.

06 A가 10시에 만날 수 있는지 묻고 있으므로 빈칸에는 제안을 수락하는 표현이 알맞다. ④는 제안을 거절하는 표현이다.

07 Can you make it at ten?은 Can we meet at ten? 으로 바꿔 쓸 수 있다.

08 A가 체육관에서 만나자고 했으므로 만날 장소를 정하는 표현인 ②가 알맞다.

09 A와 B는 10시에 학교 체육관에서 만날 것이다.

10 종하가 지금은 몸이 나아졌다고 했으므로 몸이 괜찮은지를 묻는 ③이 알맞다.

11 by the way: 그런데

12 ④를 제외하고 나머지는 모두 내일 만나자고 제안하는 표현 이다.

13 '～하자'고 제안하는 표현은 Let's ~.이다.

14 평소보다 또는 예상되는 때보다 늦게: late(늦게)

15 그들의 과학 과제를 언제까지 끝내야 하는지는 위 대화를 통해 알 수 없다.

서술형 시험대비   p.19

01 |모범답안| What's wrong? / What's the problem? / What seems to be the problem? 등

02 Why don't you get some rest?

03 meeting

04 Where should we meet?

05 at the school gym

06 matter[problem]

07 Can you make it next Monday?

08 (A) scratching   (B) ago

09 계속해서 자기의 몸을 긁는다. / 털이 빠졌다.

01 증상을 묻는 표현에는 What's wrong? / What's the problem? / What's the matter? / What seems to be the problem? 등이 있다.

02 Why don't you + 동사원형 ～?: ～하는 게 어때?

03 10시에 만날 수 있느냐는 의미이다.

04 Where should we meet?: 우리 어디서 만날까?

05 there는 앞에 나온 at the school gym을 가리킨다.

06 What's wrong with ~?는 어떤 증상이 있는지 물어보는 표현으로 What's the matter with ~? / What's the problem with ~? 등으로 바꿔 쓸 수 있다.

07 make it은 시간이나 장소의 표현과 함께 쓰여 '시간에 맞춰 가다, 도착하다'라는 의미를 갖는다.

08 (A) keep -ing: 계속해서 ～하다 (b) ~ ago: ～ 전에(과거 시제에 쓰임)

09 She keeps scratching herself. Actually, she lost some hair.를 통해서 알 수 있다.

교과서

Grammar

핵심 Check   p.20~21

1 (1) to understand   (2) It   (3) to exercise   (4) of   (5) for

2 (1) to go   (2) to help   (3) to write with   (4) cold to drink

시험대비 기본평가   p.22

01 (1) It   (2) to do   (3) to visit   (4) for   (5) of

02 (1) to change   (2) to visit   (3) to offer

03 (1) exercise → to exercise   (2) finish → to finish
    (3) That → It   (4) for → of   (5) of → for

01 (1) 가주어 it이 필요하다. (2), (3) 형용사적 용법의 to부정사가 필요하다. (4) 형용사가 hard이므로 의미상의 주어는 'for+목적격'을 쓴다. (5) 형용사가 kind이므로 의미상의 주어는 'of+목적격'을 쓴다.

02 형용사적 용법의 to부정사를 이용한다.

03 (1), (2) 가주어 It이 있는 구문이므로 동사원형을 to부정사로 바꾼다. (3) 가주어는 It으로 나타낸다. (4) 형용사가 brave이므로 의미상의 주어는 'of+목적격'을 쓴다. (5) 형용사가 easy이므로 의미상의 주어는 'for+목적격'을 쓴다.

시험대비 실력평가   p.23~25

01 ③   02 ③   03 ④   04 to write
05 It, to change   06 ①   07 ①
08 Do you want anything to eat? [Do you want to eat anything?]   09 ④   10 ④   11 It is difficult to fix the machine.   12 ②   13 ①
14 ①   15 to   16 ⑤   17 sit → sit on[in]   18 ①   19 ③   20 ③
21 It is pleasant to listen to music.   22 ⑤
23 going → to go

01 ③은 부사적 용법의 to부정사이다. '~하기 위해'로 해석한다. 나머지는 모두 형용사적 용법이다.

02 가주어 It의 진주어로 to부정사가 필요하다.

03 부정대명사 anything을 수식하는 형용사적 용법의 to부정사가 와야 한다.

04 '써야 할 편지들'이라는 뜻으로 명사 letters를 수식하는 to부정사의 형용사적 용법이다.

05 주어로 쓰인 to부정사가 긴 경우, 이를 뒤로 보내고 그 자리에 가주어 it을 쓴다.

06 <보기>의 to read는 앞에 나온 명사 books를 수식하는 형용사적 용법의 to부정사이다. ① 형용사적 용법 ② 명사적 용법 ③ 부사적 용법 ④ 명사적 용법 ⑤ 부사적 용법

07 가주어 – 진주어 구문으로 「It is+형용사+to부정사」 형태가 적절하다.

08 부정대명사를 수식하는 to부정사의 형용사적 용법을 쓴다.

09 ④의 it은 인칭대명사이고 나머지는 가주어 it[It]이다.

10 ④ to going 대신 time을 수식하는 형용사적 용법의 to부정사가 필요하다.

11 '그 기계를 고치는 것은'은 to fix the machine으로 나타낸다.

12 첫 문장은 형용사가 kind이므로 의미상의 주어는 'of+목적격'을 쓴다. 두 번째 문장은 형용사가 natural이므로 의미상의 주어는 'for+목적격'을 쓴다.

13 honest와 wise는 의미상의 주어로 'of+목적격'을 쓴다.

14 It이 가주어이므로 진주어인 to부정사가 와야 한다.

15 don't have to: ~할 필요가 없다 / reason to be angry at: ~에게 화낸 이유

16 ①, ④ 진주어로 쓰인 to부정사 ② hopes는 to부정사를 목적어로 취한다. ③ enough to+동사원형: ~하기에 충분히 …한 ⑤ 사역동사의 목적격보어는 동사원형이 와야 한다.

17 to부정사의 수식을 받는 명사가 전치사의 목적어일 경우 뒤에 전치사가 온다.

18 ①은 '때'를 나타내는 비인칭 주어이다. 나머지는 가주어 it으로 쓰였따.

19 to부정사의 수식을 받는 명사가 전치사의 목적어일 경우 to부정사 뒤에 전치사를 쓴다. ③은 to talk with라고 해야 옳다.

20 ③은 형용사적 용법의 to부정사이고, 나머지는 모두 명사적 용법으로 쓰였다.

21 to부정사로 쓰인 주어가 길거나 의미를 강조하고 싶을 때 가주어 it을 주어 자리에 쓰고 진주어인 to부정사를 문장 뒤로 보낸다.

22 time을 수식하는 to부정사와 「don't have to+동사원형」의 형태가 필요하다.

23 진주어로 to부정사가 와야 한다.

서술형 시험대비   p.26~27

01 to   02 It to
03 (1) It is difficult to learn English.
   (2) He bought a magazine to read on the train.
04 to receive
05 (1) It wasn't easy to visit him every weekend.
   (2) It is an exciting experience to live in another country.
06 (1) She has a strong desire to be a singer.
   (2) We had something to talk about.
   (3) I want a sheet[piece] of paper to write on.
   (4) Please give me something hot to drink.
07 (1) play → to play   (2) of → for
08 (1) It   (2) on   (3) with   (4) to
09 to play with   10 to
11 It, to learn
12 (1) for → of   (2) of → for
13 It's a place to sell many things for 24 hours.

01 앞의 명사를 수식하는 형용사적 용법의 to부정사가 필요하다.

02 가주어 it을 문장 앞에 두고 진주어 to부정사구를 뒤로 보낸다.

03 (1) 가주어 it, 진주어 to부정사 구문이다. (2) '읽을 잡지'이므로 to부정사의 형용사적 용법을 쓴다.

04 가주어인 It의 진주어에 해당하는 to부정사구가 되어야 하므로 to receive로 쓴다.

05 (1) '주말마다 그를 방문하는 것'은 to visit him every weekend로 나타낸다. (2) '다른 나라에서 사는 것'은 to live in another country로 나타낸다.

06 (1), (2) to부정사의 형용사적 용법을 이용해 「명사+to부정사」의 형태로 쓴다. (3) to부정사의 목적어가 있고 to부정사의 동사가 자동사일 때는 전치사가 필요하다. (4) -thing으로 끝나는 부정대명사는 「-thing+형용사+to부정사」의 이 순을 따른다.

07 (1) time을 수식하는 to부정사로 바꾼다. (2) important는 의미상의 주어로 'for+목적격'을 쓴다.

08 (1) 가주어 it이 필요하다. (2) '~ 위에' 쓰는 것이므로 전치사 on이 필요하다. (3) '칼을 가지고 로프를 자르는' 것이므로 전치사 with가 필요하다. (4) 형용사적 용법의 to부정사가 온다.

09 '같이 놀 친한 친구가 필요하다.'이므로 my best friend를 꾸며주는 to부정사는 전치사 with와 함께 써야 한다.

10 time을 수식하는 to부정사와 「don't have to+동사원형」의 형태가 필요하다.

11 to learn to ride a bike가 주어인 문장으로, 가주어 it이 앞에 온다. to ride는 learn의 목적어로 쓰인 to부정사이다.

12 (1) 형용사가 stupid이므로 의미상의 주어는 'of+목적격'을 쓴다. (2) 형용사가 necessary이므로 의미상의 주어는 'for+목적격'을 쓴다.

13 to부정사의 형용사적 용법 (a place to sell ~)을 이용한다.

[교과서]
Reading

확인문제   p.28

1 F   2 T   3 F   4 T   5 T

확인문제   p.29

1 F   2 T   3 T   4 F

교과서 확인학습 A   p.30~31

01 everywhere, see   02 kinds, bacteria
03 creatures   04 Some   05 digest, that
06 Others, make   07 that, inside, living
08 cause, such   09 enter, through
10 happens   11 multiply
12 body becomes, zone   13 start, weak
14 body, defense   15 sound   16 arrive, germs
17 show, eat   18 called, cells   19 goes, fight

20 few, feel   21 invader, copies, itself
22 smart   23 change, trick
24 several, protect   25 wash, warm
26 diet, healthy   27 exercise, plenty
28 Finally, shots   29 defense, germs
30 steps, victim   31 copies   32 defend
33 meal   34 there, eat   35 Next, send
36 see, another   37 can   38 ready, any
39 up   40 make

교과서 확인학습 B   p.32~33

1 Germs are everywhere, but it is impossible to see them with your eyes.
2 There are two major kinds of germs: bacteria and viruses.
3 Bacteria are very small creatures.
4 Some are good.
5 They can help you digest the food that you eat.
6 Others are bad and can make you sick.
7 Viruses are germs that can only live inside the cells of other living bodies.
8 They cause diseases such as the flu.
9 "Bad" germs can enter your body through your skin, mouth, nose, and eyes.
10 What happens when they invade?
11 The germs multiply in the body.
12 Your body becomes a war zone.
13 You start to feel tired and weak.
14 Luckily, your body has an army of defense.
15 The T cells sound the alarm!
16 The B cells arrive to fight the germs with antibodies.
17 The macrophage cells show up and eat the germs.
18 Together, this army is called the white blood cells.
19 If all goes well, they win the fight.
20 In a few days, you start to feel better.
21 The body remembers the invader, so it cannot make copies of itself again.
22 But the germs are smart, too.
23 They can change form and trick the body.
24 There are several ways to protect yourself from germs.
25 First, wash your hands with soap and warm water.

healthy.

27 It is also important to exercise regularly and get plenty of sleep.

28 Finally, get the necessary shots.

29 They are the best defense against germs.

30 If you follow these steps, you will not be a victim of "bad" germs.

31 Make more copies of me.

32 It's my job to defend the body.

33 That was a nice meal!

34 Are there any more germs to eat?

35 Next year, I'll send in my cousin.

36 He'll see you then for another fight!

37 What can I do now?

38 I'm ready to fight any germs.

39 We give up.

40 We can't make you sick.

시험대비 실력평가
p.34~37

01 ④ 02 ② 03 손대지 마라!

04 ③ 05 ⑤ 06 ⑤ 07 ①

08 ⑤ 09 like 10 multiply 11 invader

12 ① 13 ⑤ 14 ② 15 ④

16 ③ 17 ④ 18 another 19 it → itself 20 그들은 형태를 바꿔서 몸을 속일 수 있다

21 ③ 22 to protect 23 ② 24 ③

25 ③ 26 덤벼. 27 ② 28 규칙적으로 운동하고 잠을 충분히 자는 것 29 나의 사촌들도 게임 오버라고? 30 ④ 31 Finally

32 ⑤ 33 ①

01 주어진 문장은 좋은 박테리아가 있다는 뜻이므로 박테리아가 좋은 일을 하는 문장 앞인 ④에 와야 한다.

02 watch out: 조심하다

03 Hands off!: 손 떼!, 손대지 마!

04 앞뒤 절의 내용이 상반되므로 역접의 접속사 but이 필요하다.

05 선행사가 사물이고 목적격이므로 관계대명사 which나 that을 쓸 수 있다.

06 ⑤ 박테리아는 유익한 것과 해로운 것이 있다.

07 문맥상 '공격하다'가 알맞다.

08 선행사가 사물이고 주격이므로 관계대명사 which나 that을 쓸 수 있다.

09 such as: ~와 같은

10 수나 양이 크게 증가하다: multiply(증식하다, 번식하다)

11 invade: 침략하다 / invader: 침략자, 침입자

12 문맥상 '몸을 방어하다'가 알맞다.

13 ⓒ, ⑤ 부사적 용법 ①, ③, ④ 명사적 용법 ② 형용사적 용법

14 show up: 나타나다

15 T 세포가 어떻게 경보를 발하는지는 언급되지 않았다.

16 game over: 게임 오버, 경기 종료

17 send in: ~을 파견하다

18 뒤에 단수명사가 오므로 another가 알맞다.

19 주어 it의 목적어가 주어 자신이므로 재귀대명사 itself를 써야 한다.

20 change form: 형태를 바꾸다 / trick: 속이다

21 ③ 몸이 자신을 침입한 균을 기억한다고 언급되었다.

22 명사 ways를 수식하는 형용사적 용법의 to부정사이다.

23 protect A from B: B로부터 A를 보호하다

24 ⓒ와 ③은 '~으로'의 뜻으로 수단을 나타낸다. ①, ② ~에게(는) ④ ~에게 ⑤ ~으로(원인)

25 문맥상 '균들과 싸우다'가 알맞다.

26 Bring it on.: 덤벼.

27 ⓒ, ② 5문형 ① 2문형 ③ 1문형 ④ 4문형 ⑤ 3문형

28 It은 가주어로 진주어인 to exercise 이하를 받는다.

29 game over: 게임 오버, 경기 종료.

30 give up: 포기하다

31 final의 부사형 finally로 고친다.

32 against: ~에 대항하여

33 조건의 접속사 if가 알맞다

서술형 시험대비
p.38~39

01 Watch 02 cannot[can't] 03 Others

04 좋은 박테리아는 우리가 먹는 음식을 소화시키는 데 도움이 된다. 05 of 06 enter into → enter

07 나쁜 균들 08 Because the germs multiply in the body. 09 Are there any more germs to eat?

10 defense 11 calling → called 12 며칠 후에 여러분은 기분이 더 좋아지기 시작한다. 13 They sound the alarm. 14 different 15 that

16 snacks 17 with 18 손에 있는 균이 우리의 몸속으로 들어올 수 있기 때문이다.

01 watch out: 조심하다

02 impossible: 불가능한

03 some ~, others ...: 어떤 것들은 ~하고, 또 어떤 것들은 ...하다

05 make copies of: ~을 복사[복제]하다

06 enter는 타동사이므로 전치사 없이 목적어를 취한다.

07 they는 앞 문장에 나온 Bad germs를 받는다.

09 Are there ~?의 구문을 쓴다.

10 defend의 명사형으로 고친다.

11 문맥상 진행형이 아니라 수동태가 되어야 한다.

12 in a few days: 며칠 후에 / start to: ~하기 시작하다

14 differ: 다르다 / different: 다른, 여러 가지의

15 선행사가 everything이므로 which보다 that을 더 자주 쓴다.

16 요리하고 먹기에 빠른 간단한 식사: snack(간식

17 with: ~으로

01 ④는 '명사 - 명사' 관계인데, 나머지는 '동사 - 행위자' 관계이다.

02 • 이것은 매우 어려운 문제이다. • 성공의 비결은 열심히 일하는 데 있다. • 옛날 지폐는 복제하기 너무 쉽다. • 그녀는 피부에 바이러스가 있다.

03 반의어 관계이다. 쉬운 : 어려운 = 안전한 : 위험한

04 by the way: 그런데 / watch out: 조심하다

05 모든 생물들을 구성하는 아주 작은 부분들의 어느 하나: 세포 (cell)

06 at last: 마침내(=finally)

07 give up: 포기하다

08 상대방의 증상을 묻는 표현이 쓰여야 한다.

09 No problem.: 문제없어.(제안에 승낙하는 표현)

10 제안에 거절하는 표현이 와야 한다.

11 (C) 무슨 일 있니? - (A) 목이 아파. - (D) 안됐구나. 너는 물을 좀 마셔야 해. - (B) 알았어, 그렇게.

12 문맥상 약속 정하기 표현이 알맞다. Can you make it at 5?: 5시에 만날 수 있니?

13 What seems to be the problem?은 어떤 증상이 있는지 물어보는 표현으로 What's the matter (with ~)? / What's the problem (with ~)? / Is something wrong (with ~)? 등으로 바꿔 쓸 수 있다.

14 인칭대명사 it은 앞에 나온 get some medicine을 가리킨다.

15 위통이 있는 사람에게 해 줄 수 있는 말은 ③이 알맞다.

16 소년은 배가 몹시 아프다고 했다.

17 -thing으로 끝나는 부정대명사를 수식하는 to부정사가 필요하다.

18 가주어 It을 설명하는 진주어 to부정사가 필요하다.

19 형용사가 stupid와 clever이므로 의미상의 주어는 'of+목적격'을 쓴다.

20 뒤에 진주어인 to부정사구가 왔으므로 빈칸에는 가주어인 it과 be동사가 와야 한다.

21 -thing으로 끝나는 부정대명사는 「-thing+형용사+to부정사」의 어순을 취한다.

22 ②는 날씨를 나타내는 비인칭 주어 it이고, 나머지는 to부정사구를 진주어로 하는 가주어 it이다.

23 <보기>와 나머지는 모두 형용사적 용법이고 ②는 부사적 용법이다.

24 to부정사의 수식을 받는 명사가 전치사의 목적어일 경우 뒤에 전치사가 온다.

25 형용사적 용법의 to부정사는 명사나 대명사를 뒤에서 수식하여 형용사처럼 쓰인다. 또한, food는 보통 단수로 쓰인다.

26 To read this book이 주어인 문장으로, 가주어 it이 앞에 온다.

27 anything: 어떤 것이든

28 주어진 문장은 여러분의 몸이 전쟁 지역이 된다는 뜻이므로 피곤하고 약해지는 것을 느낀다는 문장 앞에 와야 한다.

29 균들이 몸을 공격하는 상황이므로 attack이 알맞다.

30 한정적 용법으로 쓰이고 있으므로 living이 와야 한다.

31 때를 나타내는 접속사 when이 알맞다.

32 ① 균은 자신을 복제할 수 있다.

33 another: 또 다른, 다른 하나의

34 so: 그래서

35 문맥으로 보아 '몸을 속이다'가 알맞다.

36 주어진 문장의 too로 보아 전화기와 컴퓨터에 손을 댄다는 말 다음에 와야 한다.

37 접촉해서 '~ 위에'는 on을 쓴다.

38 여러분 자신을 씻거나 또는 때때로 옷을 세탁하기 위해 물과 함께 사용하는 물질: soap(비누)

01 ④는 유의어 관계이고 나머지는 반의어 관계이다.

02 give up: 포기하다 / show up: 나타나다

03 그림을 그리다 : 화가 = 발명하다 : 발명가

04 ⑤는 dangerous(위험한)의 영영풀이다.

05 (1) be ready to: ~할 준비가 되어 있다

　　(2) have a runny nose: 콧물이 나다 / have a sore throat: 목이 아프다

06 감기에 걸렸을 때 병원에 가보라고 하는 충고가 어울린다.

07 콘서트에 가자는 A의 제안에 B가 동의를 했으므로, 뒤에는 만나는 시간 약속을 하는 내용이 이어지는 것이 자연스럽다.

08 주어진 문장은 '그 말을 들으니 기쁘다.'는 뜻으로 지금은 나 아졌다는 문장 다음에 와야 한다.

09 '시간에 맞춰 가다'는 make it이다. '너는 내일 올 수 있니?' 라는 뜻의 의문문을 만든다.

10 Let's ~.는 Why don't we ~?로 바꿔 쓸 수 있다.

11 it이 가주어이므로 진주어인 to부정사가 와야 한다.

12 첫 문장은 형용사가 wise이므로 의미상의 주어는 'of+목적 격'을 쓴다. 두 번째 문장은 형용사가 impossibl

13 to부정사의 수식을 받는 명사가 전치사의 목적어일 경우 뒤 에 전치사가 온다.

14 To finish this homework이 주어인 문장으로 가주어 it 이 앞에 온다.

15 ①에서 sit은 자동사이므로 chair를 목적어로 취하기 위해 서는 전치사 in이나 on이 필요하다.

16 <보기>와 ③의 It은 가주어이다.
　　①, ④ 비인칭 주어 ②, ⑤ 인칭대명사

17 many places to visit(방문할 많은 장소)에서 to visit은 형용사적 용법의 to부정사로 명사인 many places를 수식 한다.

18 ①은 to부정사의 형용사적 용법이고, 나머지는 모두 '~하기 위해서'라는 목적을 나타내는 부사적 용법이다.

19 be ready to: ~할 준비가 되다 / any: (긍정문에서) 어떤 ~이라도

20 Bring it on.: 덤벼라.

21 동사 exercise를 수식하는 부사로 고쳐야 한다.

22 ⓐ, ⑤ 부사적 용법
　　①, ③, ④ 명사적 용법
　　② 형용사적 용법

23 open: 열다 / close: 닫다

24 관계대명사는 선행사가 everything이므로 that을 쓴다.

25 조건을 나타내는 접속사 if가 알맞다.

26 get into: ~으로 들어가다

27 game over: 게임 오버, 경기 종료

28 'make+목적어+목적보어' 구문이다.

29 They는 앞 문장의 the necessary shots를 받는다.

30 다치거나 살해당한 사람: victim(희생자)

01 |모범답안| What's the matter[problem] with you? / Is (there) something wrong with you? / What seems to be the problem? 등

02 I have a sore throat.

03 Let's / make, it / afraid, How[What] / See

04 (B) - (C) - (D) - (A)

05 (1) It isn't easy to go down the hill.
　　(2) I like the photographs which my little[younger] brother takes.

06 (1) It is difficult for me to park a car.
　　(2) It is safe to ride a bike with a helmet.
　　(3) It is an exciting experience to live in another country.

07 (1) to go to school
　　(2) to have[eat] lunch
　　(3) to play on the playground
　　(4) to do my homework

08 What　　09 yourself　　10 with

11 여러분이 비누와 따뜻한 물로 손을 씻고 있기 때문이다.

12 up　　13 the necessary shots　　14 defense

15 여러분이 이 조치들을 따른다면, 나쁜 균들의 희생자가 되 지 않을 것이다.

01 어떤 증상이 있는지 물을 때 사용하는 표현에는 What's wrong with ~? / What's the matter[problem] with ~? / Is (there) something wrong with ~? / What seems to be the problem? 등이 있다.

02 have a sore throat: 목이 아프다

03 Let's ~: ~하자 / make it: 시간에 대다 / I'm afraid I can't.: 나는 할 수 없을 것 같다. / How about ~?: ~은 어떠니? / See you then.: 그때 보자.

04 (B) 무슨 문제 있니? - (C) 음, 이가 아파. - (D) 그것 참 안 됐구나. 치과에 가 보는 게 어때? - (A) 알았어. 그렇게.

05 (1) 「It ~ to부정사」 구문을 이용하여 문장을 완성한다. (2) 관계대명사 which를 이용하여 선행사 the photographs 를 수식하도록 한다.

06 to부정사가 이끄는 구가 주어로 오는 경우, to부정사 주어 를 문장 뒤로 보내고 그 자리에 It을 쓴다.

07 to부정사의 형용사적 용법을 이용하여 문장을 완성한다.

08 '내가 지금 무엇을 할 수 있는가?'의 뜻이 되어어 자연스럽다.

09 목적어가 주어 자신이므로 재귀대명사를 써야 한다.

10 수단을 나타내는 전치사 with가 알맞다.

12 give up: 포기하다

13 They는 인칭대명사로 앞에 나온 복수명사를 받는다.

14 defend: 방어하다 / defense: 방어

15 follow: 따르다 / step: 단계, 조치

p.52

창의사고력 서술형 문제

|모범답안|

01 (1) I need something to drink
   (2) I need a chair to sit on[in].
   (3) He needs friends to talk with

02 (1) It is kind of her to help the poor.
   (2) It is exciting for us to play the game.
   (3) It is boring for me to watch basketball games.
   (4) It is possible for you to finish the work on time.
   (5) It is difficult for foreigners to learn Korean.

03 (1) a movie to watch
   (2) a baseball game to watch
   (3) a piano lesson to take
   (4) four comic books to read

단원별 모의고사

p.53~56

01 ④	02 ④	03 ④	
04 cartoonist	05 of	06 ④	07 ②
08 the school gym, ten, play basketball		09 ③	
10 make	11 How[What] about	12 ④	
13 ③	14 ③	15 ③	16 to finish
17 ②	18 ⑤		
19 ⓐ to find ⓑ to find	20 ⑤		
21 impossible	22 ③	23 ①, ④	24 ⑤
25 ④	26 ③	27 ⑤	28 called
29 ②	30 ④		
31 Because the body remembers the invader.			

01 섭취한 음식물을 신체가 사용할 수 있도록 생리 과정을 거쳐 더 단순한 형태로 변화시키다: 소화시키다(digest)

02 watch out for: ~을 조심하다

03 shot: 주사, (농구나 축구 같은 구기에서) 슛

04 '명사 : 행위자' 관계이다. 예술, 미술 : 예술가, 미술가 / 만화 : 만화가

05 plenty of: 많은 / think of -ing: ~할 생각이다

06 A가 10시에 만날 수 있는지 묻고 있으므로 빈칸에는 제안에 승낙하는 표현인 ④가 알맞다.

07 ②를 제외하고 나머지는 모두 10시에 만나자고 제안하는 표현이다.

08 A와 B는 농구를 하기 위해 이번 토요일 10시에 학교 체육관에서 만날 것이다.

09 ⓐ be thinking of: ~할 생각 중이다 ⓒ be fine with: ~에게는 괜찮다

10 make it: 시간에 대다, 만나다

11 Let's ~.는 How[What] about -ing? / Why don't we ~? 등으로 바꿔 쓸 수 있다.

12 명사 things를 수식하는 형용사적 용법의 to부정사가 와야 한다.

13 문맥상 '함께 여행할 친구를 찾고 있다'는 흐름이 자연스러우므로, 빈칸에는 '~와 함께'에 해당하는 with가 알맞다.

14 기숙사를 사는 것이 아니라, 기숙사에서 사는 것이므로 live 다음에 전치사 in이 필요하다.

15 <보기>의 to eat는 형용사적 용법의 to부정사이다. ①, ②, ⑤ 부사적 용법 ③ 형용사적 용법 ④ 명사적 용법

16 it은 가주어이고, 진주어는 형용사 뒤에 to부정사 형태로 와야 한다.

17 ②의 경우, 두 개의 동사(is, skate)가 같이 쓰일 수는 없다. 가주어 it과 진주어 to부정사구(to skate ~)의 구문으로 만든다.

18 ⑤ -thing이나 -body로 끝나는 부정대명사의 경우 형용사와 to부정사의 수식을 동시에 받으면 「대명사+형용사+to 부정사」의 순서로 써야 한다. something important to tell이 올바르다.

19 가주어 It의 진주어로 to부정사 형태가 필요하다.

20 to부정사의 형용사적 용법이다.

21 possible: 가능한 / impossible: 불가능한

22 some ~, others ...: 어떤 것들은 ~하고, 또 어떤 것들은 …하다

23 help는 목적보어로 원형부정사나 to부정사를 취한다.

24 ⑤ 바이러스가 박테리아보다 더 해롭다는 말은 언급되지 않았다.

25 주어진 문장의 they는 the white blood cells를 받는다.

26 germs를 수식하는 형용사적 용법의 to부정사가 와야 한다.

27 show up: 나타나다(=appear)

28 수동태이므로 'be동사+과거분사'의 형을 취한다.

29 other 뒤에는 복수명사, another 뒤에는 단수명사가 온다.

30 ④ 몸이 기억하는 것은 균의 사촌이 아니라 이번에 침입한 균이다.

Lesson 4

Earth, Our Only Home

시험대비 실력평가 — p.60

01 ③	02 ⑤	03 ④	04 artificial
05 ④	06 (e)ffect	07 ③	08 to

01 ③은 -y를 붙여 형용사형을 만드는 단어이고, 나머지는 -ful을 붙여 형용사형을 만드는 단어이다.

02 make a fire: 불을 피우다 / take action: 조치를 취하다

03 어떤 사람의 작업, 수면 등을 방해하다: disturb

04 반의어 관계이다. 어두운 : 밝은 = 자연적인 : 인공적인

05 be familiar with: ~을 잘 알다 / in danger: 위험에 처한

06 빛 오염은 인간과 야생 동물에 심각한 영향을 미칠 수 있다. effect: 영향

07 in fact: 사실(actually)

08 according to: ~에 따르면 / be not supposed to: ~ 해서는 안 된다

서술형 시험대비 — p.61

01 (1) bright (2) wrong (3) well-known (4) waste
02 (1) turn down (2) Millions of (3) because of
03 (1) effect (2) light (3) volunteer
04 (1) rhythm (2) environment (3) trash
05 (1) be over (2) suffer from (3) care about
06 (1) (a)rtificial (2) (a)llow (3) (m)igrate (4) (p)rotect

01 (1), (2)는 반의어 관계이다. (1) 같은 : 다른 = 어두운 : 밝은 (2) 쉬운 : 어려운 = 잘못된 : 옳은 / (3), (4)는 유의어 관계이다. (3) 종류 : 종류 = 유명한 : 잘 알려진 (4) 맛있는 : 맛있는 = 쓰레기 : 쓰레기

02 (1) turn down: (볼륨을) 줄이다 (2) millions of: 수백만의 (3) because of: ~ 때문에

03 (1) effect: 영향; 결과 (2) light: 가벼운; 빛 (3) volunteer: 자원봉사자; 자원봉사를 하다

04 (1) 그는 리듬에 맞춰 춤추고 있다. rhythm: 리듬 (2) 우리는 환경을 오염으로부터 보호해야 한다. environment: 환경 (3) 아이들은 쓰레기를 줍고 있다. trash: 쓰레기

05 (1) be over: 끝나다 (2) suffer from: ~로 고통 받다 (3) care about: ~에 관심을 가지다

06 (1) artificial: 인공의, 인위적인 (2) allow: 허락하다 (3) migrate: 이동하다 (4) protect: 보호하다

교과서 Conversation

핵심 Check — p.62~63

1 (1) okay to / No, can't   (2) Am, allowed
2 (1) shouldn't use / sorry   (2) Don't eat
   (3) No, can't, not supposed to
   (4) take a picutre / allowed[supposed]

교과서 대화문 익히기

Check(√) True or False — p.64

1 F 2 T 3 T 4 F

교과서 확인학습 — p.66~67

Communicate: Listen - Listen and Answer Dialog 1
okay to put, bulletin / about / Let, see, Did, make / members, together, about / agree, right now / can, put / ahead

Communicate: Listen - Listen and Answer Dialog 2
are, doing / throwing away / supposed / not / can pollute, put, in danger / see, what, do / must take, care / didn't, be, careful

Communicate: Listen - Listen More
love, place / forgot, didn't bring / on our way / go get / getting dark, should, carefully / Don't / it, to cook / course, not supposed to / care about

Communicate: Listen - All Ears
not supposed to / care more about

Communicate: Speak - Talk in groups
You're not, during / wrong / class rule, shouldn't / remember

My Writing Portfolio - Step 1
Welcome to, listen, follow, supposed, make, sick, to touch, dangerous, Lastly, throw, at, at

Wrap Up - Listening ❺
is it okay to / plans / favorite, have a concert / by /

problem, be over

Wrap Up - Listening ⑥

look at / What / over there, pick / sorry, didn't know

시험대비 기본평가   p.68

01 ②   02 ②   03 ②   04 ⑤

01 '~해도 되는지' 허가 여부를 물어보는 표현이다.

02 May I ~?는 허락 여부를 묻는 표현이므로 승낙의 표현인 Sure.가 들어가야 한다.

03 허가 여부를 묻는 표현이다. 'Am I allowed to ~?'로 바꾸어 쓸 수 있다.

04 You're not allowed to ~는 허락을 구하는 말에 대한 불허의 표현으로 You're not supposed to ~로 바꿔 쓸 수 있다.

시험대비 실력평가   p.69~70

01 ④   02 ②   03 ④   04 ⑤

05 It is about World Oceans Day.   06 ④

07 ⑤   08 ④   09 away   10 ④

11 ②   12 그것은 물을 오염시키고 사람과 동물들을 위험에 빠뜨릴 수 있기 때문이다. 13 if   14 ②

15 ②

01 주어진 문장은 '음, 지금은 공간이 없다.'라는 뜻으로 '그럼 문에 붙일까요?'라는 질문 앞에 오는 것이 자연스럽다.

02 '제가 ~해도 괜찮나요?'의 뜻으로 허락 여부를 묻는 표현이 들어가야 한다. Is it okay to+동사원형 ~?: ~해도 괜찮겠어요?

03 care about: ~에 관심을 가지다

04 빈칸 뒤의 말로 보아, 문에 포스터를 붙이는 것을 허락하겠다는 뜻인데, ⑤ Maybe next time.은 다음에 허락하겠다는 뜻이므로 어색하다.

05 Q: 그 포스터는 무엇에 관한 것인가? A: 그것은 세계 해양 의 날에 대한 것이다.

06 ⓐ는 불허하는 표현이므로 ④와 바꿔 쓸 수 있다.

07 should not: ~해서는 안 된다(금지)

08 주어진 문장은 '그러면 내가 어떻게 해야 하지?'라는 뜻으로 충고를 구하는 표현이므로, '약국에 그것을 가지고 가야 해.'라는 충고의 말 앞에 오는 것이 알맞다.

09 throw away: ~을 버리다

10 You're not supposed to+동사원형 ~.은 '~해서는 안 된다' 라는 의미로 금지를 나타낸다.

11 put ~ in danger: ~을 위험에 빠뜨리다

12 It can pollute the water. It can also put people and

---

animals in danger.를 통해서 알 수 있다.

13 Is it okay to + 동사원형 ~?은 Is it OK if I ~?로 바꿔 쓸 수 있다.

14 by: ~까지

15 No problem.은 당부하기에 수락하는 표현으로 Why not?으 로 바꿔 쓸 수 있다.

서술형 시험대비   p.71

01 Is it okay to / you're not supposed to

02 Is it okay if I ~? / Am I allowed to ~? / Can[May] I ~? 등

03 You're not allowed to do that

04 (D) – (A) – (C) – (B)   05 on

06 내가 가서 칫솔 좀 사 올게.   07 to

08 not supposed[allowed / permitted] to

09 She cares about the environment.

01 Is it okay to ~?: ~해도 될까요? / You're not supposed to ~: 너는 ~하면 안 돼.

02 Is it okay to ~?은 허가 여부를 묻는 표현으로 Is it okay If I ~?, Am I allowed to ~?, Can[May] I ~? 등으로 바꿔 쓸 수 있다.

03 You're not allowed to ~.: 너는 ~해서는 안 돼.

04 (D) 쉬는 시간에 공부하면 안 돼. -(A) 그게 뭐가 문젠데? - (C) 새로운 학급 규칙이야. 그렇게 해선 안 돼. (B) 알았어. 규칙을 기억할게.

05 on one's way here: 여기 오는 길에

06 go get = go and get / get = buy

07 '~해도 되나요?'는 「Is it okay+to부정사 ~?」로 나타낼 수 있다.

08 '허락되지 않는다.'의 의미로 not supposed[allowed / permitted] to가 들어가야 한다.

교과서
Grammar

핵심 Check   p.72~73

1 (1) The window was broken by Brian.

  (2) Many poor kids are helped by Mrs. Smith.

  (3) The cars were stopped by the police officer.

2 (1) as tall as your father

  (2) not as long as the yellow one

  (3) as new as mine

01 (1) broke, broken　(2) brought, brought
　(3) kept, kept　(4) saw, seen
　(5) spoke, spoken　(6) taught, taught
　(7) wrote, written　(8) stole, stolen
　(9) made, made　(10) knew, known

02 (1) by　(2) was　(3) built　(4) from
　(5) in　(6) were　(7) with

03 (1) run as fast as
　(2) not as[so] delicious as
　(3) as large as Seoul's (population)
　(4) as heavy as mine
　(5) as difficult

01 A-B-C형: break, see, speak, write, steal, know / A-B-B형: bring, keep, teach, make

02 (1) 수동태 문장에서는 행위자 앞에 전치사 by를 쓴다. (2) 역사적 사실을 나타낼 때는 과거시제로 쓴다. (3) build의 과거분사는 built이다. (4) 화학적 변화로 인한 것은 be made from으로 나타낸다. (5) be interested in: ~에 관심이 있다 (6) The children이 복수이므로 were가 알맞다. (7) be satisfied with: ~에 만족하다

03 (1) fast의 정도를 비교하는 것이므로 run as fast as ~가 맞다. (2) as ~ as의 부정문은 not as/so ~ as로 쓴다. (3) 도쿄의 인구와 서울의 인구를 비교하는 것이므로 Seoul은 적절하지 않다. (4) your bag과 my bag을 비교하는 것이므로 me를 mine으로 고친다. (5) 뒤의 비교 대상 앞에 as가 있으므로 동등비교로 만들어야 한다.

01 ③　02 ③　03 (1) bigger (2) long
(3) happiest　04 was invented　05 ②
06 ①　07 ③　08 be fixed　09 ①
10 ⑤　11 made　12 (1) cold (2) hotter, than　13 ①　14 ②　15 ②
16 is → be　17 ⑤　18 ⑤　19 ④
20 This refrigerator can be fixed by him.　21 (1) old
(2) younger (3) shortest (4) large (5) of (6) could
22 ②

01 케이크가 주어이므로 수동태인 「be동사+과거분사」 형태가 알맞다.
02 ③ catch의 과거분사형은 caught이다.
03 (1) big는 '단모음+단자음'으로 끝난다. (2) as+원급+as의 구문이다. (3) 최상급 구문이다.
04 수동태의 과거형이 되어야 하므로 「be동사의 과거형+과거 분

사」로 나타낸다.
05 과거시제 부정문을 수동태로 바꿀 때는 「was[were]+not+ 과거분사」의 어순으로 쓴다.
06 the same ~ as는 as ~ as로 바꿔 쓸 수 있다.
07 내용상 수동태로 표현해야 하므로 「be동사+과거분사」의 형태로 나타낸다. speak의 과거분사는 spoken이다.
08 능동에서 수동으로 바꿀 때 동사는 「be동사+과거분사」 형태로 쓴다.
09 '…만큼 ~한'의 뜻을 나타내는 동등비교이다.
10 ⑤ 「by+목적격」이 와야 한다.
11 수동태로 과거분사형인 made가 알맞다. 재료의 성질과 형태가 모두 변하는 경우에는 be made from을 쓴다. 반면에, 재료의 성질은 그대로이고, 형태만 변하는 경우에는 be made of를 쓴다.
12 (1) 비교급의 문장을 not as ~ as …의 문장으로 바꾼다. (2) not as ~ as …의 문장을 비교급의 문장으로 바꾼다.
13 조동사가 있는 수동태는 「조동사+be+과거분사」의 형태로 쓴다.
14 ②에서 was는 annoyed라는 형용사를 주격보어로 취하는 be동사이며, 나머지는 모두 수동태를 나타내는 be동사이다.
15 첫 번째 문장은 '~만큼 많이'의 동등 비교 표현이고, 두 번째 문장은 'more+원급+than …'의 비교 표현이다.
16 조동사가 있는 수동태에서는 조동사 뒤에 be동사의 원형인 be가 와야 한다.
17 ⑤ find(찾다, 발견하다) – found – found / found(설립하다) – founded – founded
18 ⑤는 '~할 때'라는 뜻의 접속사이고 나머지는 as ~ as … 구문의 부사로 쓰였다.
19 ④ 주어가 these wall paintings로 바뀌며 「By+whom(who의 목적격)」이 쓰여야 한다. 동사는 과거 시제이므로 were painted가 알맞다.
20 주어가 냉장고이고 '고쳐지다'라는 수동의 의미를 나타내야 하므로 「주어+조동사+be동사+과거분사+by+목적격」의 수동태 문장으로 써야 한다.
21 (1), (4) as 다음에는 원급이 온다. (2) 비교급 (3) 최상급 (5) of 뒤에는 복수 명사나 복수 대명사가 온다. (6) as+원급 +as+주어 +can[could] 구문이다.
22 ②에서 두 번째 as 뒤에 오는 절의 주어가 George로 3인칭 단수이므로 do를 does로 바꾸어야 한다.

01 (1) was broken　(2) was written
　(3) appeared　(4) are sold
02 was
03 (1) just　(2) young　(3) twice　(4) early
04 (1) drawing → drawn

(2) is invented → was invented

(3) found → founded

(4) does → is

(5) Did → Were

05 (1) faster than   (2) as, as

(3) as old   (4) possible

06 (1) Paper money was first invented around the 10th century by Chinese people.

(2) English is spoken by people in the United States.

(3) These pictures were taken by Tom yesterday.

(4) Shells and rice were used as money by Koreans in the past.

07 (1) stolen   (2) hit   (3) caught   (4) broken

(5) found   (6) with   (7) to

08 (1) Ella has as many hats as I have.

(2) This new tool is as useful as the old one.

(3) Tom drank as much wine as water.

09 (1) Paper boxes were carried by them.

(2) I was given the book by her.

10 (1) Jimin is not as[so] tall as Taemin.

(2) Jane isn't as[so] heavy as Kirk.

---

01 수동태는 「be+과거분사」 형태로 쓴다. 시제와 수의 일치에 주의한다. (3) appear는 수동태로 쓰이지 않는다.

02 수동태에서 be동사는 주어의 수와 시제에 영향을 받는다.

03 (1) 비교 대상의 정도가 완전히 같을 때는 as 앞에 just를 붙인다. (2) '예전만큼 젊지 않다'의 뜻이므로 young이 적절하다. (3) '몇 배의 ~'는 배수사를 as 앞에 둔다. (4) '동생만 큼 일찍'이므로 early를 쓴다.

04 (1) 주어가 사물이므로, 과거진행형이 아니라 수동태가 되어야 한다. (2) 역사적 사실은 과거시제로 나타낸다. 주어인 비행기가 발명된 것이므로 수동태가 되어야 한다. (3) find(찾다)의 과거분사는 found이고, found(설립하다)의 과거분사는 founded이다. 위 문장에서 the company가 발견 된 것이 아니고 설립된 것이므로 was founded가 알맞다. (4) 수동태의 부정문이므로 be동사+not+과거분사가 알맞다. (5) 의문문이므로 Be동사+주어+과거분사 ~?가 알맞다.

05 (1) not ... as ~ as는 비교급 구문으로 바꿔 쓸 수 있다. (2) less ~ than ...은 not as ~ as 구문으로 바꿔 쓸 수 있다. (3) the same age는 as old as로 바꿔 쓸 수 있다. (4) as ~ as 주어+can = as ~ as possible

06 수동태는 「주어(+조동사)+be동사+과거분사(+by+목적격)」의 형태로 나타낸다.

07 (1) steal – stole – stolen (2) hit – hit – hit (3) catch – caught – caught (4) break – broke – broken (5) find(찾다)의 과거분사는 found / found(설립하다)의 과거분사는

---

founded (6) be filled with: ~으로 가득하다 (7) be known to: ~에게 알려져 있다

08 (1) Ella has ~와 I have를 동등 비교한다. (2) This new tool 과 The old one을 동등 비교한다. one은 tool의 반복을 피하기 위해 쓴 부정대명사이다. (3) wine과 water를 비교한다.

09 (1) carry - carried (2) give - given

10 'A는 B보다 덜 ~하다'는 A not as[so] ~ as B로 바꾸어 쓸 수 있다.

확인문제   p.80

1 T   2 T   3 F   4 F   5 T

확인문제   p.81

1 F   2 T   3 T   4 F   5 F

교과서 확인학습 A   p.82~83

01 Look, painting 02 created, artist

03 time, look, starry   04 many, lucky

05 fact, world, sky

06 because, pollution   07 familiar, land

08 that, problems, action   09 know, cause

10 Light, wrong, everywhere

11 effects, wildlife

12 report, population, enough

13 Especially, see

14 suffer, because, disturbed 15 threatened

16 migrate, natural, cause   17 millions, hitting

18 easily, since, bright

19 die, draws, ocean   20 Clearly, serious

21 find, solve   22 may, only

교과서 확인학습 B   p.84~85

1 Look at this beautiful painting.

2 It was created by the famous Dutch artist Vincent van Gogh in 1889.

3 In Van Gogh's time, almost everyone could look up and see a wonderful starry night sky.

4 Now, how many of us are as lucky as Van Gogh?

5 In fact, many people in today's world cannot enjoy a starry night sky.

6 This is so because of light pollution.

7 Most of us are familiar with air, water, and land pollution.

8 We know that they are serious problems, and we are taking action to solve them.

9 But did you know that light can also cause pollution?

10 Light pollution—too much light in the wrong place at the wrong time—is almost everywhere around the world.

11 It can have serious effects on humans and wildlife.

12 According to a recent report, about 89% of the world's population lives under skies that are not dark enough at night.

13 Especially in big cities, people often cannot see a starry night.

14 They can also suffer from sleep problems because the natural rhythm of day and night is disturbed by artificial light.

15 Wildlife is threatened by light pollution, too.

16 Birds that migrate or hunt at night find their way by natural light, but light in big cities can cause them to wander off course.

17 Every year millions of birds die after hitting buildings that have bright lights.

18 Sea turtles cannot easily find a place to lay eggs since beaches are too bright at night.

19 Also, many baby sea turtles die because artificial light draws them away from the ocean.

20 Clearly, light pollution is as serious as other forms of pollution.

21 We have to find ways to solve the problem.

22 If we do not, we may see stars only in our dreams or paintings.

시험대비 실력평가
p.86~89

01 ③　　02 artist　　03 ①　　04 오늘날
세계의 많은 사람들이 별이 빛나는 밤하늘을 즐길 수 없는 것ㅣ
05 ④　　06 air, water, and land pollution
07 ③　　08 ③, ⑤　　09 starry　　10 ②
11 artificial　　12 세계 인구의 89퍼센트가 밤에 충분히
어둡지 않은 하늘 아래서 살고 있는 것　　13 ④

14 ③　　15 hitting　　16 ②, ⑤　　17 ④
18 ②　　19 We have to find ways to solve the problem.　　20 ③　　21 ①　　22 by
23 우리들 중 많은 사람들은 별이 총총한 멋진 밤하늘을 볼 수 없다.　　24 ③　　25 ③　　26 ②
27 Light pollution　　28 ①　　29 ⑤
30 disturbed　　31 ②

01 주어진 문장은 얼마나 많은 사람이 별이 총총한 하늘을 볼 수 있느냐는 뜻이므로 많은 사람들이 볼 수 없다는 문장 앞인 ③에 와야 한다.

02 art: 미술, 예술 / artist: 미술가, 예술가

03 in fact: 사실

04 This는 앞 문장의 내용을 받는 지시대명사이다.

05 be familiar with: ~에 익숙하다

06 they는 앞 문장의 복수명사를 받는 인칭대명사이다.

07 ③ 빛 오염에 대해 알고 있었느냐고 묻고 있으므로 많은 사람들이 알고 있다고 말할 수 없다.

08 선행사가 사물인 skies이므로 주격 관계대명사로 쓰이는 that이나 which가 올 수 있다.

09 star의 형용사형 starry로 고쳐야 한다.

10 suffer from: ~으로 고통을 받다

11 natural: 자연적인 / artificial: 인공적인

13 'be동사+과거분사'의 수동태가 되어야 한다.

14 cause A to ~: A가 ~하도록 야기하다

15 'after+동명사' 구문이다.

16 문맥상 이유를 나타내는 접속사가 알맞다.

17 ④ 해변이 너무 밝은 이유는 언급되지 않았다.

18 'as+원급+as'의 동등 비교 구문이다.

19 have to ~: ~해야 한다

20 ⓒ와 ③의 may는 '~일지도 모르다'의 뜻으로 약한 추측을 나타낸다.

21 look at: ~을 보다 /
look up: 위를 올려다보다, 쳐다보다

22 'be+과거분사+by ~'의 수동태 구문이다.

23 Van Gogh만큼 운이 좋다는 말은 Van Gogh처럼 멋진 밤하늘을 즐길 수 있다는 의미이다.

24 in fact=as a matter of fact: 사실

25 take action: 조치를 취하다

26 문맥상 '오염을 일으키다'가 자연스러우므로 cause가 알맞다.

27 It은 인칭대명사로 앞 문장에 나온 단수명사를 받는다.

28 according to: ~에 의하면

29 문맥상 이유를 나타내는 접속사가 알맞다.

30 수동태 구문이 되어야 하므로 disturb의 과거분사로 바꾼다.

31 ② 공기, 물, 토양 오염이 왜 심각한지는 언급되지 않았다.

서술형 시험대비　　　　　　　p.90~91

01 threatened 　02 but　　03 million ➡ millions

04 because[as, since]　　05 From

06 volunteers

07 그의 일은 어두워진 후에 거북들이 돌아올 때 시작된다.

08 Because they want to lay eggs on the beach.

09 created

10 almost everyone could look up and see a wonderful starry night sky

11 in　　　　12 enjoy[see], of

13 우리들 대부분은 공기 오염, 물 오염, 토양 오염은 잘 알고 있다.

14 that　　　15 solve　　16 wildlife

17 잘못된 시간에 잘못된 장소에 너무나 많은 빛이 있는 것.

01 수동태 구문이 되어야 하므로 threaten의 과거분사로 바꾼다.

02 상반되는 내용의 두 절을 연결하므로 but이 알맞다.

03 millions of: 수백만의

04 이유를 나타내는 접속사 because, as, since 등을 쓴다.

05 from A to B: A에서 B까지

06 어떤 일을 하도록 강제 받지 않고 자청해서 하다: volunteer(자원 봉사하다)

07 after dark: 어두워진 후에

09 수동태 구문이 되어야 하므로 create의 과거분사로 바꾼다.

10 시제가 과거이므로 can의 과거형 could를 쓴다. night을 수식하는 형용사가 되어야 하므로 star의 형용사형 starry 로 바꿔야 한다.

11 in fact: 사실

12 enjoy 대신 see를 쓸 수 있다.

13 most of: ~의 대부분 / be familiar with: ~에 익숙하다, ~을 잘 알고 있다

14 명사절을 이끄는 접속사 that을 쓴다.

15 solution의 동사형 solve로 고친다.

16 야생에 사는 동물들: wildlife(야생 동물)

영역별 핵심문제　　　　　　　p.93~97

01 ⑤　　　02 ④　　03 care about 04 natural

05 (m)igrate　06 ③　　07 ②　　08 ④

09 ③　　10 ⑤　　11 ①　　12 ③

13 ④　　14 ②　　15 ②　　16 He plays tennis as well as Tom.　　17 ④

18 ⑤　　19 ③　　20 ⑤　　21 This refrigerator can be fixed by him.　　22 ①

23 All kinds of things were used as money.

24 ③　　25 ②　　26 that[which]27 ④

28 ②　　29 ⑤　　30 ②　　31 town

01 ⑤는 유의어 관계이고, 나머지는 반의어 관계이다.

02 run away: 도망가다 / throw away: 버리다

03 care about: ~에 관심을 가지다

04 반의어 관계이다. 쉬운 : 어려운 = 인공적인 : 자연적인

05 migrate: 이동하다

06 • 규칙을 따르세요. • 그는 그의 칫솔을 가져오지 않았다. • 그녀는 게시판에 포스터를 붙일 것이다. • 너는 꽃을 꺾어서는 안돼. / feed: 먹이를 주다

07 식사 때 다 먹지 않고 남은 음식: 남은 음식(leftover)

08 금지의 표현은 명령문 「Don't+동사원형 ~.」을 사용하거나 조동사 shouldn't를 사용하여 표현할 수 있다.

09 B의 응답은 허가 여부에 대한 응답이므로 Is it okay if ~?의 형태로 물어봐야 한다.

10 ⑤ 허가를 구하는 표현이 적절하다. Do you mind ~?에 대해 거절할 때는 Yes로 답해야 한다.

11 '~해도 되니?'라고 허락을 요청할 때는 「Is it okay if 주어+ 동사 ~?」를 쓴다.

12 ⓑ should: ~해야 한다 ⓒ Can[May] I ~?: 제가 ~해도 되나요?

13 ④ 세계 해양의 날이 언제인지는 알 수 없다.

14 ② take의 과거분사는 taken이다.

15 태어난 것은 과거의 일이므로 수동태의 과거시제 문장이 되어야 한다. be born: 태어나다

16 '~만큼 잘'은 as well as로 나타낸다.

17 ④ be filled with: ~로 가득 차 있다

18 ⑤ appear는 자동사이므로 수동태가 아니라 능동태로 쓰여야 한다.

19 「as+형용사+a(n)+명사+as ~」의 어순이므로 as great a statesman as ~가 되어야 한다.

20 ⑤ 행위의 주체가 일반인이거나 굳이 말하지 않아도 알 수 있는 경우에는 'by+목적격'을 생략할 수 있다.

21 주어가 냉장고이고 '고쳐지다'라는 수동의 의미를 나타내야 하므로 「주어+조동사+be동사+과거분사+by+목적격」의 수동태 문장으로 써야 한다.

22 just the same ~ as는 just as ~ as로 바꿔 쓸 수 있다.

23 사물이 주어이므로 수동태를 사용한다.

24 수동태 문장은 「be+과거분사」로 나타낸다. 주어 Honey가 3인칭 단수이므로 be동사는 is를 사용한다.

25 They can also suffer ...의 They는 문맥상 people을 받으므로 ②에 들어가야 한다.

26 주어가 사물이고 주격이므로 that이나 which가 와야 한다.

27 문맥상 빛 오염에 의해 '위협을 받는다'가 알맞다.

28 ⓒ, ② ~으로, ~에 의해(수단) ① ~ 옆에(장소나 위치) ③ ~ 까

15

지는(시간) ④ ~ 단위로(단위) ⑤ ~을 지나

29 ⑤ 인공의 빛은 길을 찾는 데 방해가 된다.

30 주어진 문장은 Lucas가 자원 봉사를 한다는 내용이므로 그의 일을 설명하는 문장 앞에 와야 한다.

31 사람들이 살고 일하며 많은 거리와 건물들이 있는 장소로 마을보다 더 크다: town(읍, 소도시)

32 from A to B: A에서 B까지

33 turn off: ~을 끄다

34 ② 얼마나 많은 바다 거북이가 그 마을에 오는지는 알 수 없다.

단원별 예상문제
p.98~101

01 ⑤	02 (e)nough	03 ③	04 In[in]
05 ①	06 ②	07 ③	08 ⑤
09 to	10 ⑤	11 It will be over by about 8:00.	12 ②
13 ④	14 as much as he used to	15 Who used shells and rice as money?	16 ②
17 ①	18 ①	19 ②	20 ③
21 fish	22 They live in southern Africa.	23 ④	24 ⑤
25 hit → hitting	26 ②	27 ③, ⑤	28 It , clear
29 ④			

01 ⑤는 명사에 -ful을 붙여 형용사형을 만드는 단어이고 <보기>와 나머지는 명사에 -y를 붙여 형용사형을 만드는 단어 들이다.

02 enough: 충분한

03 ③은 pet(애완동물)의 영영풀이이다.

04 in fact: 사실 / put ~ in danger: ~을 위험에 빠뜨리다

05 take care of: ~을 처리하다 / because of: ~ 때문에

06 B의 답변으로 보아, 빈칸에는 금지를 나타내는 should not을 사용한 문장이 들어가야 한다.

07 ③ Certainly.는 허락을 나타내는 표현인데, 뒤에 이어지는 말은 가지고 오지 않았다고 했으므로 어울리지 않는다.

08 빈칸에는 허락을 구하는 표현이 들어가야 어울린다. ⑤ Do you mind if I ~?도 허락을 구하는 표현이지만 '~하는 것을 꺼리세요?'의 뜻이므로 Yes, you can.으로 대답할 수 없다.

09 Is it okay to ~?: ~해도 될까요? / be going to: ~할 것이다

10 빈칸 다음의 말로 보아 당부하기에 수락하는 표현이 알맞다. ⑤는 당부하기에 거절하는 표현이다.

11 콘서트는 약 8시쯤 끝날 것이다.

12 '~에 의해 발명되었다'의 의미이므로 by가 적절하다.

13 <보기>의 was는 수동태를 나타내는 be동사이다. ④는 형용사 disappointed를 보어로 취하는 be동사이다.

14 '예전만큼 많이'는 as much as he used to로 나타낸다.

15 먼저 평서문으로 고치면 Shells and rice were used as money by someone.이 된다. 여기서 능동태로 변환 하고 다시 의문문으로 바꾼다.

16 ② letters가 복수이므로 was는 were가 되어야 한다.

17 첫 번째 문장은 '~만큼 많은'의 동등 비교 표현이고, 두 번째는 비교급을 강조하는 much가 적절하다.

18 이 문장의 목적어인 this cake를 앞으로 보내고, 동사 made를 was made로 바꾼다.

19 ②의 by는 '~까지(는)'의 의미이고, 나머지는 '~에 의해'라는 의미로 쓰였다.

20 suffer from: ~으로 고통 받다

21 물에 살며 꼬리와 지느러미를 가지고 있는 생물: fish(물고기)

23 '~에 의해, ~으로'의 뜻으로 행위자나 수단을 나타내는 전치사 by가 알맞다.

24 cause는 목적보어로 to부정사를 취한다.

25 이 문장에서의 after는 전치사이므로 hit을 동명사로 고쳐야 한다.

26 ⓔ, ② 형용사적 용법 ①, ⑤ 명사적 용법 ③, ④ 부사적 용법

27 이유를 나타내는 접속사로는 because, as, since 등이 있다.

28 clearly는 문장 수식 부사로 It is clear that으로 바꿔 쓸 수 있다.

29 ④ 밤에 왜 해변이 너무 밝은지는 알 수 없다.

서술형 실전문제
p.102~103

01 you're not permitted to

02 Is it okay if I eat this grape juice?

03 you're not allowed to do that / you're not permitted to do that 등

04 (C) - (A) - (D) - (B)

05 (1) My bicycle was fixed by Tom.
(2) Our school was founded in 1976.

06 (1) Meg sings as well as you (do).
(2) This street is just as wide as that one.
(3) Seoul Tower is about three times as high as this tower.
(4) I can't[cannot] cook as well as my sister.

07 (1) This song is not[isn't] liked by everybody. / Is this song liked by everybody?
(2) My computer wasn't used by Alice. / Was my computer used by Alice?

08 lay   **09** on

10 His work starts when turtles arrive after dark.

11 (q)uiet   **12** painting

13 우리들은 별이 총총한 멋진 밤하늘을 볼 수 있는 사람이 많지 않다.

14 because of

01 You're permitted to ~.: 너는 ~해서는 안 된다.

02 Is it okay if I ~?: 제가 ~해도 되나요?

03 You're not supposed to do that.은 상대방의 요청을 불

허 하는 표현으로 You're not allowed to do that. / You're not permitted to do that. / You shouldn't do that. / You can't do that. 등으로 바꿔 쓸 수 있다.

04 (C) 이봐요, 표지판을 보세요! - (A) 무슨 표지판이요?- (D) 저쪽에 있는 거요. 여기서 꽃을 따면 안 돼요. - (B) 아, 미안해요. 전 몰랐어요.

05 (1) 수동태의 과거형: was[were]+과거분사+by+목적격 (2) be founded: 설립되다

06 as ~ as ...는 동등 비교를 나타낸다.

07 능동태의 시제가 과거형이므로 수동태는 was used가 되어야 한다. 부정문은 be동사 뒤에 not을 붙여 만들고, 의문문은 be동사를 문장의 맨 앞으로 보내고 문장의 끝에 물음표를 붙여 만든다.

08 lie: 놓여 있다, 눕다 / lay: 놓다, (알을) 낳다

09 on weekends: 주말에

10 after dark: 어두워진 후에

11 소리가 거의 나지 않는: quiet(조용한)

12 paint: 그리다 / painting: 그림

13 이 문장의 lucky는 별을 볼 수 있는 행운을 의미한다.

14 because 다음에는 절이 오고, because of 다음에는 명사(구)가 온다.

창의사고력 서술형 문제   p.104

|모범답안|

01 Sure, go ahead. / Why not? / No problem. / That's fine with me. / I'm afraid not. / Certainly not. / No, I'm sorry. / Not for any reason. 등

02 (1) *Zootopia* was directed by Byron Howard.
   (2) *The Scream* was painted by Edward Munch.
   (3) *Anne of Green Gables* was written by Lucy Maud Montgomery.
   (4) iPhone was made by Steve Jobs.
   (5) *The Starry Night* was painted by Vincent van Gogh.

03 (1) I am as popular as Kathy.
   (2) I run as fast as my brother does.
   (3) I study as hard as you do.
   (4) I am not as diligent as Frank.

03 「as+형용사/부사의 원급+as」와 「not as+형용사/부사의 원급+as」의 구문을 활용하여 자신의 입장에서 자유롭게 써 보도록 한다.

단원별 모의고사   p.105~108

01 ⑤	02 ④	03 starry	04 ⑤
05 ②	06 ⑤	07 ④	08 ②
09 ②	10 ②	11 이곳에서 꽃을 꺾으면 안	
되는 것	12 ①	13 ⑤	14 ④
15 ②	16 as	17 ⑤	18 ③
19 ①	20 ③	21 not, easy	22 ①
23 familiar	24 ④	25 Yes, it can.	26 ①
27 natural	28 ③	29 ⑤	

30 바다거북들은 밤에 해변이 너무 밝기 때문에 알을 낳을 장소를 쉽게 찾을 수 없다.   31 artificial   32 Light in big cities does.

01 ⑤는 명사형이고 나머지는 형용사형이다.

02 turn down: (소리를) 낮추다

03 starry: 별이 총총한

04 be familiar with: ~을 잘 알다 / according to: ~에 따르면

05 ② be over: 끝나다

06 TV를 켜도 되느냐는 질문에 숙제를 하는 중이라고 했으므로 거절하는 표현이 적절하다. ⑤를 제외하고는 모두 승낙하는 표현이다.

07 불허하는 말이므로 ④와 바꾸어 쓸 수 있다.

08 ②를 제외하고는 모두 허가 여부를 묻는 표현이다. ②는 어디서 그것을 발견했는지 말해 줄 것을 부탁하는 표현이다.

09 B가 춥다고 했으므로 승낙의 표현이 와야 한다. Would you mind if ~?로 묻는 경우 부정으로 답해야 승낙의 표현이 된다.

10 you're not supposed to는 금지를 나타내는 표현으로 ①, ③, ④, ⑤와 바꿔 쓸 수 있다. You don't have to ~는 '너는 ~할 필요가 없다'는 의미이다.

12 주어가 books이므로 수동태(be+p.p.)로 써야 한다.

13 must be chosen을 수식해야 하므로 부사 형태가 알맞다.

14 주어가 you이므로 be동사는 are가 온다. be interested in: ~에 관심이 있다

15 수동태 문장은 「be동사+과거분사」의 어순으로 쓴다. be동사가 있으므로 빈칸에는 invite의 과거분사만 오면 된다.

16 less ~ than ...은 not as ~ as 구문으로 바꿔 쓸 수 있다. less ~ than ... …보다 적은 ~

17 hold의 과거분사는 held이다.

18 'Romeo and Juliet'은 책 이름이므로 단수로 취급하고 과거에 쓰여진 것이므로 was written으로 고쳐야 한다.

19 ① 두 번째 as 뒤에 오는 절의 주어가 Mike로 3인칭 단수이므로 do를 does로 바꾸어야 한다.

20 ③ 수동태이므로 write의 과거분사가 알맞다. (wrote → written)

21 '…만큼 ~하지 않다'는 not as ~ as로 나타낸다.

22 be covered with: ~로 덮여 있다 / be known for: ~로 알려

지다[유명하다]

23 어떤 사람이나 어떤 것을 알아보거나 또는 잘 아는: familiar(익숙한, 잘 아는)

24 목적을 나타내는 to부정사의 부사적 용법이다.

26 주어진 문장은 야생 동물이 빛 오염에 위협을 받는다는 뜻이므로 그 구체적인 예들을 서술하는 문장 앞에 온다.

27 nature: 자연 / natural: 자연의, 자연적인

28 앞뒤의 절의 내용이 상반되므로 상반의 접속사 but이 와야 한다.

29 선행사가 사물이고 주격인 관계대명사는 that이나 which가 쓰인다.

30 a place to lay eggs: 알을 낳을 장소 / since: ~이기 때문에

31 자연적으로 일어나지 않고 예를 들면 과학이나 기술을 써서 인간에 의해 만들어진: artificial(인공의, 인조의)

Laugh Out Loud

교과서 Reading

확인문제 p.112

1 T 2 F 3 F 4 T 5 T 6 F

확인문제 p.113

1 T 2 F 3 T 4 F 5 T 6 F

교과서 확인학습 A p.114~115

01 Clock, Talks   02 invited, to, one evening

03 was proud of, in, comic books

04 In, had, metal dish   05 asked, What's

06 special, talks, proudly   07 If, hit, the time

08 hit, with   09 made, loud

10 Suddenly, on the other side, shouted, crazy

11 It's, at, go to bed   12 Flat

13 university   14 in, on

15 come back early, because

16 got up late, make

17 being late, decided to tell, got, tire

18 that, bad luck, allowed, to, on

19 When, to take, on, put, different 20 As, sat down

21 global warming

22 a piece of cake, continued   23 answer

24 Which   25 Special

26 One day, to buy

27 How much, one

28 costs, pet shop

29 Why, expensive

30 special one, play the piano   31 What about

32 because, jump rope   33 what about

34 responded, costs

35 surprised, does, do

36 said, other, call

1 A Clock That Talks

2 Dean invited his friends to his room one evening.

3 He was proud of everything in his room: a nice bed, many comic books, and a new computer.

4 In the corner, he also had a very big metal dish.

5 A friend asked, "What's that big dish?"

6 "Oh, that's my special clock. It talks," Dean replied proudly.

7 "If you hit the dish, you'll know the time."

8 Then he hit the dish with his hand.

9 It made a really loud noise.

10 Suddenly, his sister who was on the other side of the wall shouted, "Are you crazy?

11 It's eleven o'clock at night. Time to go to bed!"

12 A Flat Tire

13 Jessie and Nicole are university friends.

14 They visited Jessie's grandma in Florida on Saturday.

15 They planned to come back early on Monday because they had a big test that afternoon.

16 But they got up late and could not make it to the test.

17 They needed a good excuse for being late, so they decided to tell the professor that their car got a flat tire.

18 The professor agreed that it was just bad luck and allowed them to take the test on Wednesday.

19 When they came to take the test on Wednesday morning, the professor put Jessie and Nicole in different rooms.

20 As they sat down, they read the first question.

21 For 5 points, explain global warming.

22 It was a piece of cake to them. Then, the test continued.

23 For 95 points, answer the question.

24 Which tire?

25 A Special Parrot

26 One day Abril went to a pet shop to buy a parrot.

27 "How much is this blue one?" she asked.

28 "It costs $2,000," said the pet shop owner.

29 "Why is it so expensive?" asked Abril.

30 "This parrot is a very special one. It can play the piano!"

31 "What about the green one?" she asked.

32 "It costs $5,000 because it can play the piano, paint pictures, and jump rope."

33 "Then what about the red one?" Abril asked.

34 The owner responded that it costs $10,000.

35 She was surprised and asked, "What does it do?"

36 "I don't know," said the owner, "but the other two birds call it 'teacher.'"

01 (1) surprised (2) global (3) excuse (4) special
02 (1) a piece of (2) get up late (3) one evening
03 (1) flat (2) shout (3) owner (4) invite
04 (1) You had better not go out because a typhoon is coming.
   (2) He is the only friend that[who/whom] I have.
05 (1) to go (2) to sweep
06 (1) If (2) when (3) Though
07 of   08 there was   09 (s)pecial   10 that
11 She was on the other side of the wall.
12 parrot   13 about   14 that   15 surprised
16 It can play the piano.

01 (1) surprised: 놀란 (2) global: 지구의 (3) excuse: 변명, 핑계 거리 (4) special: 특별한

02 (1) a piece of cake: 식은 죽 먹기 (2) get up late: 늦잠 을 자다 (3) one evening: 어느 날 저녁

03 (1) 충분한 공기가 없는: flat(펑크 난) (2) 뭔가를 아주 크게 말 하다: shout(외치다) (3) 어떤 것을 소유한 사람: owner(주 인) (4) 누군가에게 파티, 결혼식, 식사 등에 오라 고 부탁하다: invite(초대하다)

04 (1) because는 이유를 나타내는 접속사이다. (2) 선행사가 사람 인 목적격 관계대명사이다.

05 let과 make는 사역동사이므로 목적보어로 원형부정사를 취하 고, allow와 force는 목적보어로 to부정사를 취한다.

06 though는 양보, when은 때, if는 조건을 나타낸다.

07 be proud of: ~을 자랑스럽게 여기다

08 there was: ~이 있었다

09 어떤 사람이나 어떤 것보다 더 좋거나 더 중요한: special(특별한)

10 선행사가 사람이고 주격이므로 who나 that을 쓸 수 있다.

12 one은 부정대명사로 앞에 나온 단수명사를 받는다.

13 What about ~?: ~은 어때요?

14 명사절을 이끄는 접속사 that이 알맞다.

15 사람이 놀란 것이므로 과거분사형의 형용사를 쓴다.

19

01 ④	02 ③	03 ②	04 is
proud of	05 (e)xcuse	06 ②	07 same
08 ⑤	09 to	10 ②	11 ④
12 ②	13 ④	14 ②	15 ③
16 ④	17 ②, ⑤	18 ③	19 being
20 let, take	21 ⑤	22 ①	23 proudly
24 ③	25 of	26 ⑤	27 ④
28 ①	29 owner	30 ④	31 ⑤
32 ④	33 ④	34 ②	35 ①
36 ④	37 ⑤	38 그것은 그들에게 아주	
쉬웠다.			

01 ④는 유의어 관계이고 나머지는 반의어 관계이다.

02 뭔가를 명료하게 또는 쉽게 이해하도록 해 주다: explain(설명하다)

03 flat: 펑크 난, 편평한

04 be proud of: ~을 자랑스러워하다

05 실수, 그릇된 행동 따위의 구실로 대는 이유: excuse(변명, 핑계 거리)

06 on the other side of: ~의 반대편에 / laugh out loud: 큰 소리로 웃다

07 반의어 관계이다. 다른 : 같은 = 시끄러운 : 조용한

08 • 그것은 비용이 얼마나 들죠? • 그는 망치로 못을 쳤다. • 그는 시험을 칠 것이다. • 우리는 이 땅을 태양의 섬이라 부른다.

09 앞의 명사를 수식하는 형용사적 용법의 to부정사가 필요하다.

10 ③은 부사적 용법의 to부정사이다. '~하기 위해'로 해석한다. 나머지는 모두 형용사적 용법이다.

11 ④는 간접목적어와 직접목적어를 취하는 4형식 문장이다. 나머지는 목적어와 목적격보어를 취하는 5형식 문장이다.

12 손은 두 개이므로 나머지 한 손은 the other로 나타낸다.

13 ④ 5형식에서 동사 see는 목적격보어로 분사나 동사원형을 취한다. to play → playing[play]

14 선행사가 사람이고 주격이므로 관계대명사 who가 들어가야 알맞다

15 '~하면'이라는 조건의 접속사가 필요하다

16 조건을 나타내는 if절은 미래의 의미이더라도 현재시제로 써야 한다.

17 이유를 나타내는 접속사 because나 as가 알맞다.

18 make it: 시간에 대다, 해내다

19 전치사 for의 목적어이므로 동명사가 되어야 한다.

20 allow와 let은 둘 다 '~하게 허용하다'의 뜻이지만, allow는 목적보어로 to부정사, let은 목적보어로 원형부정사를 취한다.

21 ⑤ 95점짜리 문제는 쉽지 않았다.

22 be proud of=take pride in: ~을 자랑스럽게 여기다

23 동사 replied를 수식하므로 부사형이 되어야 한다.

24 문맥상 조건을 나타내는 접속사가 알맞다.

25 suddenly=all of a sudden: 갑자기

26 위 글은 Dean의 재미있는 행동을 서술한 글이다.

27 문맥상 '비싼'이 알맞다.

28 as는 이유를 나타내는 접속사로도 쓰인다.

29 own: 소유하다 / owner: 소유자

30 ⓓ, ④ 5문형 ① 3문형 ② 2문형 ③ 1문형 ⑤ 4문형

31 ⑤ 빨간 앵무새가 하는 일은 본문에 언급되지 않았다.

32 일찍 일어날 계획이었다는 말 다음에 와야 한다.

33 ⓐ, ④ 명사적 용법 ①, ③ 형용사적 용법 ②, ⑤ 부사적 용법

34 a good excuse for+동명사: ~에 대한 좋은 핑계

35 결과를 나타내는 접속사 so가 알맞다.

36 allow는 목적보어로 to부정사를 취한다.

37 문맥상 각각 다른 방에서 시험을 치르는 것이 알맞다.

38 a piece of cake: 아주 쉬운, 식은 죽 먹기

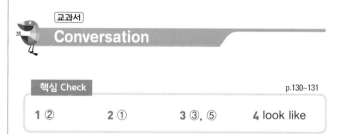

Lesson 5

Understanding Others

시험대비 실력평가
p.128

01 (o)rdinary   02 announcement   03 ⑤
04 ②   05 ⑤   06 mind   07 ③
08 ④

01 둘은 반의어 관계다. 친절한 : 불친절한 – 비범한 : 평범한
02 무언가에 대한 새로운 정보를 주며 누군가가 공식적으로 말하는 것
03 whisper는 '속삭이다'는 뜻이다.
04 위험하거나 나쁜 것으로부터 사람이나 사물을 지키다
05 부모가 매주 아이에게 주는 돈: 용돈
06 mind는 동사로 '신경을 쓰다, 언짢아하다'는 뜻이다.
07 사람들은 긴 턱수염을 매우 싫어했다. 그래서 턱수염을 가진 사람을 피했다.
08 '싸워 물리치다'는 의미로 fight off가 적절하고, 두 번째 빈칸은 그들을 공격한 것 때문에 그를 고소했다(accused)가 적절하다.

서술형 시험대비
p.120

01 (1) appearance   (2) freedom
02 (1) change   (2) train   03 (1) judge   (2) mean
04 (1) do well on   (2) cared for   (3) thanks to
05 (1) face difficulties   (2) looked different from
     (3) in prison, protecting

01 (1) 소유격 their 뒤에는 명사형이 적절하므로 appearance를 쓴다. (2) 정관사 the 뒤에 명사형이 적절하므로 freedom을 써야 한다.
02 (1) '어떤 것을 다르게 만들다'라는 동사의 의미와 '비용보다 더 많은 돈을 지불했을 때 돌려받는 돈(거스름 돈)'이라는 명사의 의미를 가지는 change가 적절하다. (2) '사람이나 동물들에게 어떤 일을 하는 방법을 가르치다(훈련하다)'라는 동사의 의미와 '철도 위에 함께 연결된 많은 차량(기차)'이라는 명사의 의미를 가지는 train이 적절하다.
03 (1) 첫 번째 빈칸은 명사 '판사', 두 번째 빈칸은 동사로 '판단하다'라는 의미이므로 judge가 맞다. (2) 첫 번째 빈칸은 '의미하다'라는 동사이고 두 번째는 be동사 뒤에 형용사 '못된'의 의미인 mean이 적절하다.
04 (1) '네가 시험을 잘 보길 바란다.'는 의미로 do well on이 적절하다. (2) '42살의 Joseph Palmer'는 평범한 사람이었다. 그는

직업이 있었고 가족을 돌보았다.'는 의미로 과거형 cared for가 적절하다. (3) '그는 아들의 편지 덕분에 석방되었다'는 의미로 thanks to가 적절하다.
05 (1) 어려움에 직면하다는 표현은 face difficulties. (2) 'look+형용사'는 '~처럼 보이다'는 의미로 과거형 looked different from이 적절하다 (3) be in prison: 감옥에 갇히다 / 전치사 for 뒤에 동명사 protecting이 적절하다.

교과서
Conversation

핵심 Check
p.130~131

1 ②   2 ①   3 ③, ⑤   4 look like

교과서 대화문 익히기

Check(√) True or False
p.132

1 T   2 F   3 T   4 T

교과서 확인학습
p.134~135

Communicate: Listen-Listen and Answer. Talk
from, ago, worried, shy, good, lucky, friendly, playing, call, I hope

Communicate: Listen-Listen and Answer. Dialog
winning / great / mean / what, look like / has, ponytail / who scored / seventh

Communicate: Listen-Listen More
What / lost / calm down / What, look like / has / wearing / wearing / carrying / look for, announcement, missing / I hope

Communicate: Speak 2-Talk in pairs
have, important / do well on / so

Communicate: Speak 2-Talk in groups
What / What does, like / no / have

Communicate: Speak-Rap Time
I hope, find / do, best / the same / look like / straight / wearing / reading

My Speaking Portfolio
bulletin board, are / made, choice, vote for / mean, promises / choose / seems okay / friendly, talent shows

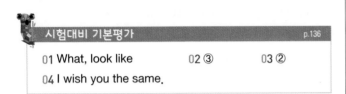

Wrap Up

over there / Which, What does, look / curly, wearing / sad, wrong / happened / fell off / That's too bad, I hope, get better

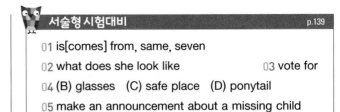

서술형 시험대비 p.139

01 is[comes] from, same, seven

02 what does she look like   03 vote for

04 (B) glasses   (C) safe place   (D) ponytail

05 make an announcement about a missing child

01 Gacha는 몽골에서 왔고, Minsol과 같은 반이다. Gacha는 7골을 넣었다.

03 공식적인 서류에 표시를 해서 선거에 출마할 사람을 고르다

시험대비 기본평가 p.136

01 What, look like   02 ③   03 ②

04 I wish you the same.

01 사람의 외모를 물어보는 표현으로 'What ~ look like?'를 사용한다.

02 강아지를 잃어버렸다는 말에 이어지는 대답으로 희망이나 바람을 나타내는 'I hope ~.'가 적절하다.

03 내일 중요한 시험이 있으므로 시험을 잘 보길 바란다는 표현이 적절하다.

04 '~이기를 바라'라는 표현은 'I wish ~'를 사용한다.

교과서
Grammar

핵심 Check p.140~141

1 (1) expected, to be   (2) (c)aused, to (j)ump

  (3) (f)orced, to sign

2 (1) Before   (2) comes   (3) after

시험대비 실력평가 p.137~138

01 ③   02 who scored the goal just now

03 ⑤   04 ③   05 ②

06 That's too bad

07 I hope she'll get better soon.

08 (A) What does he look like?   (B) Can you tell me more?   09 ④   10 ②

11 curly hair, glasses

시험대비 기본평가 p.142

01 ⑤   02 ①   03 ④

04 (1) I want you to clean the windows.

  (2) Before I have dinner, I will clean my room.

  (3) He took my hand and asked me to marry him.

  (4) Tell her to buy a comfortable pair of shoes!

05 Justin had some fruit after he played soccer.

01 상대방의 말을 확인하기 위한 표현으로 '~을 말하니?'의 의미다.

02 명사 the girl을 수식하는 관계대명사절을 만든다.

03 Ben의 'I've heard a lot about her.'라는 말을 통해 Gacha에 관해 알고 있다는 것을 알 수 있다.

04 대화의 내용으로 보아 차기 학생회장 선거라는 것을 알 수 있다.

05 그녀의 외모를 묻는 표현이 오는 것이 적절하다.

06 상대방의 슬픔을 위로하는 표현으로 That's too bad., 또는 I'm sorry to hear that. 등으로 쓸 수 있다.

07 희망이나 바람을 표현하는 말로 'I hope+주어+동사 ~'를 사용한다.

08 (A)는 남동생의 외모를 묻는 표현이 적절하고, (B)는 추가적으로 남동생에 대해 묻는 표현이 적절하다.

09 여자의 남동생이 어디에 있는지는 대화에 언급되어 있지 않아 답할 수 없다.

10 '자전거에서 떨어졌어'라는 A의 말에 '그 말을 들으니 기뻐'라는 답은 어색하다.

11 주어진 문장은 새로 온 학생에 대한 외모를 묘사하는 글이다.

01 ask의 목적격보어는 to부정사이다.

02 잠자리에 들기 전에 손을 씻었다고 하는 것이 자연스럽다.

03 before와 after는 두 개의 절을 연결해 주는 접속사로 어떤 일이 일어나기 전이나 후의 시간 관계를 나타내며 before는 '~하기 전에', after는 '~한 후에'를 뜻한다. ① Before → After ② Before → After ③ after → before ⑤ After → Before

04 (1), (3), (4) want, ask, tell은 to부정사를 목적격보어로 취하는 동사이다. (2) 시간의 부사절에서는 현재시제를 사용하여 미래를 나타낸다.

05 접속사 after(~한 후에)를 이용하여 영작한다.

시험대비 실력평가 p.143~145

01 ⑤   02 ②   03 ③   04 ④

05 (1) to come   (2) to do   (3) expects   (4) to go

  (5) after   (6) before   06 ①   07 ②

08 ②   09 ②   10 (1) to tell

(2) to study   (3) (to) push   11 before   12 ③

13 (1) After they played tennis, they went shopping.

(2) Before Eunji watched the movie, she bought a hat.

(3) The teacher told us to gather at the gym.

(4) Jiho asked Dohun to clean the window.

14 ⑤   15 ③   16 ①   17 ④   18 ②

19 (1) She asked her brother to help her with her homework.

(2) Jim wanted her to go shopping with him.

(3) They advised him to leave the place as soon as possible.

(4) Before he rode his bike, Jason put on his helmet.

(5) She will be a good wife when she gets married.

01 want는 목적격보어로 to부정사가 온다.

02 Before는 접속사로 어떤 일이 일어나기 전의 시간 관계를 나타낸다.

03 tell은 목적격보어로 동사원형이 아니라 to부정사가 온다. to be가 되어야 한다.

04 before: ~하기 전에

05 (1), (2), (4) tell, want, allow는 목적격보어로 to부정사가 온다. (3) hope는 5형식으로 쓰이지 않는다. (5) 문맥상 after가 적절하다. (6) 문맥상 before가 적절하다.

06 빈칸에는 to부정사를 목적격보어로 취할 수 있는 동사가 들어가야 한다.

07 ② 시간의 부사절에서는 현재시제를 사용하여 미래를 나타낸다.

08 ② 해가 떠오른 시점이 다르므로 두 문장의 의미가 다르다.

09 before 부사절은 after를 사용하여 주절과 부사절을 바꿔 쓸 수 있다.

10 ask, encourage, help는 to부정사를 목적격보어로 취하는 동사이다. help는 동사원형을 쓸 수도 있다.

11 after 부사절은 before를 사용하여 주절과 부사절을 바꿔 쓸 수 있다.

12 ask는 목적격보어로 to부정사를 쓴다.

13 (1), (2) before와 after는 접속사로 어떤 일의 시간 관계를 나타내며 before는 '~하기 전에', after는 '~한 후에'를 뜻한다. (3), (4) tell, ask의 목적격보어로 to부정사가 온다.

14 ⑤ make는 사역동사로 동사원형을 목적격보어로 취한다. 나머지는 모두 to부정사를 목적격보어로 취하는 동사들로 to do가 들어가야 한다.

15 ① I read a book before I went to bed last night. ② I brushed my teeth before I went to bed. ④ After he bought the book, he read it. ⑤ Eric will go swimming when Sue arrives.

16 cause, expect, ask, want, tell 모두 목적격보어로 to부정사가 와야 한다. ceremony: 식, 의식 / wake ~ up: ~을 깨우다

17 주절은 미래이지만, 빈칸이 이끄는 절은 현재형이므로 빈칸에는 시간이나 조건의 부사절이 적절하므로 양보절을 이끄는 Even if는 적절하지 않다.

18 ask와 tell은 모두 to부정사를 목적격보어로 취하는 동사이므로 빈칸에는 to부정사가 들어가는 것이 적절하다.

19 (1), (2), (3) ask, want, advise는 모두 목적격보어로 to부정사가 와야 한다. (4) 의미상 After를 Before로 고쳐야 한다. (5) 시간의 부사절에서는 현재시제를 사용하여 미래를 나타낸다.

서술형 시험대비   p.146~147

01 (1) Lucy's dad wants her to be a police officer.

(2) My mother asked me to buy milk on my way home.

(3) The teacher told the students to bring some water.

(4) She got her two sons to divide a cake exactly in half.

(5) Her family environment forced her not to continue her studies.

02 (1) I will let you know my mind as soon as I make a decision.

(2) Nancy wanted her brother to cook ramyeon for her.

03 (1) to help   (2) to go   (3) to stay   (4) not to take

(5) comes   (6) have

04 (1) watches, after   (2) Before, did

(3) to call[phone], comes   (4) to feed

05 (1) They bought their swimming suit before they went to the beach.

(2) After the students took a bus for one hour, they arrived at their destination.

(3) After they arrived at the museum, they appreciated the works in the museum.

06 (1) before she studies math in her room

(2) after she has lunch with her family 또는 before she goes to the movie with James

(3) after she studies math in her room

07 Laura to study history

08 (1) Before → After   (2) after → before

(3) will come → comes   (4) meeting → to meet

09 (1) My parents always tell me to do my best in school.

(2) Good health enabled him to carry out the plan.

(3) Yuri will put on her uniform after she has breakfast.

01 (1) want, (2) ask, (3) tell, (4) get 등의 동사는 목적격보어로 to부정사가 와야 한다. (5) force의 목적격보어로 쓰인 to부정사의 부정형은 'not to 동사원형'으로 쓴다.

02 (1) 시간의 부사절에서는 현재시제로 미래를 표현한다. make a decision: 결정을 내리다 (2) want는 목적격보 어로 to부정사가 온다.

03 (1), (2), (3), (4) ask, allow, order, warn의 목적격보어로 to부정사가 적절하다. to부정사의 부정형은 'not to 동사원형'으로 쓴다. (5), (6) 시간의 부사절이므로 주절이 미래시제일지라도 현재시제로 써야 한다.

04 (3), (4) 시간의 부사절에서는 현재시제를 사용하여 미래를 나타내며 ask나 tell은 목적격보어로 to부정사가 온다.

05 before와 after는 접속사로 어떤 일이 일어나기 전이나 후의 시간 관계를 나타내며 before와 after가 이끄는 부사절은 보통 주절의 앞이나 뒤에 올 수 있다. destination: 목적지

06 before(~하기 전에)와 after(~한 후에)가 이끄는 부사절은 보통 주절과 부사절을 바꿔 쓸 수 있으며, before와 after를 서로 바꿔 쓸 수 있다.

07 encourage는 목적격보어로 to부정사를 사용한다.

08 (1), (2) before: ~하기 전에, after: ~한 후에 (3) 시간의 부사절에서는 현재시제를 사용하여 미래를 나타낸다. (4) would like는 목적격보어로 to부정사를 취한다. set: (해 따위가) 지다, 저물다 migrate: 이주하다 migrating bird: 철새

09 (1), (2) tell과 enable은 목적격보어로 to부정사가 온다. (3) 시간의 부사절에서는 미래시제 대신에 현재시제를 사용한다.

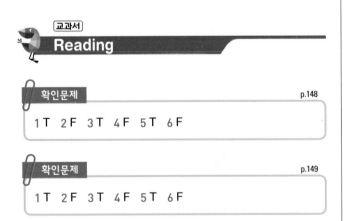

교과서 Reading

확인문제 p.148

1 T 2 F 3 T 4 F 5 T 6 F

확인문제 p.149

1 T 2 F 3 T 4 F 5 T 6 F

교과서 확인학습 A p.150~151

01 Be Different
02 an ordinary person
03 cared for
04 to face difficulties
05 looked different
06 did not like it
07 the man with a beard
08 sit next to him
09 behind his back
10 broke his windows

11 threw stones at
12 stop growing
13 mind
14 to have
15 attacked, threw
16 cut off
17 fight them off
18 accused him of
19 was arrested
20 the victim
21 a man with a beard, went to prison
22 wanted, to know
23 sent, to
24 was in prison, protecting himself
25 became angry, to set, free
26 was freed
27 attitudes toward beards
28 with a beard
29 His name
30 popular, fought for

교과서 확인학습 B p.152~153

1 The Right To Be Different
2 In many ways, 42-year-old Joseph Palmer was an ordinary person.
3 He had a job and cared for his family.
4 But in 1830, after he moved to a small town in Massachusetts, he began to face difficulties.
5 Joseph looked different from other people: he had a long beard.
6 People did not like it very much.
7 The town's people avoided the man with a beard.
8 They did not want to sit next to him.
9 They even whispered behind his back, "What is he trying to hide?"
10 Some neighbors broke his windows.
11 Others threw stones at him when he walked down the street.
12 They told him to stop growing a beard.
13 Joseph did not mind.
14 He just wanted the freedom to have his beard.
15 One day, four men attacked Joseph and threw him on the ground.
16 "We're going to cut off your beard!" they shouted.
17 Joseph was a big man, and he was able to fight them off.
18 But the men called the police and accused him of attacking them.
19 Poor Joseph was arrested.
20 He said to the judge, "I'm the victim here."
21 Sadly, no one believed a man with a beard, and he went to prison for over a year.
22 Joseph's son, Thomas, wanted people to know the truth.
23 He sent letters to newspapers across the country.

24 People learned that Joseph was in prison just for protecting himself and his beard.

25 Many people became angry about this, so the judge finally decided to set Joseph free.

26 After he was freed, Joseph traveled and told his story to lots of people.

27 Slowly, people's attitudes toward beards changed.

28 Before Joseph died, a man with a beard became the President of the United States.

29 His name was Abraham Lincoln.

30 He made beards popular, but Joseph Palmer fought for the right to have them.

시험대비 실력평가
p.154~157

01 ②, ⑤	02 ③	03 ⑤	04 to stop
05 (A) them (B) Sadly (C) for			06 ③
07 ②	08 ③	09 ①, ④	10 ②, ③
11 appearance		12 students who talk about other people's appearance	13 ④
14 extraordinary → ordinary		15 behind his back	
16 ①, ④	17 ③	18 ⑤	19 ④
20 reading	21 (A) differently (B) hungry (C) foolish	22 ②	23 ②	24 ⑤
25 ①			

01 ⓐ와 ②, ⑤: ~을 돌보다, ① care about: ~에 마음을 쓰다, ~에 관심을 가지다, ③ look for: ~을 찾다, ④ take off: ~을 벗다, 이륙하다

02 ⓑ different from: ~와 다른, ⓒ the man with a beard: 턱수염을 가진 남자

03 ⑤ 마을 사람들은 Joseph Palmer를 피했고 심지어 그의 등 뒤에서 "그가 무엇을 숨기려는 거지?"라고 속삭였다.

04 tell+목적어+to부정사

05 (A) 'four men'을 가리키므로 them이 적절하다. (B) '슬프게도', 아무도 턱수염을 가진 남자를 믿지 않았다고 해야 하므로 Sadly가 적절하다. Luckily: 운 좋게, (문장이나 동사를 수식하여) 다행히도, (C) 'during+특정 기간을 나타내는 명사', 'for+숫자'이므로 for가 적절하다.

06 ③ 부당한, 불공평한, 자신이 희생자인데 체포되었기 때문에 '부당하다'는 심경을 나타낸다고 하는 것이 적절하다. ① 지루한, ② 무서워하는, 겁먹은, ④ 흥분한, ⑤ 부끄러운

07 위 글은 턱수염을 기를 권리를 위하여 싸웠던 Joseph에 관한 글이므로, 제목으로는 '어렵게 얻은 턱수염을 기를 권리'가 적절하다. hard-won: 어렵게 얻은, ① inform A of B: A에게 B를 알리다, ③ 여론의 압력, ④ notice: ~을 알아차리다

08 ⓐ Joseph's son, ⓑ, ⓒ Joseph, ⓓ, ⓔ Abraham Lincoln을 가리킨다.

09 ①, 즉시, ④ 정확히, Ⓐ와 나머지는 '마침내, 결국'

10 Ⓑ와 ①, ④, ⑤는 형용사적 용법, ② 명사적 용법, ③ 부사적 용법(원인)

11 소유격 다음에 명사로 쓰는 것이 적절하다. appearance: 외모

12 추천 독자층은 '다른 사람들의 외모에 관해 이야기하는 학생들'이다.

13 ④ 구입 장소는 알 수 없다. ① The Right to Be Different, ② Joseph Palmer, ③ we should not judge people by their appearance. ⑤ Why did Joseph Palmer want to have a beard?

14 직업이 있고 가족을 돌보았던 Joseph Palmer는 여러 면에서 '평범한' 사람이었지만 1830년에 매사추세츠주의 작은 도시로 이사를 한 후에 어려움에 직면하기 시작했던 것이므로, ordinary로 고쳐야 한다. extraordinary: 보기 드문, 비범한; 대단한

15 behind somebody's back: ~의 등 뒤에서, ~가 없는 곳에서

16 ⓒ와 ②, ③, ⑤는 명사적 용법, ① 형용사적 용법, ④ 부사적 용법(목적)

17 some ~, others ...: 어떤 것[사람]들은 ~, 다른 것[사람]들은 ...

18 ⑤ 모난 돌이 정 맞는다(모난 돌이 석공의 정을 만난다.) 남들과 달리나 행동 등이 남과 다름을 빗대는 속담으로 'A cornered stone meets the mason's chisel.'이라고도 한다. ① 불행한 일은 겹치기 마련이다. (엎친 데 덮친다.) ② 쥐구멍에도 볕 들 날이 있다. ③ 제때의 바늘 한 뜸이 아홉 번의 수고를 던다. ④ 떡줄 사람은 꿈도 안 꾸는데 김칫국부터 마신다.

19 Joseph은 덩치가 큰 사람이어서, 그들을 싸워 물리칠 수 있었다.

20 enjoy는 목적어로 동명사를 취한다.

21 (A) 동사 think를 수식하므로 부사 differently가 적절하다. (B), (C) Stay 다음에 보어를 써야 하므로 형용사 hungry와 foolish가 적절하다.

22 위 글은 '독서기록장'이다. ① (신문·잡지의) 글, 기사, ③ 일기, ④ 수필, ⑤ 전기

23 ②번 다음 문장의 this에 주목한다. 주어진 문장의 'Joseph was in prison just for protecting himself and his beard.'를 받고 있으므로 ②번이 적절하다.

24 Joseph은 석방된 뒤에 순회를 하며 많은 사람들에게 자신의 이야기를 전하면서 턱수염을 기를 권리를 위하여 싸웠기 때문에 '의지가 강한' 성격이라고 하는 것이 적절하다. ② 호기심 많은, ③ 관대한, ④ 창의적인, ⑤ 의지가 강한

25 ⓐ와 ①번은 권리(명사), ② 맞는(형용사), ③ 정확히, 바로(부사), ④ 오른쪽의(형용사), ⑤ 바라던 대로(부사)

01 (A) 42-year-old　(B) different　(C) to sit

02 a long beard

03 (1) 마을 사람들은 그의 기다란 턱수염을 별로 좋아하지
　　　않았다.
　　(2) 마을 사람들은 그 턱수염을 가진 남자를 피했다.
　　(3) 마을 사람들은 그의 곁에 앉고 싶어 하지 않았다.
　　(4) 마을 사람들은 심지어 그의 등 뒤에서 "그가 무엇을
　　　숨기려는 거지?"라고 속삭였다.

04 The four men called the police and accused
　 Joseph of attacking them.

05 he had a beard

06 Joseph's son, Thomas, wanted people to know
　 the truth.　　　　　　　　07 ⑤ → for

08 Abraham Lincoln　　　09 The others → Others

10 growing　　11 accused him of attacking them

12 victim　　　13 (A) over a year　(B) a beard

01 (A) 뒤에 나오는 명사를 꾸며주는 형용사의 역할을 할 때는
　 42-year-old로 쓰는 것이 적절하다. (B) 감각동사 looked의
　 보어는 형용사를 써야 하므로 different가 적절하다. (C) want
　 는 목적어로 to부정사를 취하므로 to sit이 적절하다.

02 '기다란 턱수염'을 가리킨다.

03 본문의 difficulties 다음의 내용을 쓰면 된다.

04 네 명의 남자들은 경찰을 불렀고, 자신들을 공격한 것으로
　 Joseph을 고발했다.

05 아무도 턱수염을 가진 남자를 믿지 않았다고 했으므로, '그가 턱
　 수염을 길렀기' 때문이라고 하는 것이 적절하다.

06 want+목적어+to부정사: 목적어가 ~하기를 원하다, Thomas
　 의 앞과 뒤에 동격을 나타내는 콤마를 찍는 것이 적절하다.

07 Joseph Palmer는 턱수염을 기를 권리를 '위하여' 싸웠다고 해
　 야 하기 때문에, for로 고쳐야 한다. fight for: ~을 위해 싸우
　 다, ~을 얻기 위해 싸우다, fight against: ~에 맞서 싸우다

08 Abraham Lincoln(에이브러햄 링컨)을 가리킨다.

09 '어떤 사람들은 ~, 또 어떤 사람들은 …'의 뜻이 되어야 하므로
　 The others를 Others로 고쳐야 한다.

10 문맥상 stop 뒤에 동명사가 와야 한다.

11 'of'를 보충한다. accuse A of B: B 때문에 A를 고발하다

12 피해자, 다쳤거나 죽임을 당한 사람

13 Joseph은 그저 자신의 턱수염을 기를 자유를 원했지만 '턱수염'
　 을 가진 남자에 대한 이웃들의 편견 때문에 '일 년이 넘는 기간'
　 동안 감옥에 갔다.

01 appearance　　　02 ⑤　　　03 ④
04 ②　　　05 like　　　06 was arrested

07 ③　　　08 ④　　　09 ②　　　10 ⑤
11 ①　　　12 ③　　　13 ①, ③, ④
14 (1) she saw a giraffe　(2) before　(3) after she saw
a giraffe　　15 ②　　　16 ②
17 (1) we ate ice cream, we watched the movie
　 (2) I untie my hair, I pass the school gate
18 (1) I will take a photo of myself after I get a haircut
　　 tomorrow.
　 (2) Fiona wants Andrew not to come to the party.
　 (3) The situation required me to have strong belief.
19 ①　　　20 Brush your teeth before you go to
bed.　　　21 ③　　　22 beard
23 ②, ③, ⑤　　24 ④　　25 ①
26 Joseph was in prison just for protecting himself
and his beard.　　　27 it → them　28 ④
29 ③　　　30 ⑤

01 동사 : 명사의 관계이다.

02 네 명의 남자들이 그를 바닥에 던졌다고 했으므로 ⓐ에는 '공격
　 하다'가 적절하다. ⓑ는 '수염을 자르다'는 의미로 cut off가 적
　 절하다.

03 ④번의 judge는 명사로 '판사'다.

04 어떤 일이 일어나도록 하다 / 어떤 일이 발생하는 이유[원인]

05 like는 전치사로 '~와 같은', 동사로 '좋아하다'라는 의미이다.

06 Joseph이 체포가 되었다는 수동의 의미이므로 'be+p.p.' 형태
　 를 사용한다.

07 '그녀는 어떻게 생겼니?'라고 외모를 묻는 표현이므로 She's
　 very tall and has a ponytail. 앞에 오는 것이 적절하다.

08 그는 지도를 보고 있다는 말은 사람의 외모를 묻는 말에 대한 답
　 으로 적절하지 않다.

09 실종된 동생을 빨리 찾기를 바란다는 바람을 나타내는 표현이
　 적절하다.

10 ⑤번은 대화 속의 남자가 할 일을 묘사한 것이다.

11 빈칸 다음의 대답으로 보아 외모를 물어보는 말이 적절하다.

12 '무슨 일이니?'라는 물음에 (C) 여동생의 팔이 부러졌다는 답이
　 오고, (A) 무슨 일이 있었는지 묻는다. (B) my sister를 받는
　 대명사 she로 구체적으로 무슨 일이 있었는지 언급하고, 마지막
　 으로 (D) 빨리 낫기를 바라는 말이 오는 것이 적절하다.

13 빈칸이 이끄는 절은 현재시제이지만 주절은 미래이므로, 빈칸에
　 는 시간이나 조건의 부사절이 들어가야 한다.

14 동물을 본 순서에 맞게 after나 before를 이용하여 쓴다.

15 첫 번째 문장은 5형식이고 두 번째 문장은 3형식이다. 3형식과
　 5형식에 쓰이면서, to부정사를 목적격보어와 목적어로 받을 수
　 있는 동사는 want이다.

16 ② persuade는 to부정사를 목적격보어로 취하는 동사이다.

17 Before+주어1+동사1 ~, 주어2+동사2 … = After+주어2+
　 동사2 …, 주어1+동사1 ~

18 (1) 시간의 부사절에서는 미래시제 대신에 현재시제를 사용한다. (2) want는 that절을 목적어로 취하지 않으며 to부정사의 부정형은 'not[never]+to 동사원형'이다. (3) require는 목적격보어로 to부정사를 취한다.

19 warn과 ask는 목적격보어로 to부정사가 오며, to부정사의 부정형은 'not[never]+to 동사원형'이다.

20 brush one's teeth: 양치질하다

21 ⓐ와 ③번은 직면하다, ① 얼굴, ② 표면, 겉면, ④ (시계의) 문자판, ⑤ 체면, lose one's face: 체면을 잃다 crisis: 위기

22 beard: (턱)수염, 사람의 턱과 뺨에 나는 털

23 ⓐ와 ②, ③, ⑤는 형용사적 용법, ① 명사적 용법, ④ 부사적 용법

24 이 글은 '턱수염을 가진 남자에 대한 부당한 행동'에 관한 글이다. ① bully: (약자를) 괴롭히다[왕따시키다], 협박하다, ② 희생자를 수감시킨 판사

25 ① 이웃들이 Joseph의 창문을 언제 깼는지는 대답할 수 없다. ② Joseph's neighbors did. ③ He just wanted the freedom to have his beard. ④ He said to the judge, "I'm the victim here." ⑤ For over a year.

26 'Joseph이 단지 자신과 자신의 턱수염을 지키려다 감옥에 갔다는 것'을 가리킨다.

27 beards를 받는 것이므로 them이 적절하다.

28 ④ 턱수염을 대중적으로 만든 것은 'Abraham Lincoln'이었다.

29 앞에 나오는 내용과 상반되는 내용이 뒤에 이어지므로 However가 가장 적절하다. ① 게다가, ② 그러므로, ④ 예를 들면 ⑤ 게다가, 더욱이

30 위 독서 기록장의 교훈은 'We should not judge people by their appearance.'이므로, 어울리는 속담은 '표지만 보고 책을 판단하지 말라.(뚝배기보다는 장 맛이다.)'가 적절하다. ① 사공이 많으면 배가 산으로 올라간다. ② 기회를 놓치지 마라. ③ 엎질러진 우유를 놓고 울어봐야 소용없다. ④ 남의 떡이 더 커 보인다.

단원별 예상문제
p.166~169

01 unfriendly 02 (A) attack (B) attitude
03 worried, lost   04 ②   05 ③
06 vote for, short hair, friendly, fun and exciting,
promises   07 ⑤   08 hopes, class will win,
handball   09 ④   10 ①
11 ③, ⑤   12 ③
13 (1) The teacher asked me to close the door.
  (2) Dr. Smith advised her to go to bed early.
  (3) After the soccer match was over, the players
     lay on the grass.
14 (1) Judy asked him to make sandwiches.
  (2) Tom expected Jane to be thin.
  (3) My advice caused him to stop smoking.
15 looked like → looked   16 Joseph Palmer
17 (A) growing (B) to have (C) was arrested 18 ②
19 ⑤   20 (A) The judge (B) his beard
21 ③   22 ④

01 반의어 관계이다. 유죄의 : 무죄의 = 친절한 : 불친절한

02 (A) 어떤 개가 나를 공격하려고 했을 때, 나의 고양이가 큰 소리로 울었다. (B) 나는 당신의 좋은 태도가 좋아요. 당신은 항상 긍정적으로 생각해요. meow: 야옹하고 울다

04 ⓑ는 남동생의 외모를 물어보는 표현이므로 look for를 look like로 바꾸어야 한다.

05 삼촌과 낚시하러 간다는 말에 네가 꼭 그것을 찾기를 바란다는 말은 어색하다. oval: 달걀 모양의, 타원형의

07 Jiho가 Somin이의 친구인지는 대화에서 언급되어 있지 않다.

08 다음 주 운동회에 대한 Gacha의 바람은 무엇인가?

09 (A) 약간 수줍음을 탔고 한국어를 잘 못했다고 했으므로 무척 걱정이 되었다가 적절하다. (B) 뒤 문장이 '나는 운이 좋은 아이다'로 앞 문장과 대조되므로 '하지만'이 적절하다. (C) 반 친구들이 자신을 '황금 손'이라고 부른다고 했으므로 핸드볼을 잘한다는 것을 알 수 있다.

10 (A)에는 사람의 외모를 묻는 표현이 적절하고, (B)에는 무슨 옷차림을 하고 있는지 묻는 표현이 적절하다.

11 ③ beg는 목적격보어로 to부정사를 취한다. ⑤ 시간의 부사절에서 현재시제로 미래를 나타낸다.

12 ⓑ Would you like me to bring any food to the party? ⓒ Her parents expected her to win the contest. ⓔ She told him to be on time.

13 (1), (2) ask, advise는 목적격보어로 to부정사를 취한다. (3) after: ~한 후에

14 (1) ask (2) expect (3) cause 등의 동사는 목적격보어로 to부정사가 와야 한다.

15 looked+형용사, looked like+명사: ~하게 보이다

16 Joseph Palmer를 가리킨다.

17 (A) '턱수염을 그만 기르라고 말했다'고 해야 하므로 growing이 적절하다. stop+~ing: ~하기를 그만두다, stop+to부정사: ~하기 위해 멈추다, (B) 턱수염을 '기를' 자유라고 해야 하므로 to have가 적절하다. (C) 불쌍한 Joseph은 '체포되었다'고 해야 하므로 수동태인 was arrested가 적절하다.

18 ⓐ와 ②번은 상관하다, 신경 쓰다(동사), ① 기억(력), 마음, 보지 않으면 마음도 멀어진다. ③ 신경, 생각, 관심, ④ (마음을 가진 자로서의) 인간, the greatest mind of the time: 그 시대의 가장 훌륭한 사람, ⑤ 마음, 정신, 건전한 신체에 건전한 정신이 깃든다.

19 ⑤ 판사에게 자기가 '희생자'라고 말했다고 하는 것이 적절하다.

① 공격[폭행]을 한 사람, ② 변호사, ③ 죄수, ④ (약자를) 괴롭히는 사람, ⑤ 피해자[희생자]

20 Joseph이 단지 자신과 '자신의 턱수염'을 지키려다 감옥에 갇혔다는 사실에 대해 많은 사람들이 분개했기 때문에, '판사'는 결국 Joseph을 석방하기로 결정했다.

21 이 글은 Joseph이 자신의 턱수염을 지키려다 감옥에 갇히기까지 했지만, 석방된 뒤에 순회를 하며 많은 사람들에게 자신의 이야기를 전함으로써 사람들의 턱수염에 대한 태도를 서서히 변화시켰다는 내용의 글이다. 따라서 이에 어울리는 속담은 '뜻이 있는 곳에 길이 있다'가 적절하다. ① 무소식이 희소식이다. ② 남의 떡이 더 커 보인다. ④ 뛰기 전에 살펴봐라.(신중하게 행동하라.) ⑤ 연습이 완벽하게 만들어 준다.

22 ④ 몇 사람이 턱수염에 대한 그들의 태도를 바꿨는지는 알 수 없다. ① Because he wanted people to know the truth. ② They learned that Joseph was in prison just for protecting himself and his beard. ③ He traveled and told his story to lots of people. ⑤ Abraham Lincoln did.

서술형 실전문제 p.170~171

01 what does she look like?
02 school president / vote / confident / our school a safe place
03 (A) I hope you'll do well on the exam.
   (B) I hope so, too.
04 (1) My history teacher told us to hand in the project by tomorrow.
   (2) The teacher warned the students to be quiet in class.
   (3) Amy's best friend wants her to listen to his songs.
   (4) Her manager always forces Melanie to throw away the trash.
   (5) The doctor encouraged Jack not to give up doing exercise.
05 (1) Mom told me to walk the dog.
   (2) Mark will control Maria's customers until she returns.
06 I set my alarm clock, I went to bed
07 freedom
08 Joseph was a big man, and he was able to fight them off.
09 (A) victim   (B) beard
10 (A) protecting   (B) angry   (C) free
11 Joseph's son, Thomas, sent letters to newspapers across the country

01 외모를 묻는 표현은 'What ~ look like?'를 사용한다.

03 (A) 바람을 나타내는 표현으로 'I hope+주어+동사 ~' 형태를 이용한다. '시험을 잘 보다'는 표현은 'do well on the exam'이다. (B) '또한'의 의미로 문장 끝에 too를 사용한다.

04 (1) tell (2) warn (3) want (4) force 등의 동사는 목적격보어로 to부정사가 와야 한다. (5) to부정사의 부정형은 'never[not] to 동사원형'으로 쓴다.

05 (1) tell은 목적격보어로 to부정사를 취한다. (2) 시간의 부사절에서는 현재시제를 사용하여 미래를 나타낸다.

06 Before+주어1+동사1 ~, 주어2+동사2 … = After+주어2+동사2 …, 주어1+동사1 ~

07 to부정사로 수식받고 있기 때문에 명사 형태로 쓰는 것이 적절하다.

08 목적어가 인칭대명사이므로 fight off them이 아니라, fight them off가 적절하다.

09 Joseph은 따돌림의 '희생자'였지만, 아무도 '턱수염'을 가진 남자를 믿지 않았기 때문에 일년이 넘는 기간 동안 감옥에 갔다. bully: (약자를) 괴롭히다[왕따시키다], 협박하다

10 (A) 자기 자신과 턱수염을 '지키려고'라고 해야 하므로 protecting이 적절하다. prevent: 막다, 예방하다, (B) become 뒤에 형용사가 보어로 와야 하므로 angry가 적절하다. (C) set free 석방하다

11 'Joseph의 아들인 Thomas가 전국에 있는 신문사에 편지를 보냈기' 때문에 알게 되었다.

창의사고력 서술형 문제 p.172

|모범답안|
01 [A] (1) A: What does Minsu look like?
          B: He has short hair and is wearing jeans.
      (2) A: What does Sumi look like?
          B: She is tall and has a ponytail. She is wearing glasses.
   [B] (1) A: I lost my puppy this afternoon.
          B: I hope you'll find it soon.
      (2) A: I have an important exam tomorrow!
          B: I hope you'll do well on the exam.
      (3) A: I'm going to my favorite singer's concert tonight.
          B: I hope you have a good time.
02 (1) Dad wants me to come home early.
   (2) My classmates asked me to be quiet in class.
   (3) She told him to fix the computer.
   (4) She didn't allow us to play the piano.
   (5) I advised her to go home early after the concert.
   (6) The teacher forced the students to attend the class.

03 (A) reading   (B) differently   (C) who
   (D) How   (E) Stay hungry.

01 ③   02 difficulty   03 ①   04 ④
05 ⑤   06 ②   07 ③   08 ②
09 ⑤   10 ②   11 ⑤
12 is she the girl who scored the goal just now?
13 ③   14 ②   15 ①
16 (1) not to drive so fast   (2) to play the piano for her
17 after she had dinner / before she studied history
18 he had a long beard   19 ④   20 ①
21 four men   22 ②   23 People learned that
Joseph was in prison just for protecting himself and
his beard.   24 Abraham Lincoln did.

01 ③번의 attack은 '공격하다'라는 의미로 'to use violence
   to hurt or damage someone'을 뜻한다. ③의 설명은
   bullying(괴롭히기)에 대한 것이다.

02 반의어 관계이다. 유죄의 : 무죄의 = 쉬움 : 어려움

03 동사로 '바닥으로 떨어지다', 명사로 '여름과 겨울 사이에 있
   는 계절'을 뜻하는 fall이 적절하다.

04 What does he look like?는 외모를 묻는 표현으로 ④번은 사
   람의 성격이나 성질을 말하는 것이므로 적절하지 않다.

05 (A) 여동생의 팔이 부러졌다고 했으므로 자전거에서 떨어졌다
   (fell off)가 적절하다. (B) '곧 회복하기를 바라'라는 바람을 나
   타내는 말이 적절하다.

06 (B) 너희 반에 새로운 학생이 왔다는 말을 들었다는 말이 먼저
   오고 → (D) 긍정의 답을 하고 저기에 있다는 말 다음에 → (C)
   어느 아이인지 묻고 외모를 묻는 말이 온다. → (A) 마지막으로
   외모를 설명하는 말이 오는 것이 적절하다.

07 결선 경기에서 최선을 다하길 바란다는 말에 '너도 그러길 바라.'
   라는 말이 가장 자연스럽다.

08 잃어버린 남동생에 관한 정보를 제공하고 있는 상황에서 추가적
   인 정보를 묻는 것이 가장 적절하다.

10 여학생이 어디서 동생을 잃어버렸는지는 대화에서 알 수 없다.

11 '우리는 훌륭한 핸드볼 선수가 있어.'라는 말에 그 선수가 누구인
   지에 대한 정보를 확인하는 말이 오는 것이 적절하다.

12 의문문이므로 be동사로 문장을 시작한다. 그리고 '막 골을 넣은
   소녀'는 관계대명사 who를 이용하여 the girl을 수식하는 문장
   을 만든다.

13 ① Do you want me to clean your house for you? ②
   He told Perry to put on a penguin shirt. ④ The doctor
   advised Kathy to stop smoking. ⑤ Ms. Green asked
   him to carry the boxes.

14 ② 시간의 부사절에서는 미래시제 대신에 현재시제를 사용한다.

15 첫 번째 문장: expect는 to부정사를 목적격보어로 받는다. 두
   번째 문장: 시간의 부사절에서는 현재시제를 사용하여 미래를
   나타낸다.

16 tell과 ask는 목적격보어로 to부정사를 쓰고 부정사의 부정은
   not[never]을 to부정사 앞에 붙인다.

17 before와 after는 접속사로 어떤 일이 일어나기 전이나 후의 시
   간 관계를 나타낸다.

18 Joseph Palmer는 '기다란 턱수염을 기르고 있었기 때문에' 다
   른 사람들과 달라 보였다.

19 behind somebody's back: ~의 등 뒤에서

20 ⓐ throw A at B: A를 B에게 던지다, ⓒ accuse A of B: A
   를 B 때문에 고발하다

21 '네 명의 남자'를 가리킨다.

22 ⓐ와 ②번은 판사, sentence: …에게 판결을 내리다[형을 선고
   하다], ① 판결하다, guilty: 유죄의, ③ 심판하다, ④ 감정가,
   감식가, ⑤ 판단하다, 평가하다

23 'for'를 보충하면 된다.

24 did = made beards popular

교과서 파헤치기

Lesson 3

1 successc, 성공   2 defend, 방어하다
3 appointment, 약속   4 major, 주요한, 중대한
5 bacteria, 박테리아, 세균   6 cell, 세포
7 multiply, 증식[번식]하다   8 shot, 주사
9 germ, 세균, 미생물   10 invade, 침입하다
11 balanced, 균형잡힌, 안정된   12 luckily, 다행히도
13 scratch, 긁다, 할퀴다   14 flu, 독감
15 victim, 피해자, 희생자   16 digest, 소화하다, 소화시키다

단어 TEST Step 1   p.02

01 어려운	02 약속	03 공격하다, 공격
04 박테리아, 세균	05 세포	06 생물
07 다른	08 소화하다, 소화시키다	
09 부러지다	10 운동하다	11 위험한
12 항체	13 방어하다	14 약
15 증식[번식]하다	16 방어	17 불가능한
18 침입하다	19 대식 세포	20 균형 잡힌, 안정된
21 위통, 복통	22 주요한, 중대한	23 피부
24 규칙적으로	25 긁다, 할퀴다	26 건강한
27 열	28 기억하다	29 세균, 미생물
30 마지막으로, 마침내		31 성공
32 끔찍한, 소름끼치는		33 다행이도
34 필요한	35 ~에 좋다	36 많은
37 ~와 같은	38 마침내, 드디어	
39 A를 B로부터 보호하다		40 그런데
41 포기하다	42 며칠 후에	43 ~으로 유명하다

단어 TEST Step 2   p.03

01 stomachache	02 attack	03 bacteria
04 actually	05 several	06 shot
07 skin	08 antibody	09 cell
10 creature	11 different	12 digest
13 exercise	14 dangerous	15 defend
16 finally	17 appointment	18 germ
19 impossible	20 invade	21 defense
22 fever	23 luckily	24 macrophage
25 balanced	26 break	27 major
28 necessary	29 regularly	30 medicine
31 virus	32 victim	33 multiply
34 scratch	35 success	36 at last
37 be famous for	38 be ready to	39 by the way
40 give up	41 plenty of	42 show up
43 watch out		

대화문 TEST Step 1   p.05~06

Communicate: Listen - Listen and Answer Dialog 1

Can, early, don't feel / seems to, problem / terrible stomachache, hurts / Why don't you, nurse's office / already, didn't help / can, Go see / Sure

Communicate: Listen - Listen and Answer Dialog 2

heard, sick, okay / went to, feel better / Good to, By the way, to talk / should meet, make it / Let's meet, at / early, sleep late / How about / sounds

Communicate: Listen - Listen More

wrong with / keeps scratching, lost / have the problem / About, ago / Let, see, has a virus, you some medicine / neet to, Can make, it / fine with / See you

Communicate: Listen - All Ears

make it / wrong with

Communicate: Speak 2 - Talk in pairs

What's, with / have, sore throat / too bad, should drink / I will

Communicate: Speak 2 - Talk in group

Let's play / why not / make it at / fine with, should, meet / Let's, meet / See, there

Wrap Up - Listening ⑤

don't feel / seems to be / have a fever / Let me see, have a fever, get, medicine / Thank you

Wrap Up - Listening ⑥

thinking of going, come with / want to go / Can, make / fine with / Let's meet at

대화문 TEST Step 2   p.07~08

Communicate: Listen - Listen and Answer Dialog 1

B: Can I go home early, Ms. Song? I don't feel so good.
W: What seems to be the problem?
B: I have a terrible stomachache. It really hurts.

W: Why don't you get some medicine at the nurse's office.

B: I already did. But it didn't help.

W: Okay. You can go. Go see a doctor, okay?

B: Sure. Thanks.

Communicate: Listen - Listen and Answer Dialog 2

B: Hello, Sora.

G: Hi, Jongha. I heard you were sick. Are you okay now?

B: Yes, I went to the doctor, and I feel better now.

G: Good to hear that. By the way, I called you to talk about our science project.

B: Yeah, we should meet. Can you make it tomorrow?

G: Okay. Let's meet at Simpson's Donuts at nine.

B: At nine? That's too early. I sleep late on the weekend.

G: How about 10 then?

B: That sounds fine.

Communicate: Listen - Listen More

M: Hi, Minsol. What's wrong with your dog?

G: She keeps scratching herself. Actually, she lost some hair.

M: When did she first have the problem?

G: About three days ago.

M: Let me see. (pause) She has a virus on her skin. I'll give you some medicine.

G: Thank you

M: I need to check your dog again. Can you make it next Monday?

G: That's fine with me.

M: Okay. See you.

Communicate: Listen - All Ears

M: 1 Can you make it next Friday?

2 What's wrong with your cat?

Communicate: Speak 2 - Talk in pairs

A: What's wrong with you?

B: I have a sore throat.

A: That's too bad. You should drink some water.

B: Okay, I will.

Communicate: Speak 2 - Talk in group

A: Let's play basketball this Saturday.

B: Sure, why not?

A: Can you make it at ten?

B: That's fine with me. Where should we meet?

A: Let's meet at the school gym.

B: Okay. See you there.

Wrap Up - Listening ⑤

B: Mom, I don't feel well.

W: What seems to be the problem?

B: I think I have a fever.

W: Really? Let me see. Umm, you do have a fever. I'll get you some medicine.

B: Thank you, Mom.

Wrap Up - Listening ⑥

G: I'm thinking of going to the Comics Museum tomorrow. Will you come with me?

B: I really want to go.

G: Can you make it at 11?

B: That's fine with me.

G: Okay. Let's meet at the subway station.

본문 TEST Step 1   p.09~10

01 everywhere, it, with
02 are, kinds, bacteria
03 Bacteria, creatures   04 Some, good
05 can, digest, that   06 Others, make
07 that, inside, living   08 cause, such
09 enter, through, skin
10 happens, invade   11 multiply, body
12 becomes, zone   13 feel, weak
14 body, defense   15 sound alarm
16 arrive, germs with
17 macrophage, up, eat
18 Together, called, cells   19 goes, fight
20 In, few, feel   21 invader,copies, itself
22 smart, too   23 change, trick
24 several, protect, from
25 wash, with, warm
26 diet, keep, healthy
27 It, exercise, plenty   28 Finally, shots
29 defense, germs
30 follow, steps, victim   31 Make, copies
32 my, defend   33 was, meal   34 there, eat
35 Next, send   36 see, another   37 What can
38 ready, any   39 give up   40 make, sick

본문 TEST Step 2   p.11~12

01 everywhere, impossible to see
02 major kinds, bacteria, viruses   03 are, creatures
04 Some, good   05 help you digest
06 Others, make, sick
07 germs, inside, other living bodies
08 cause, such as

09 can enter, through, skin mouth

10 happens, invade   11 multiply, body

12 becomes, zone

13 feel, tired, weak

14 Luckily, army of defense   15 sound, alarm

16 to fight, germs, antibodies

17 macrophage, show up

18 white blood cells   19 goes well, win

20 few days, feel better

21 invader, cannot make, copies

22 But, smart, too   23 change form

24 several ways to protect

25 wash, with soap

26 keep, strong, healthy

27 important to exercise, plenty of

28 Finally, necessary shots

29 defense against

30 steps, be a victim

31 Make. copies of   32 job to defend

33 nice meal   34 more germs to eat

35 send in   36 for another fight

37 What, do   38 I'm ready to   39 give up

40 make you sick

1 세균은 어디에나 있지만 눈으로 세균을 보는 것은 불가능하다.

2 세균에는 두 가지 주요한 종류가 있다: 박테리아와 바이러스이다.

3 박테리아는 매우 작은 생물이다.

4 어떤 것들은 좋다.

5 그것들은 당신이 먹는 음식을 소화하는 데 도움을 줄 수 있다.

6 다른 것들은 나쁘고 당신을 아프게 할 수 있다.

7 바이러스는 다른 살아있는 몸의 세포 안에서만 살 수 있는 세균이다.

8 그들은 독감과 같은 질병을 일으킨다.

9 '나쁜' 세균은 피부, 입, 코, 눈을 통해 몸에 들어갈 수 있다.

10 그들이 침입하면 어떻게 되는가?

11 세균은 몸속에서 증식한다.

12 당신의 몸은 전쟁 지역이 된다.

13 당신은 피곤하고 약해지기 시작한다.

14 다행히도, 당신의 몸은 방어 군대를 가지고 있다.

15 T세포가 경보를 발한다!

16 B세포는 항체로 세균과 싸우기 위해 도착한다.

17 대식 세포가 나타나서 세균을 먹는다.

18 이 군대는 함께 백혈구라고 부른다.

19 모든 것이 잘되면 싸움에서 이긴다.

20 며칠 후면 당신은 회복되기 시작한다.

21 몸은 침입자를 기억하므로 다시 복제할 수 없다.

22 하지만 세균들도 영리하다.

23 그들은 형태를 바꿀 수 있고 몸을 속일 수 있다.

24 세균으로부터 당신 자신을 보호하는 몇 가지 방법이 있다.

25 먼저 비누와 따뜻한 물로 손을 씻어라.

26 균형 잡힌 식단은 당신의 몸을 튼튼하고 건강하게 해줄 것이다.

27 규칙적으로 운동하고 충분한 잠을 자는 것도 중요하다.

28 마지막으로 필요한 주사를 맞아라.

29 그것들은 세균을 막는 최고의 방어이다.

30 만약 당신이 이 단계를 따른다면, 당신은 "나쁜" 세균의 희생자가 되지 않을 것이다.

31 나를 더 복제해 주세요.

32 몸을 지키는 게 내 일이야.

33 정말 맛있는 식사였어!

34 먹을 세균이 더 있니?

35 내년에는 내 사촌을 보낼게.

36 그때 그가 또 싸우려고 널 보게 될 거야!

37 나는 어떤 세균과도 싸울 준비가 되어 있어.

38 우리는 널 아프게 할 수 없어.

1 Germs are everywhere, but it is impossible to see them with your eyes.

2 There are two major kinds of germs: bacteria and viruses.

3 Bacteria are very small creatures.

4 Some are good.

5 They can help you digest the food that you eat.

6 Others are bad and can make you sick.

7 Viruses are germs that can only live inside the cells of other living bodies.

8 They cause diseases such as the flu.

9 "Bad" germs can enter your body through your skin, mouth, nose, and eyes.

10 What happens when they invade?

11 The germs multiply in the body.

12 Your body becomes a war zone.

13 You start to feel tired and weak.

14 Luckily, your body has an army of defense.

15 The T cells sound the alarm!

16 The B cells arrive to fight the germs with antibodies.

17 The macrophage cells show up and eat the germs.

18 Together, this army is called the white blood cells.

19 If all goes well, they win the fight.

20 In a few days, you start to feel better.

21 The body remembers the invader, so it cannot make copies of itself again.

22 But the germs are smart, too.

23 They can change form and trick the body.

24 There are several ways to protect yourself from germs.

25 First, wash your hands with soap and warm water.

26 A balanced diet will keep your body strong and healthy.

27 It is also important to exercise regularly and get plenty of sleep.

28 Finally, get the necessary shots.

29 They are the best defense against germs.

30 If you follow these steps, you will not be a victim of "bad" germs.

31 Make more copies of me.

32 It's my job to defend the body.

33 That was a nice meal!

34 Are there any more germs to eat?

35 Next year, I'll send in my cousin.

36 He'll see you then for another fight!

37 What can I do now?

38 I'm ready to fight any germs.

39 We give up.

40 We can't make you sick.

구석구석지문 TEST Step 1   p.19

My Speaking Portfolio - Step 1

1. Less, More
2. dangerous, play
3. to out
4. Healthy
5. Eating, good
6. important, enough

Around the World

1. Mexican painter
2. famous, unique
3. cartoonist, character
4. great, writer
5. spent, writing
6. director
7. inventor, created

Think and Write

1. use, to touch
2. touch
3. close, with, too
4. are, that
5. with, get into
6. what should
7. Wash, with

구석구석지문 TEST Step 2   p.20

My Speaking Portfolio - Step 1

1. Sit Less, Move More
2. It is dangerous to play online games too much.
3. It is time to go out and exercise.
4. Stay Healthy
5. Eating too many snacks is not good for your health.
6. It is important to eat enough fruit and vegetables.

Around the World

1. Frida Kahlo was a Mexican painter[artist].
2. She is famous for her unique paintings.
3. Charles Schulz was a cartoonist who created the famous character Charlie Brown.
4. Park Gyeongri was a great Korean writer.
5. She spent 25 years writing Toji.
6. James Cameron is the director of the movie, Avatar .
7. Jang Yeongsil was a(n) inventor[scientist] who created water clocks.

Think and Write

1. Every day you use your hands to touch different things.
2. You touch your phone and computer.
3. You open and close doors with your hands, too.
4. There are germs on everything that you touch.
5. If you eat snacks with your hands, the germs on your hands can get into your body.
6. Then what should you do?
7. Wash your hands with soap!

단어 TEST Step 1
p.21

01 야생 동물	02 잘못된, 틀린	03 남은 음식
04 오염	05 인공의, 인위적인	06 밝은
07 주의 깊은	08 창조[창작]하다	09 음량, 볼륨
10 (꽃을) 꺾다	11 방해하다	12 영향, 결과
13 충분히; 충분한	14 허락하다	15 리듬
16 거의	17 환경	18 주의 깊게
19 특히, 특별히	20 유명한	21 분명히
22 ~을 따르다	23 위협하다, 위태롭게 하다	
24 인간, 사람	25 마지막으로	26 이동하다, 이주하다
27 해결하다	28 자연의, 자연적인	29 보호하다
30 규칙	31 심각한	32 별이 총총한
33 쓰레기	34 자원 봉사로 일하다; 자원 봉사자	
35 먹이를 주다	36 ~에 따르면	
37 ~에 익숙하다, ~을 잘 알다		
38 ~을 처리하다, ~을 돌보다		39 ~에 관심을 가지다
40 영향을 주다	41 위험에 처한	42 사실
43 ~을 버리다		

단어 TEST Step 2
p.22

01 threaten	02 human	03 lastly
04 lay	05 everywhere	06 migrate
07 solve	08 protect	09 recent
10 leftover	11 pollution	12 artificial
13 bright	14 careful	15 wildlife
16 create	17 effect	18 almost
19 environment	20 carefully	21 natural
22 especially	23 famous	24 rule
25 serious	26 starry	27 toothbrush
28 trash	29 volunteer	30 feed
31 volume	32 pick	33 disturb
34 wrong	35 rhythm	36 care about
37 according to	38 take action	39 turn down
40 in danger	41 suffer from	42 be familiar with
43 millions of		

단어 TEST Step 3
p.23

1 starry, 별이 총총한   2 artificial, 인공의, 인위적인
3 create, 창조[창작]하다   4 lay, (알을) 낳다
5 pollution, 오염   6 feed, 먹이를 주다   7 rhythm, 리듬

8 disturb, 방해하다   9 wildlife, 야생 동물
10 effect, 영향   11 environment, 환경
12 migrate, 이동하다   13 protect, 보호하다
14 trash, 쓰레기   15 leftover, 남은 음식
16 volume, 음량

대화문 TEST Step 1
p.24~25

Communicate: Listen - Listen and Answer Dialog 1

okay to put, bulletin board / about, Oceans Day / Let, see, Did, make / members, together, should care more about / agree, right now / can, put, on / Go ahead

Communicate: Listen - Listen and Answer Dialog 2

are, doing / throwing away unused medicine / not supposed to / not / can pollute, also put, in danger / see, what should, do / must take, care / didn't, be more careful

Communicate: Listen - Listen More

love, place / forgot, didn't bring / saw, on our way / go get, toothbrushes / getting dark, should drive carefully / Don't worry / it okay to cook / course, not supposed to throw away / care about, environment

Communicate: Listen - All Ears

not supposed to / should care more about

Communicate: Speak - Talk in groups

You're not supposed to, during / wrong with / class rule, shouldn't / remember the rule

My Writing Portfolio - Step 1

Welcome to, listen, follow, supposed to feed, make, sick, not supposed to touch, dangerous, Lastly, don't throw, at, Enjoy, at

Wrap Up - Listening ❺

is it okay to go out / What, plans / favorite, is going to have a concert / come home by / problem, be over

Wrap Up - Listening ❻

look at / What / over there, not supposed to pick / sorry, didn't know

대화문 TEST Step 2
p.26~27

Communicate: Listen - Listen and Answer Dialog 1

G: Is it okay to put a poster on the bulletin board, Mr. Cha?

M: A poster?

G: Here. It's a poster about World Oceans Day.

M: Let me see. It's a great poster. Did you make it?

G: My club members made it together. I think people should care more about our oceans.

M: I agree. Well, we don't have space right now.

G: Then can I put it on the door?

M: Sure. Go ahead.

Communicate: Listen - Listen and Answer Dialog 2

G: What are you doing, Minsu?

B: I'm throwing away unused medicine.

G: Well, you're not supposed to do that.

B: Why not?

G: It can pollute the water. It can also put people and animals in danger.

B: I see. Then what should I do?

G: You must take it to a drugstore. They'll take care of it.

B: Oh, I didn't know that. I'll be more careful.

Communicate: Listen - Listen More

G: Wow! I love this place, Dad.

M: Oh, I forgot something. I didn't bring our toothbrushes.

G: I saw a store on our way here.

M: Okay. I'll go get some toothbrushes.

G: Sure. It's getting dark. You should drive carfully.

M: Don't worry.

G: Dad, is it okay to cook some ramyeon ?

M: Of course. But you're not supposed to throw away any leftovers.

G: I know that. I really care about the environment.

Communicate: Listen - All Ears

M: 1. You're not supposed to do that.

　　2. People should care more about our oceans.

Communicate: Speak - Talk in groups

A: You're not supposed to study during breaks.

B: What's wrong with that?

A: It's a new class rule. You shouldn't do that.

B: Okay. I'll remember the rule.

My Writing Portfolio - Step 1

M: Welcome to K-Zoo. Please listen carefully and follow the rules. First, you're not supposed to feed the animals. It can make them sick. And you're not supposed to touch the animals. It can be very dangerous. Lastly, don't throw stones or trash at them. Enjoy your time at K-Zoo. Thank you.

Wrap Up - Listening ⑤

G: Dad, is it okay to go out with my friends this Saturday?

M: What are your plans?

G: Well, my favorite singer is going to have a concert at Olympic Park.

M: Okay, but come home by 9 o'clock.

G: No problem. The concert will be over by about 8:00.

Wrap Up - Listening ⑥

W: Hey, look at the sign!

B: What sign?

W: The one over there. You're not supposed to pick flowers here.

B: Oh, I'm sorry. I didn't know that.

본문 TEST Step 1　　　　　　　　　　　　　p.28~29

01 Look, painting 02 created, artist, in

03 time, look, starry 　　　　 04 many, are, as

05 fact, world, sky

06 because, pollution

07 Most, familiar, land

08 that, problems, action

09 know, light, cause

10 Light, wrong, everywhere

11 effects on, wildlife

12 report, population, enough

13 Especially, often, see

14 suffer, because, disturbed 　 15 threatened, too

16 migrate, natural, cause

17 millions, hitting, that

18 easily, since, bright

19 die, draws, ocean

20 Clearly, serious, forms

21 have, find, solve 　　　　　 22 If, may, only

본문 TEST Step 2　　　　　　　　　　　　　p.30~31

01 Look at, painting

02 was created by, artist

03 time, look up, wonderful starry night sky

04 many, are lucky as

05 fact, world, sky

06 because, light pollution

07 are familiar with, land pollution

08 that, problems, are taking action to solve

09 know, cause pollution

10 Light, wrong place, wrong time, everywhere

11 serious effects on, wildlife

12 According to, report, population, dark enough

13 Especially, often cannot see

14 suffer from, because, disturbed

15 is threatened by, too

16 migrate, by natural light, cause, wander off course

17 millions of birds , after hitting

18 easily, place to lay, since, bright

19 die, draws, away from, ocean

20 Clearly, serious, other forms

21 have to find, solve

22 If, do not, may see, only

22 만약 우리가 하지 않으면, 우리는 우리의 꿈이나 그림에서만 별을 볼 수 있을지 모릅니다.

1 이 아름다운 그림을 보세요.

2 그것은 1889년에 유명한 네덜란드 미술가 빈센트 반 고흐에 의해 만들어졌습니다.

3 반 고흐의 시대에는 거의 모든 사람들이 위를 쳐다보고 멋진 별이 빛나는 밤하늘을 볼 수 있었습니다.

4 이제, 우리들 중 얼마나 많은 사람이 반 고흐만큼 운이 있을까요?

5 사실, 오늘날 세계의 많은 사람들은 별이 빛나는 밤하늘을 즐길 수 없습니다.

6 이것은 빛의 오염 때문에 그렇습니다.

7 우리 대부분은 공기, 물, 토양 오염에 익숙합니다.

8 우리는 그것들이 심각한 문제라는 것을 알고 있으며, 그것들을 해결하기 위해 조치를 취하고 있습니다.

9 하지만 여러분은 빛이 오염도 일으킬 수 있다는 것을 알고 있었나요?

10 빛의 오염—잘못된 시간에 잘못된 장소에서의 너무 많은 빛—은 전 세계의 거의 모든 곳에 있습니다.

11 그것은 인간과 야생동물에게 심각한 영향을 미칠 수 있습니다.

12 최근 보고서에 따르면, 세계 인구의 약 89%가 밤에 충분히 어둡지 않은 하늘 아래서 살고 있습니다.

13 특히 대도시에서는 별이 빛나는 밤을 종종 볼 수 없습니다.

14 그들은 또한 인공적인 빛에 의해 낮과 밤의 자연적인 리듬이 방해를 받기 때문에 수면 문제로 고통을 겪을 수도 있습니다.

15 야생동물도 빛의 오염으로 위협받고 있습니다.

16 밤에 이동하거나 사냥하는 새들은 자연광을 통해 길을 찾지만, 대도시의 빛은 길을 벗어나도록 할 수 있습니다.

17 매년 수백만 마리의 새들이 밝은 불빛이 있는 건물에 부딪치고서 죽습니다.

18 바다거북들은 밤에 해변이 너무 밝기 때문에 알을 낳을 장소를 쉽게 찾을 수 없습니다.

19 또한, 많은 아기 바다거북들은 인공 빛이 그들을 바다에서 멀어지게 하기 때문에 죽습니다.

20 분명히, 빛 오염은 다른 형태의 오염만큼이나 심각합니다.

21 우리는 그 문제를 해결할 방법을 찾아야 합니다.

1 Look at this beautiful painting.

2 It was created by the famous Dutch artist Vincent van Gogh in 1889.

3 In Van Gogh's time, almost everyone could look up and see a wonderful starry night sky.

4 Now, how many of us are as lucky as Van Gogh?

5 In fact, many people in today's world cannot enjoy a starry night sky.

6 This is so because of light pollution.

7 Most of us are familiar with air, water, and land pollution.

8 We know that they are serious problems, and we are taking action to solve them.

9 But did you know that light can also cause pollution?

10 Light pollution—too much light in the wrong place at the wrong time—is almost everywhere around the world.

11 It can have serious effects on humans and wildlife.

12 According to a recent report, about 89% of the world's population lives under skies that are not dark enough at night.

13 Especially in big cities, people often cannot see a starry night.

14 They can also suffer from sleep problems because the natural rhythm of day and night is disturbed by artificial light.

15 Wildlife is threatened by light pollution, too.

16 Birds that migrate or hunt at night find their way by natural light, but light in big cities can cause them to wander off course.

17 Every year millions of birds die after hitting buildings that have bright lights.

18 Sea turtles cannot easily find a place to lay eggs since beaches are too bright at night.

19 Also, many baby sea turtles die because artificial light draws them away from the ocean.

20 Clearly, light pollution is as serious as other forms of pollution.

21 We have to find ways to solve the problem.

22 If we do not, we may see stars only in our dreams or paintings.

구석구석지문 TEST Step 1 p.38

My Writing Portfolio - Step 1

1. African
2. Home, southern
3. fish
4. Size, up to be
5. Life span
6. in danger
7. suffer from sea pollution
8. catch, fish, don't have enough

Have Fun Together

1. not supposed to
2. shouldn't feed
3. get sick
4. look at
5. not supposed to touch
6. take, trash home
7. shouldn't leave
8. rule
9. supposed to pick, or
10. it's, but, isn't allowed in
11. turn down
12. supposed to play, loudly
13. not supposed to fish

4. Please look at the sign.
5. It says you're not supposed to touch the birds.
6. Will you please take your trash home?
7. You shouldn't leave it in the mountains.
8. That's the rule here.
9. Excuse me. You're not supposed to pick flowers or fruits.
10. I understand it's hot, but swimming isn't allowed in this national park.
11. Will you turn down the volume please?
12. You're not supposed to play music loudly.
13. Excuse me. You're not supposed to fish here.

구석구석지문 TEST Step 2 p.39

My Writing Portfolio - Step 1

1. African penguin
2. Home : southern Africa
3. Food: fish
4. Size : grows up to be 60-70 cm
5. Life span : 10-30 years
6. Why are they in danger ?
7. Sometimes they suffer from sea pollution .
8. Also, people catch too many fish, and African penguins don't have enough food.

Have Fun Together

1. Excuse me. You're not supposed to make a fire and cook here.
2. In this park, you shouldn't feed wild animals.
3. They can get sick, you know.

Lesson SP

12 invite, 초대하다　13 professor, 교수

14 excuse, 변명, 핑계 거리　15 respond, 응답하다

16 university, 대학

단어 TEST Step 1　　　　　　　　　　p.40

01 교수　　　　　02 사다

03 ~라고 부르다, 전화하다　　04 계속하다

05 허락하다　06 ~때문에　07 놀란

08 (값 · 비용이) ~이다[들다]　09 다른

10 자랑스럽게　11 접시, 요리　12 일찍

13 시계　14 만화책　15 모든 것

16 계획하다, 의도하다　　17 변명, 핑계 거리

18 설명하다　19 벽　20 바람이 빠진, 펑크 난

21 지구 온난화　22 치다, 때리다　23 대학

24 초대하다　25 줄넘기하다　26 미친, 정신이상인

27 결정하다　28 갑자기　29 시끄러운

30 특별한　31 외치다, 소리치다　32 금속

33 주인　34 대답하다　35 대답(응답)하다

36 식은 죽 먹기　37 ~에 늦다　38 ~을 자랑으로 여기다

39 ~의 반대편에(는)　40 돌아오다　41 늦잠을 자다

42 시험을 보다　43 큰 소리로 웃다

단어 TEST Step 2　　　　　　　　　　p.41

01 buy　02 call　03 surprised

04 professor　05 expensive　06 respond

07 invite　08 jump rope　09 wall

10 proudly　11 early　12 different

13 continue　14 allow　15 flat

16 reply　17 special　18 global warming

19 metal　20 everything　21 university

22 point　23 noise　24 crazy

25 decide　26 suddenly　27 explain

28 owner　29 loud　30 shout

31 corner　32 excuse　33 hit

34 cost　35 laugh out loud　36 go to bed

37 be proud of　38 on the other side of

39 come back　40 get up late　41 on Saturday

42 be late for　43 take a test

단어 TEST Step 3　　　　　　　　　　p.42

1 flat, 펑크 난　2 expensive, 값비싼　3 noise, 소음

4 shout, 외치다, 소리치다　5 crazy, 미친　6 owner, 주인

7 continue, 계속하다　8 dish, 접시　9 suddenly, 갑자기

10 cost, (값 · 비용이) ~이다[들다]　11 explain, 설명하다

본문 TEST Step 1　　　　　　　　　　p.43~44

01 Clock, Talks　02 invited, to, one

03 proud, in, comic　04 In, had, dish

05 asked, What's　06 special, talks, proudly

07 If, hit, time　08 hit, with　09 made, loud

10 on, shouted, crazy　11 It's, at, bed

12 Flat Tire　13 university friends

14 in, on　15 back, because, had

16 got, late, make

17 being, decided, got

18 that, allowed, to

19 When, take, put　20 As, down, first

21 global warming

22 piece, cake, continued　23 points. answer

24 Which tire　25 Special Parrot　26 One, to buy

27 How much, one　28 costs, pet shop

29 Why, expensive

30 special one, play　31 about, one

32 costs, because, jump

33 about, one, asked

34 responded, costs

35 surprised, asked　36 said, other, call

본문 TEST Step 2　　　　　　　　　　p.45~46

01 Clock, Talks　02 invited, to, one evening

03 was proud of, in, comic books, new computer

04 In, had, metal dish

05 asked, What's, big dish

06 special, talks, proudly　07 If, hit, the time

08 hit, with his hand

09 made, loud noise

10 Suddenly, on the other side of, shouted, Are, crazy

11 It's, at, Time go to bed　12 Flat Tire

13 are university friends

14 visited, in, on Saturday

15 come back early, because, big test

16 got up late, make it to

17 for being late, decided to tell, got, flat tire

18 agreed that, bad luck, allowed, to take

19 When, came to take, on, put, different rooms

20 As, sat down 21 explain global warming

22 a piece of cake, continued   23 answer

24 Which   25 Special

26 One day, went to, to buy

27 How much, one, asked

28 costs, pet shop owner

29 Why, so expensive

30 special one, play the piano   31 What about

32 because, can play, paint, jump rope

33 what about   34 responded, costs

35 surprised, does, do

36 said, other two birds call

26 어느 날 Abril은 앵무새를 사러 애완동물 가게에 갔다.

27 "이 파란 앵무새는 얼마죠?" 그녀가 물었다.

28 "이것은 2,000달러예요." 애완동물 가게 주인이 말했다.

29 "왜 그렇게 비싸죠?" Abril이 물었다.

30 "이것은 아주 특별한 앵무새입니다. 피아노를 칠 수 있어요!"

31 "초록색 앵무새요?" 그녀가 물었다.

32 "이것은 피아노를 치고, 그림을 그리고, 줄넘기를 할 수 있기 때문에 5,000달러입니다."

33 "그럼 빨간 앵무새는요?" Abril이 물었다.

34 주인은 10,000달러라고 대답했다.

35 그녀는 놀라서 물었다. "그것은 뭘 할 수 있죠?"

36 "모르겠어요, 하지만 다른 두 새들이 그것을 '선생님'이라고 불러요."라고 주인이 말했다.

1 말하는 시계

2 어느 날 저녁 Dean은 친구들을 자기 방으로 초대했다.

3 그는 방에 있는 모든 것 즉, 멋진 침대, 많은 만화책들, 그리고 새 컴퓨터를 자랑스러워했다.

4 구석에 그는 커다란 금속 접시도 가지고 있었다.

5 한 친구가 "저 큰 접시는 뭐니?"라고 물었다.

6 "아, 저건 내 특별한 시계야. 그건 말을 해." Dean이 자랑스럽게 대답했다.

7 "접시를 치면, 시간을 알게 될 거야."

8 그리고 나서 그는 손으로 접시를 쳤다.

9 그것은 정말 큰 소리를 냈다.

10 갑자기 벽 반대편에 있던 그의 누나가 소리쳤다. "너 미쳤니?"

11 밤 11시야. 잘 시간이야!"

12 펑크 난 타이어

13 Jessie와 Nicole은 대학 친구이다.

14 그들은 토요일에 플로리다에 계시는 Jessie의 할머니를 방문했다.

15 그들은 월요일 오후에 큰 시험이 있기 때문에 그날 일찍 돌아올 계획이었다.

16 하지만 그들은 늦게 일어나서 시험에 맞춰 올 수 없었다.

17 그들은 지각한 것에 대한 좋은 핑계 거리가 필요해서 교수에게 차의 타이어에 펑크가 났다고 말하기로 결정했다.

18 교수는 그것이 단지 불운이라는 것에 동의했고 수요일에 그들이 시험을 볼 수 있도록 허락했다.

19 수요일 아침에 그들이 시험을 보러 왔을 때, 교수는 Jessie와 Nicole을 다른 방에 들어가게 했다.

20 그들은 앉아서 첫 번째 문제를 읽었다.

21 5점짜리, 지구 온난화를 설명하시오.

22 그것은 그들에게 식은 죽 먹기였다. 그러고 나서, 시험은 계속되었다.

23 95점짜리, 질문에 답하시오.

24 어느 타이어였는가?

25 특별한 앵무새

1 A Clock That Talks

2 Dean invited his friends to his room one evening.

3 He was proud of everything in his room: a nice bed, many comic books, and a new computer.

4 In the corner, he also had a very big metal dish.

5 A friend asked, "What's that big dish?"

6 "Oh, that's my special clock. It talks," Dean replied proudly.

7 "If you hit the dish, you'll know the time."

8 Then he hit the dish with his hand.

9 It made a really loud noise.

10 Suddenly, his sister who was on the other side of the wall shouted, "Are you crazy?

11 It's eleven o'clock at night. Time to go to bed!"

12 A Flat Tire

13 Jessie and Nicole are university friends.

14 They visited Jessie's grandma in Florida on Saturday.

15 They planned to come back early on Monday because they had a big test that afternoon.

16 But they got up late and could not make it to the test.

17 They needed a good excuse for being late, so they decided to tell the professor that their car got a flat tire.

18 The professor agreed that it was just bad luck and allowed them to take the test on Wednesday.

19 When they came to take the test on Wednesday morning, the professor put Jessie and Nicole in different rooms.

20 As they sat down, they read the first question.

21 For 5 points, explain global warming.

22 It was a piece of cake to them. Then, the test continued.

23 For 95 points, answer the question.

24 Which tire?

25 A Special Parrot

26 One day Abril went to a pet shop to buy a parrot.

27 "How much is this blue one?" she asked.

28 "It costs $2,000," said the pet shop owner.

29 "Why is it so expensive?" asked Abril.

30 "This parrot is a very special one. It can play the piano!"

31 "What about the green one?" she asked.

32 "It costs $5,000 because it can play the piano, paint pictures, and jump rope."

33 "Then what about the red one?" Abril asked.

34 The owner responded that it costs $10,000.

35 She was surprised and asked, "What does it do?"

36 "I don't know," said the owner, "but the other two birds call it 'teacher.'"

11 choose, 선택하다, 고르다   12 protect, 보호하다

13 change, 잔돈   14 victim, 피해자, 희생자

15 allowance, 용돈   16 arrest, 체포하다

단어 TEST Step 1 p.53

01 태도, 자세	02 고발하다, 비난하다	
03 던지다	04 ~ 뒤에	05 공약, 약속
06 보호하다	07 피하다	08 약자 괴롭히기
09 어려움	10 석방하다	11 외모
12 등장인물, 캐릭터	13 유죄의	14 걱정하는
15 판사; 판단하다	16 부끄럼을 많이 타는, 수줍어하는	
17 감옥	18 턱수염	19 실종된, 행방불명된
20 공격하다	21 이웃	22 자유
23 자신감 있는	24 회장	25 받다
26 권리	27 용돈	28 진실
29 체포하다	30 희생자	31 평범한
32 다정한, 친절한	33 속삭이다	34 인기 있는, 대중적인
35 ~을 돌보다	36 ~을 두려워하다	37 진정하다
38 ~을 석방하다	39 B 때문에 A를 고발하다	
40 ~ 덕분에	41 ~을 지지하다, ~을 찬성하다	
42 ~을 싸워 물리치다		
43 ~을 뽑다, ~에게 투표하다		

단어 TEST Step 2 p.54

01 back	02 pass	03 activity
04 carry	05 shout	06 victim
07 vote	08 choice	09 enter
10 hide	11 whisper	12 friendly
13 appearance	14 arrest	15 lucky
16 face	17 mind	18 guilty
19 choose	20 curly	21 ordinary
22 popular	23 anytime	24 promise
25 monthly	26 score	27 freedom
28 protect	29 confident	30 allowance
31 neighbor	32 accuse	33 missing
34 prison	35 so far	36 be afraid of
37 accuse A of B	38 cut off ~	39 be good at ~
40 thanks to ~	41 vote for ~	
42 agree with+사람		43 care for ~

단어 TEST Step 3 p.55

1 cause, 야기하다   2 neighbor, 이웃   3 avoid, 피하다

4 score, 득점하다   5 attitude, 태도   6 confidence, 자신감

7 character, 등장인물   8 whisper, 속삭이다

9 attack, 공격하다   10 bullying, 괴롭히기

대화문 TEST Step 1 p.56~57

Communicate: Listen-Listen and Answer. Talk

from, ago, worried, shy, good, lucky, friendly, playing, call, will be, I hope, will win

Communicate: Listen-Listen and Answer. Dialog

Is, winning / course, great handball player / mean the girl from / her name / what, look like / very tall, has, ponytail / who scored, just now / her seventh goal / really great

Communicate: Listen-Listen More

What can I do / lost, younger brother / calm down, brother's / five years old / What, look like / has / is, wearing / wearing, green shirt / tell me more / carrying a red backpack / look for, make an announcement, missing / I hope, find

Communicate: Speak 2-Talk in pairs

have an important exam / I hope, do well on / hope so, too

Communicate: Speak 2-Talk in groups

What, your character's name / His name / What does, look like / has no hair / have big eyes / does

Communicate: Speak-Rap Time

[1] lost, this afternoon / I hope, find

[2] do your best / I wish, the same

[3] What does, look like / has long straight hair

[4] Is, wearing / reading a map

My Speaking Portfolio

Look at, bulletin board, are, school president / already made, already made, choice, vote for / mean, with glasses, looks smart, promises / who will, choose / wants to make, a sate place / always has, right / seems okay / looks friendly, talent shows

Wrap Up

1 there is / from, over there / Which, What does, look / curly, wearing glasses

2 look sad, wrong / broke her arm / happened / fell off / That's too bad, I hope, get better

대화문 TEST Step 2 p.58~59

Communicate: Listen-Listen and Answer. Talk

G: Hi, I'm Gacha. I'm from Mongolia. When I first came to Songji Middle School two months ago, I was so worried. I was a little shy, and I wasn't good at Korean. However, I'm a lucky girl. All my classmates are nice and friendly. I enjoy playing handball with them in P.E. class. I'm a good player. They call me "Golden Hand." There will be a sports day next week. I hope my class will win in the handball event.

Communicate: Listen-Listen and Answer. Dialog

B: Hi, Minsol. Is your class winning?

G: Of course. We have a great handball player.

B: You mean the girl from Mongolia?

G: Yes, her name is Gacha.

B: I've heard a lot about her. But what does she look like?

G: She's very tall and has a ponytail.

B: Oh, is she the girl who scored the goal just now?

G: Yes, that's her seventh goal.

B: Wow, she's really great.

Communicate: Listen-Listen More

M: What can I do for you?

G: I lost my younger brother.

M: Okay, calm down. What's your brother's name?

G: His name is Wally Brown. He's five years old.

M: What does he look like?

G: He has brown hair and brown eyes.

M: What is he wearing?

G: He is wearing a green shirt and black pants.

M: Can you tell me more?

G: Oh, he is carrying a red backpack.

M: All right. We'll go out and look for him. Also, we'll make an announcement about a missing child.

G: Thank you so much. I hope I'll find him soon.

Communicate: Speak 2-Talk in pairs

A: I have an important exam tomorrow!

B: I hope you'll do well on the exam.

A: I hope so, too. Thanks.

Communicate: Speak 2-Talk in groups

A: What is your character's name?

B: His name is Buster.

A: What does he look like?

B: He has no hair.

A: Does he have big eyes?

B: Yes, he does.

Communicate: Speak-Rap Time

(1) A: I lost my puppy this afternoon.
   B: I hope you'll find him soon.

(2) A: I hope you'll do your best in the final game.
   B: Thanks. I wish you the same.

(3) A: What does your sister look like, Claire?
   B: She's tall and has long straight hair.

(4) A: Is your father wearing a blue cap?
   B: Yeah. Now, he's reading a map.

My Speaking Portfolio

G: Look at the bulletin board. There are posters for the next school president.

B: Yeah, I've already made my choice. I'll vote for Jang Jimin.

G: You mean the boy with glasses? He looks smart, but I don't like his promises.

B: Then who will you choose?

G: Well, I am for number 1, Han Siwon. She wants to make our school a safe place.

B: She always has a ponytail, right?

G: Yes, and Hong Jiho seems okay.

B: She looks friendly, but I don't like talent shows.

Wrap Up

1 B: I hear there is a new student in your class.
   G: Yes. She's from Jejudo. Oh, she's over there!
   B: Which one? What does she look like?
   G: She has curly hair and is wearing glasses.

2 G: You look sad. What's wrong, Jongmin?
   B: My sister broke her arm this morning.
   G: What happened?
   B: She fell off her bike.
   G: That's too bad. I hope she'll get better soon.

본문 TEST Step 1   p.60~61

01 Right, Different

02 ways, ordinary person

03 had, cared for

04 after, moved, face difficulties

05 looked different, other   06 did, like

07 avoided, with, beard   08 did, sit, to,

09 whispered, behind, trying   10 some, broke

11 threw, at, down   12 told, stop growing

13 did, mind   14 just, to have

15 One, attacked, threw   16 cut off, shouted

17 able, fight, off   18 called, accused, of

19 was arrested   20 judge, victim

21 believed, with, prison, over

22 wanted, know, truth   23 sent, to, across

24 in prison, protecting himself

25 became angry, set, free   26 freed, traveled, lots

27 attitudes toward, changed   28 Before, died, beard

29 His name

30 made, popular, fought, right

01 Right To Be Different

02 In many ways, an ordinary person

03 had a job, cared for

04 after, moved to, to face difficulties

05 looked different from   06 did not like it

07 avoided the man with a beard

08 to sit next to him

09 behind his back, trying to hide

10 Some, broke his windows

11 Others threw stones at, walked down

12 told, to stop growing

13 did not mind   14 freedom to have

15 attacked, threw him on the ground

16 cut off, shouted

17 was able to fight them off

18 accused him of attacking   19 was arrested

20 the judge, the victim

21 a man with a beard, went to prison

22 wanted, to know

23 sent, to, across the country

24 was in prison, protecting himself

25 became angry, decided to set, free

26 was freed, lots of

27 attitudes toward beards changed

28 Before, died, with a beard   29 His name

30 made beards popular, fought for, right to have

15 어느 날, 네 명의 남자가 Joseph을 공격했고 그를 바닥에 던졌다.

16 "우리가 당신의 턱수염을 잘라 버리겠어!"라고 그들은 소리쳤다.

17 Joseph은 덩치가 큰 사람이었고, 그는 그들을 싸워 물리칠 수 있었다.

18 하지만 그 남자들은 경찰을 불렀고, 자신들을 공격한 것으로 그를 고발했다.

19 불쌍한 Joseph은 체포되었다.

20 그는 "저는 여기서 희생자입니다."라고 판사에게 말했다.

21 슬프게도, 아무도 턱수염을 가진 남자를 믿지 않았고, 그는 일 년이 넘는 기간 동안 감옥에 갔다.

22 Joseph의 아들인 Thomas는 사람들이 진실을 알기를 원했다.

23 그는 전국에 있는 신문사에 편지를 보냈다.

24 사람들은 Joseph이 단지 자신과 자신의 턱수염을 지키려다 감옥에 갇혔다는 것을 알게 되었다.

25 많은 사람들은 이에 대해 분개했고, 그래서 판사는 결국 Joseph을 석방하기로 결정했다.

26 Joseph은 석방된 뒤에 순회를 하며 많은 사람들에게 자신의 이야기를 전했다.

27 사람들의 턱수염에 대한 태도는 서서히 변해갔다.

28 Joseph이 죽기 전에, 턱수염을 가진 남자가 미국의 대통령이 되었다.

29 그의 이름은 Abraham Lincoln(에이브러햄 링컨)이었다.

30 그는 턱수염을 대중적으로 만들었지만, Joseph Palmer는 그것을 기를 권리를 위하여 싸웠다.

1 다를 권리

2 여러 면에서 42살의 Joseph Palmer는 평범한 사람이었다.

3 그는 직업이 있었고 가족을 돌보았다.

4 하지만 1830년에 매사추세츠에 있는 작은 도시로 이사를 한 후에 그는 어려움에 직면하기 시작했다.

5 Joseph은 다른 사람들과 달라 보였다. 그는 기다란 턱수염을 기르고 있었다.

6 사람들은 그것을 별로 좋아하지 않았다.

7 마을 사람들은 턱수염을 가진 그 남자를 피했다.

8 그들은 그의 곁에 앉고 싶어 하지 않았다.

9 그들은 심지어 그의 등 뒤에서 "그가 무엇을 숨기려는 거지?" 라고 속삭였다.

10 어떤 이웃들은 그의 창문을 깼다.

11 다른 사람들은 그가 길을 걸어 내려갈 때 그에게 돌을 던졌다.

12 그들은 그에게 턱수염을 그만 기르라고 말했다.

13 Joseph은 신경 쓰지 않았다.

14 그는 그저 자신의 턱수염을 기를 자유를 원했다.

1 The Right To Be Different

2 In many ways, 42-year-old Joseph Palmer was an ordinary person.

3 He had a job and cared for his family.

4 But in 1830, after he moved to a small town in Massachusetts, he began to face difficulties.

5 Joseph looked different from other people: he had a long beard.

6 People did not like it very much.

7 The town's people avoided the man with a beard.

8 They did not want to sit next to him.

9 They even whispered behind his back, "What is he trying to hide?"

10 Some neighbors broke his windows.

11 Others threw stones at him when he walked down the street.

12 They told him to stop growing a beard.

13 Joseph did not mind.

14 He just wanted the freedom to have his beard.

15 One day, four men attacked Joseph and threw him on the ground.

16 "We're going to cut off your beard!" they shouted.

17 Joseph was a big man, and he was able to fight them off.

18 But the men called the police and accused him of attacking them.

19 Poor Joseph was arrested.

20 He said to the judge, "I'm the victim here."

21 Sadly, no one believed a man with a beard, and he went to prison for over a year.

22 Joseph's son, Thomas, wanted people to know the truth.

23 He sent letters to newspapers across the country.

24 People learned that Joseph was in prison just for protecting himself and his beard.

25 Many people became angry about this, so the judge finally decided to set Joseph free.

26 After he was freed, Joseph traveled and told his story to lots of people.

27 Slowly, people's attitudes toward beards changed.

28 Before Joseph died, a man with a beard became the President of the United States.

29 His name was Abraham Lincoln.

30 He made beards popular, but Joseph Palmer fought for the right to have them.

구석구석지문 TEST Step 1   p.70

My Speaking Portfolio

1. will vote
2. looks confident, smart
3. thinks, should be
4. agree with
5. such as, bullying
6. hope, becomes
7. to be a safer place

My Writing Portfolio: My Book Report

1. Right to Be
2. About
3. about, last week
4. really enjoyed
5. learned from, that, appearance
6. who talk, must
7. However, have a question
8. Why, to have a beard

Words in Action

1. Welcome to, Admission, free
2. have in mind
3. If, to visit, look around
4. get hungry, a light snack

구석구석지문 TEST Step 2   p.71

My Speaking Portfolio

1. I will vote for Han Siwon.
2. She looks confident and smart.
3. She thinks school should be a safe place.
4. I agree with her.
5. I like her promises such as no more bullying.
6. I hope Han Siwon becomes the next school president.
7. I really want my school to be a safer place.

My Writing Portfolio: My Book Report

1. The Right to Be Different
2. A Story About Joseph Palmer
3. I read the story about Joseph Palmer last week.
4. I really enjoyed it.
5. I learned from the story that we should not judge people by their appearance.
6. Students who talk about other people's appearance must read the story.
7. However, I have a question about it.
8. Why did Joseph Palmer want to have a beard?

Words in Action

1. Welcome to the travel fair. Admission is free.
2. What countries do you have in mind?
3. If you want to visit South America, you can look around the booths on the left.
4. If you get hungry, you can have drinks and a light snack.

적중100

영어 기출 문제집

정답 및 해설

천재 | 이재영